CAMPBELL UNION HIGH SCHOOL DISTRICT
BLACKFORD HIGH SCHOOL

Textbook No. _____ **3300**

	Pupil's Name	Room No.	Teacher	Per.
1	Curtis Andrusky	10	Sharpe	2.
2	Pam Sprague	36		
3				
4				
5				
6				
7				
8				
9				
10				
11				

Introductory Algebra
1

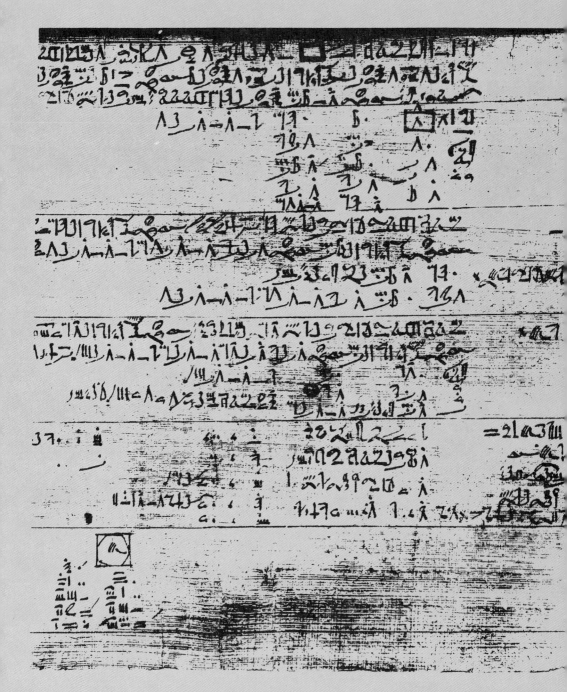

This photograph shows a portion of the Rhind Mathematical Papyrus, an ancient Egyptian manuscript written about the year 1650 B.C. The Rhind papyrus contains complicated solutions to problems in mathematics that can be easily solved by students of algebra today, for the ancient Egyptians studied mathematics during its birth.

INTRODUCTORY

ALGEBRA 1

RUSSELL F. JACOBS

HARCOURT, BRACE & WORLD, INC.

New York   Chicago   San Francisco   Atlanta   Dallas

ABOUT THE AUTHOR

Russell F. Jacobs
Mathematics Consultant
Phoenix Union High School System
Phoenix, Arizona

COVER

The cover shows a photographic enlargement of a portion of a thin disk containing miniature electronic devices called *integrated circuits*. These circuits replace much of the heavier and bulkier electronic devices that limit the effectiveness of complex electronic systems such as those found in computers. So small are these integrated circuits that those shown on the cover can easily fit within the area covered by a dime.

PICTURE CREDITS

Cover photo, Bell Telephone Laboratories; title-page photo, Oriental Division, New York Public Library; opposite p. 1, American Museum of Natural History; p. 40, top, General Electric Company; p. 40, bottom, UNIVAC; p. 82, NASA; p. 118, © Dr. Derek J. de Solla Price; p. 154, American Museum of Natural History; p. 190, Dick Hartman for Fairchild Aircraft; p. 232, New York Life Insurance Company; p. 258, International Nickel Company, Inc.; p. 286, map, Map Division, New York Public Library; p. 286, instruments, National Maritime Museum, London; p. 318, United Nations; pp. 342 and 364, Air Force Cambridge Research Laboratories; p. 402, Harbrace.

Printed in the United States of America

ISBN 0-15-357734-7

Preface

INTRODUCTORY ALGEBRA, *Book 1*, is the first of a two-volume series that includes all of the usual topics of modern elementary algebra.

The author acknowledges the influence of the work and publications of the School Mathematics Study Group in his preparation of this textbook and INTRODUCTORY ALGEBRA, *Book 2*. The author's experience in teaching courses using S.M.S.G. textbooks at various levels has provided the inspiration for this work.

INTRODUCTORY ALGEBRA, *Book 1*, is written in a way that encourages the student to become involved in the development of the mathematical concepts presented. A semi-programmed style is used with many pivotal questions provided at appropriate points. These pivotal questions are designated as **P-1, P-2, P-3,** etc. The discovery method is utilized through the pivotal questions and also in the *Oral* and *Written Exercises*. Answers to the pivotal questions are provided at the back of the book.

Each section is written to provide material for a one-day lesson. *Oral Exercises* are provided for each section. These exercises help to reinforce the student's understanding of the material presented in the section and help to prepare him to do the *Written Exercises* successfully.

The items of the *Written Exercises* that are labeled A are paired by their degree of difficulty or type. The B exercises are of two kinds. Some are written to help students discover relationships that will be presented formally in later sections. Others are of an enrichment nature and are supplementary to the basic content of the course. The C exercises are considered more difficult than the A exercises but are related to the topics presented in the accompanying section. The B and C exercises are not included in every section.

A *Chapter Summary* is provided at the end of each chapter. This summary is divided into two parts entitled *Important Terms* and *Important Ideas*. A *Chapter Review* is provided for each chapter, and a *Cumulative Review* is given at the end of every third chapter. At the end of Chapter 1, there is a *Review of Arithmetic;* and at the end of Chapter 13, there are *Review Exercises* for Chapters 1–12.

A complete *Teacher's Edition* is available, which includes a discussion of the rationale of the course, hints on the selection of students for the course, suggestions for administrative organization of the course, a suggested timetable of assignments, and hints for teaching each lesson.

A test booklet, *Tests to Accompany* INTRODUCTORY ALGEBRA, *Book 1,* is available with chapter tests and semester tests.

The author wishes to acknowledge especially the cooperation of the teachers, administrators, and students of Phoenix South Mountain High School in Phoenix, Arizona, for the initial use of the textbook in multilithed form during the time that it was being prepared for commercial publication. The author is indebted to many people for their help and inspiration but wishes to pay special tribute to the following people: George Anderson, Norma Anderson, John Black, Hazel Boegeman, Robert Haberer, Helen Jacobs, John Murphy, John Waters.

R.F.J.

Contents

13 Probability and Statistics ⠀⠀⠀⠀⠀⠀⠀⠀⠀⠀⠀ 403

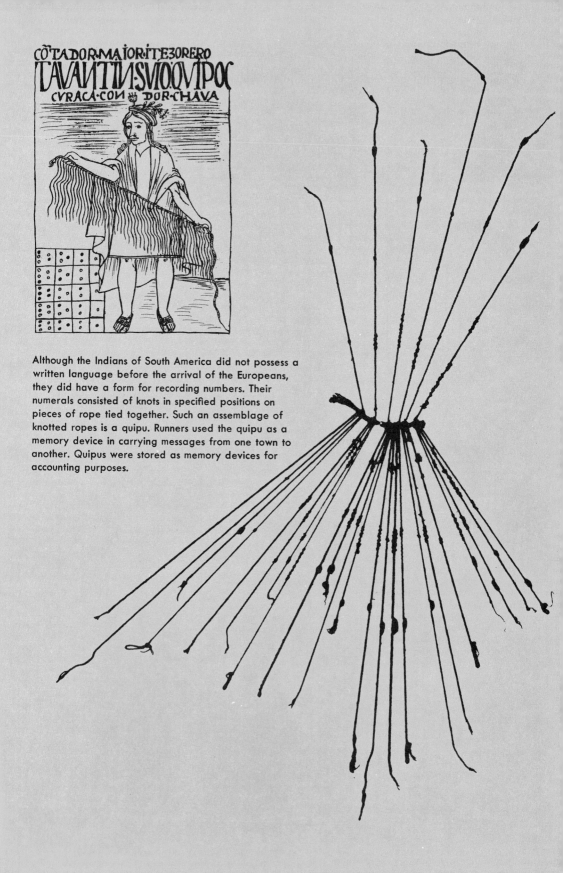

Although the Indians of South America did not possess a written language before the arrival of the Europeans, they did have a form for recording numbers. Their numerals consisted of knots in specified positions on pieces of rope tied together. Such an assemblage of knotted ropes is a quipu. Runners used the quipu as a memory device in carrying messages from one town to another. Quipus were stored as memory devices for accounting purposes.

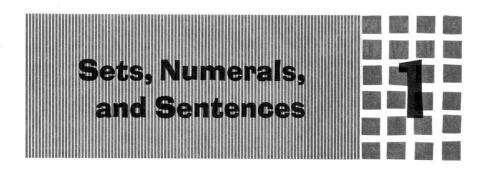

Sets, Numerals, and Sentences

1.1 Sets

Everyone is familiar with various names for groups of objects. A television announcer will refer to a "team" of football players. Hunters on a safari may see a "herd" of elephants. One of your friends probably speaks of his stereo records as a "collection."

■ **P-1** What word is usually used to describe collectively the instruments that a draftsman uses or the clubs that a golfer carries in his bag?

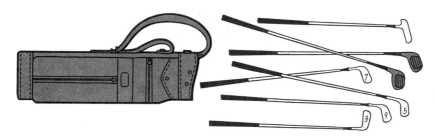

The idea of a collection of objects is very important in mathematics, and the word **set** is used to describe such collections. Generally speaking, the objects that make up a set may be of any kind. In this course, however, you will be mainly concerned with sets of numbers.

> The objects that make up a set are called its **elements**.

One way to name a set is to place symbols representing the elements inside a pair of **braces,** { }, and to separate the symbols by commas. For example, the set of vowels of the English alphabet can be represented by {a, e, i, o, u}. You would read {a, e, i, o, u} as "the set whose members are a, e, i, o, and u."

This method of naming a set is sometimes called the **roster method.**

■ **P-2** What set is represented by {Washington, Adams, Jefferson}?

■ **P-3** How would you represent the set of courses you are studying this year?

It is often convenient to use simpler names for sets, and it is common practice to name sets by capital letters. Thus you might name the set of vowels listed on the previous page as the set S. This would be indicated by the equality S = {a, e, i, o, u}.

In referring to this set several times during a problem, you would find that it is much easier to call it set S rather than to list all of its elements each time. You might, for example, refer to the set of presidents listed above as set P. You are free to choose whatever capital letter you want to represent a given set. It would not be desirable, however, to name two different sets by the same capital letter unless they are in different problems.

ORAL EXERCISES 1.1

1. By what name are collections of objects in mathematics called?

2. What are the objects called that make up a set?

Give a description of the following sets in your own words.

3. {New York, Chicago, Los Angeles}   **4.** {Alaska, Hawaii}

5. {penny, nickel, dime}   **6.** {x, y, z}

7. {April, June, September, November}   **8.** {2, 4, 6, 8, 10}

9. $\{\frac{1}{2}, \frac{1}{3}, \frac{1}{4}, \frac{1}{5}\}$ **10.** {12, 18, 3, 9, 6, 15}

Tell the elements of the sets given by the following word descriptions.

11. The set of three largest cities in your state

12. The set of whole numbers between $5\frac{1}{2}$ and $7\frac{1}{3}$

13. The set of presidents of the United States after Harry Truman

14. The set of states bordering the Pacific Ocean

15. The set of odd numbers between 0 and 10

16. The set of even numbers between $4\frac{1}{3}$ and $7\frac{2}{3}$

17. The set of persons who are members of your family

18. What simpler names are often used for sets?

19. What do you call the symbols that bound the names of the elements of a set?

20. In the roster method, how are the names of the elements of a set separated?

WRITTEN EXERCISES 1.1

A Name the following sets by the roster method. (Here you may take "between" to mean "not including.")

1. The set of whole numbers between 12 and 20
2. The set of whole numbers between 25 and 27
3. The set of fractions that show a numerator equal to 1 and a whole denominator between 5 and 10
4. The set of fractions that show a denominator equal to 7 and a whole numerator between 1 and 7
5. The set of letters of the alphabet between m and r
6. The set of letters of the alphabet between a and k
7. The set of types of United States coins in circulation having a value of less than 30 cents
8. The set of types of United States paper money less than 20 dollars
9. The set of oceans bordering the United States
10. The set of foreign countries bordering the United States

Give a word description of each of the following sets.

11. A = {1, 2, 3}
12. B = {2, 4, 6}
13. C = {Tuesday, Thursday}
14. D = {Sunday, Saturday}
15. F = {August, April}
16. G = {Los Angeles, San Francisco}
17. H = {Philadelphia, Pittsburgh}
18. P = {January, June, July}
19. E = {Pacific, Atlantic, Indian, Arctic, Antarctic}
20. Q = {Erie, Michigan, Superior, Ontario, Huron}

B Can you name the following sets by using the roster method? Explain.

21. The set of whole numbers between $5\frac{1}{3}$ and $5\frac{7}{8}$
22. The set of women who have been presidents of the United States
23. The set of tigers in this room
24. The set of elements that are in both {3, 5, 7} and {0, 1, 2}
25. The set of whole numbers greater than 100
26. The set of numbers between 1 and 2

1.2   Subsets and the Empty Set

Look carefully at the following pairs of sets.

A = {1, 2, 3}   and   B = {1, 2, 3, 4, 5}
C = {r, d, t, p}   and   D = {p, q, a, r, s, p}
E = {△, ○, □}   and   F = {○, □, △, ◇}
G = {apple, pear, peach} and   H = {banana, orange, apricot}

■ **P-1**   Are all the elements of set A also elements of set B?

> **When every element of set A is also an element of set B, A is a subset of B.**

■ **P-2**   Are all the elements of C also elements of D?

It would not be correct to say that C is a subset of D since there is an element of C that is not in D.

■ **P-3**   Is every element of set E also an element of set F? Is E a subset of F?

■ **P-4**   Is G a subset of H? Why or why not?

■ **P-5**   Would it be correct to say that B is a subset of A? Why or why not?

■ **P-6**   Can you describe some more sets that are subsets of set B?

■ **P-7**   What larger set can you name that has the set of vowels as one of its subsets?

The set of boys is a subset of the set of students in class.

Mathematicians also agree that the following sentence is true.

Every set is a subset of itself.

Thus, it is correct to say that set A is a subset of set A.

You saw in the exercises of the preceding section that it is possible to describe a set that has no elements in it.

A set that has no elements is called the empty set, or the null set.

The empty set can be named by the symbol ϕ, or it can be represented by empty braces, { }. The set of even numbers between $4\frac{1}{2}$ and $5\frac{3}{4}$ is the empty set. Likewise, the set of months that have 32 days is the empty set. Notice that it is *the* empty set. Even though there are many descriptions for it, there is actually only one empty set.

You should realize that the symbols

$$\{0\} \quad \text{and} \quad \{\phi\}$$

do not represent the empty set. These symbols represent sets that do, in fact, have an element in each!

■ **P-8** How would you describe the relationship between the following sets?

$$A = \{1, 2, 3\} \quad \text{and} \quad B = \{1, 2, 3, 4, 5\}$$

Are there any elements of A that are not in B?

You can see that this question suggests another way of looking at the subset relation.

■ **P-9** Consider the following sets.

$$R = \{ \quad \} \quad \text{and} \quad S = \{a, b, c\}$$

Are there any elements of R that are not in S?

You may conclude that the following sentence is true.

The empty set is a subset of every set.

ORAL EXERCISES 1.2

1. If every element of set Q is also an element of set Y, then what relationship does Q have to Y?
2. What name is given to the set that has no elements?
3. What symbols can be used to describe the empty set?

In each of the following pairs of sets, name one set, if possible, that is a subset of the other.

4. A $= \{2, 5, 12\}$ and B $= \{2, 13, 5, 11\}$
5. R $= \{a, x, t\}$ and S $= \{a, t\}$
6. C $= \{\triangle, \square, \bigcirc\}$ and D $= \{\triangle, \square, \bigcirc, \bigcirc\}$
7. P $= \{a, t, b, x\}$ and Q $= \{r, x, b, t\}$
8. M $= \{2, 4, 6, 8, 10\}$ and N $= \{6, 2, 8, 4, 10\}$
9. E $= \phi$ and F $= \{3\}$
10. T $= \{0\}$ and W $= \{5 - 5\}$

Indicate whether each of the following sets is *Empty* or *Nonempty*.

11. $\{\ \ \}$ 12. $\{\phi\}$ 13. $\{0\}$ 14. ϕ

Suppose you want to consider all the subsets of A if

$$A = \{a, b, c\}.$$

15. Name the subsets that have one element in each.
16. Name the subsets that have two elements in each.
17. Is there a subset that has three elements in it?
18. Have you considered all the possible subsets of A?

WRITTEN EXERCISES 1.2

A Consider the following sets.

$$A = \{2, 4, 6\} \qquad B = \{0, 2, 4, 6\}$$
$$C = \{0, 1, 2, 3, 4, 6\} \qquad D = \{0, 1, 3, 5\}$$
$$E = \{\tfrac{6}{3}, (3 + 1), (8 - 2)\}$$

Using these sets, indicate whether each of the following statements is *True* or *False*.

1. A is a subset of B.
2. B is a subset of C.
3. B is a subset of A.
4. C is a subset of B.
5. D is a subset of B.
6. D is a subset of C.
7. E is a subset of C.
8. E is a subset of B.
9. E is a subset of A.
10. A is a subset of E.

Indicate whether each of the following statements is *True* or *False*.

11. ϕ is a subset of {1, 2, 3}.
12. { } is a subset of {a}.
13. Set R is a subset of set R.
14. {a, b, c} is a subset of {a, b, c}.
15. {ϕ} is a subset of {θ, ϕ}.
16. {0} is a subset of {0, 1, 2}.
17. {x, y, z} is a subset of { }.
18. {a, b, c} is a subset of ϕ.

Indicate whether each of the following sets is *Empty* or *Nonempty*.

19. The set of numbers that can be added to 5 to obtain a sum of 5
20. The set of numbers that can be multiplied by 10 to obtain 10 as a product
21. The set of elements that belong to both A and B where A = {1, 2, 3} and B = {0, 2, 4}
22. The set of elements that belong to both P and Q where P = { } and Q = {a, b, c}
23. The set of letters of the alphabet that serve as both consonants and vowels
24. The set of cars that can be described as both 8-cylinder and 6-cylinder

25. Use the roster method to name all possible subsets of {1, 2, 3}.
26. Use the roster method to name all the subsets of {1, 2, 3, 4} that are not subsets of {1, 2, 3}.

C   Indicate whether each of the following statements is *True* or *False*.

27. The set of blue-eyed persons is a subset of the set of persons who have blond hair.
28. The set of all high school basketball players is a subset of the set of high school football players.
29. The set of United States senators from your state is a subset of the set of all United States senators.
30. The set of United States sailors is a subset of the set of men in the United States armed forces.
31. The set of states east of the Mississippi River is a subset of the set of states west of the Mississippi River.
32. The set of United States explorers who have been to Mars is a subset of the set of all United States explorers.

1.3 Finite and Infinite Sets

A set is said to be **finite** provided that either it is empty or its elements can be counted and the counting comes to an end. If a set is not finite, it is said to be **infinite**.

The set of states of the United States is finite while the set of whole numbers is infinite.

■ **P-1** Is each of the following sets finite or infinite?

$$\{\tfrac{2}{3}, \tfrac{3}{4}\}; \quad \phi; \quad \{\text{leaves on a certain tree}\};$$
$$\{\text{even numbers}\}; \quad \{\text{different names for the number 2}\}$$

You can see that the roster method for naming a set is not satisfactory for infinite sets because you cannot list all the elements. It is possible to use a **word description** for many sets and thus to avoid the necessity of listing the elements. The word description must be completely accurate so that a person can tell whether or not a particular element belongs to the set. The set must contain all the elements that fit the description and no other.

■ **P-2** Only one of the following is a good word description for a set. Which one is it?

$$\{\text{persons who walk fast}\}; \quad \{\text{good baseball players}\};$$
$$\{\text{teachers in your school}\}$$

Here are word descriptions of some infinite sets:

$$\{\text{whole numbers greater than 5}\}; \quad \{\text{numbers between 1 and 2}\};$$
$$\{\text{whole numbers}\}; \quad \{\text{different names for 3}\}$$

■ **P-3** Is it clear what elements belong to each of the above infinite sets?

■ **P-4** Is it possible to name the elements of each of the following finite sets?

$$\{\text{days of the week with names that begin with T}\};$$
$$\{\text{two largest cities of Missouri}\};$$
$$\{\text{former presidents of the United States}\}$$

For certain infinite sets of numbers, it is possible to use a modified form of the roster method. For example, the set of even whole numbers can be shown as

$$\{0, 2, 4, 6, \cdots\}.$$

The three dots here mean that there are infinitely many elements in the set and that you can obtain names for more elements just by following the pattern for those already listed. It is important that enough elements be listed to make the pattern clear.

■ **P-5** Can you give a word description for

$$\{12, 15, 18, 21, \cdots\}?$$

■ **P-6** What are the next three elements in

$$\{5, 10, 15, 20, 25, \cdots\}?$$

Notice here that a certain order for listing the elements must be used to establish the pattern. In using the regular roster method, the order in which you list the elements is not important. Thus,

$$\{2, 5, \tfrac{1}{2}\} \quad \text{and} \quad \{5, 2, \tfrac{1}{2}\}$$

are names for the same set.

The modified roster method for sets can also be used for certain finite sets that have many elements. The set of whole numbers from 1 to 20 inclusive could be described as

$$\{1, 2, 3, 4, 5, \cdots, 20\}.$$

Here the three dots represent the whole numbers between 5 and 20 that are not listed. Notice that the first and last elements are listed along with enough other elements to establish the pattern that describes the set.

■ **P-7** What elements are not listed in the set

$$\{10, 20, 30, \cdots, 90\}?$$

■ **P-8** How could you describe the set of odd numbers from 1 to 999 inclusive by the modified roster method?

■ **P-9** What is a word description of the set represented by

$$\{2, 4, 6, \cdots, 100\}?$$

ORAL EXERCISES 1.3

1. What are finite sets? infinite sets? Give examples of each.
2. Is the empty set considered to be finite or infinite?

Tell whether each of the following sets is *Finite* or *Infinite*.
3. {persons living on earth}
4. {4, 8, 12, · · ·, 36}
5. {3, 6, 9, 12, · · ·}
6. {numbers between 2 and 3}
7. {women on major league baseball teams}
8. {0, ϕ}

In each of the following sets, name three more elements of the set that are not listed.
9. {1, 2, 4, 7, 11, · · ·}
10. {$\frac{1}{2}$, $\frac{1}{3}$, $\frac{1}{4}$, $\frac{1}{5}$, · · ·}
11. {$\frac{1}{2}$, $\frac{3}{4}$, $\frac{5}{6}$, $\frac{7}{8}$, · · ·}
12. {0.5, 0.55, 0.555, · · ·}
13. {1, 2, 4, 8, 16, · · ·}

Are the following good descriptions for sets? Discuss.
14. {persons who live in cities}
15. {persons who play tennis well}
16. {buildings of modern design}
17. {numbers named by fractions that are easy to add}

WRITTEN EXERCISES 1.3

A   Indicate whether each of the following sets is *Finite* or *Infinite*.
1. {automobiles in the United States}
2. {grains of sand on all the beaches of the world}
3. {numbers greater than 1 named by fractions that show 5 as a denominator}
4. {days of the week with names that begin with a vowel}
5. {points on a three-inch-long line segment}
6. {whole numbers up to a billion trillion trillion}
7. {$\frac{2}{1}$, $\frac{2}{2}$, $\frac{2}{3}$, $\frac{2}{4}$, · · ·, $\frac{2}{13}$}
8. {0, 1, 2, · · ·, 10}
9. {0.9, 0.99, 0.999, · · ·}
10. {0.9, 0.99, 0.999, · · ·, 0.99999999}

In each of the following sets, name the next three elements of the set that are not listed.

11. $\{2, 5, 8, 11, \cdots\}$
12. $\{\frac{1}{2}, 2\frac{1}{2}, 4\frac{1}{2}, 6\frac{1}{2}, \cdots\}$
13. $\{1, 3, 9, 27, \cdots\}$
14. $\{1, 4, 9, 16, \cdots\}$
15. $\{400, 200, 100, 50, \cdots\}$
16. $\{1, \frac{1}{3}, \frac{1}{9}, \frac{1}{27}, \cdots\}$

Name the following sets using the modified roster method.

17. {whole numbers between 100 and 200}
18. {every fifth whole number beginning with 21}
19. {letters of the alphabet}
20. {Roman numerals from 1 to 20}
21. {years between 1899 and 1935}
22. {days of February in a leap year}

B In what way are the sets in each of the following pairs related?

23. {whole numbers greater than 10} and $\{11, 12, 13, 14, \cdots\}$
24. $A = \{\frac{2}{4}, \frac{2}{6}, \frac{2}{8}\}$ and $B = \{\frac{1}{2}, \frac{1}{3}, \frac{1}{4}\}$
25. {persons taller than 6 feet} and {persons taller than 72 inches}
26. $C = \{r, s, t\}$ and $D = \{s, r, t\}$

How are the sets in each of these pairs related?

27. $A = \{\frac{1}{2}, 5, 2\}$ and $B = \{c, r, w\}$
28. {United States senators from Texas}
and
{United States senators from Rhode Island}
29. $R = \{2, 4, 6, 8, \cdots, 20\}$ and $S = \{1, 3, 5, 7, \cdots, 19\}$
30. {even numbers} and {odd numbers}

C 31. It is impractical to count the number of persons on earth at a given instant. Does this mean that the set of persons on earth is infinite?

32. Is the set of stars in the sky finite or infinite? Discuss.

Are the following good set descriptions? Discuss.

33. $\{\frac{1}{2}, 5, 27, 20\frac{1}{3}, \cdots\}$
34. {students who are good in math}
35. {persons who are Democrats}
36. {persons who must file a United States income tax return}

1.4 Equal Sets and Equivalent Sets

> **Two sets are said to be equal if they contain the same elements.**

Consider the sets

$$\{1, 2, 3\} \quad \text{and} \quad \{3 - 2, 4 - 2, 2 + 1\}.$$

They are equal sets because the elements of each are the whole numbers one, two, and three. Note that, for two sets to be equal, the names for the elements in each do not have to be the same.

■ **P-1** Can you pick out some pairs of equal sets among the following?

$$A = \{e, w, b\}; \quad B = \{5, 7, 8\}; \quad C = \{w, b, e\}; \quad D = \{6, 7, 8\};$$
$$E = \{6 - 1, 6 + 1, 6 + 2\}$$

> **Two sets that contain the same number of elements are said to be equivalent.**

The set of whole numbers from 1 to 26 inclusive and the set of letters of the alphabet are equivalent.

In using the roster method for naming a set, you should never list an element more than once.

■ **P-2** Are two equal sets always equivalent?

■ **P-3** Are the sets $\{a, b, c\}$ and $\{\frac{1}{2}, \frac{1}{3}, \frac{1}{5}\}$ equivalent? Are they equal?

■ **P-4** Are two equivalent sets always equal?

> **If two sets are equivalent, the elements of one set can be put into a one-to-one correspondence with the elements of the other.**

This means that each element of one set can be paired off with exactly one element of the other set and that there are no elements left unpaired.

Consider the two sets in **P-3** on the previous page. You can demonstrate a one-to-one correspondence in this way:

$$a \qquad b \qquad c$$
$$\updownarrow \qquad \updownarrow \qquad \updownarrow$$
$$\tfrac{1}{2} \qquad \tfrac{1}{3} \qquad \tfrac{1}{5}$$

■ **P-5** Is there a one-to-one correspondence between the set of students in your math class and the set of student desks in the room?

When you count the number of elements in a set or the number of objects in a collection, you are actually forming a one-to-one correspondence between the members of the set and the elements in a subset of the set of **counting numbers,**

$$\{1, 2, 3, 4, 5, \cdots\}.$$

For the set

$$\{\text{Mary, Dick, Ann, Jean, Helen, Alan, Tom, Oscar}\},$$

you can demonstrate this counting procedure by the following correspondence.

$$\text{Mary} \quad \text{Dick} \quad \text{Ann} \quad \text{Jean} \quad \text{Helen} \quad \text{Alan} \quad \text{Tom} \quad \text{Oscar}$$
$$\updownarrow \qquad \updownarrow \qquad \updownarrow \qquad \updownarrow \qquad \updownarrow \qquad \updownarrow \qquad \updownarrow \qquad \updownarrow$$
$$1 \qquad 2 \qquad 3 \qquad 4 \qquad 5 \qquad 6 \qquad 7 \qquad 8$$

You conclude that the given set has eight elements in it. In practice, of course, you do not have to write down the correspondence.

If you consider the number zero along with the set of counting numbers, you are thinking of the set of **whole numbers.** The set of whole numbers can be represented by the modified roster method as

$$\{0, 1, 2, 3, 4, \cdots\}.$$

The **successor** of any whole number is the next greater whole number.

Notice that each whole number has a successor.

■ **P-6** What is the successor of 15? of 100? of 1,000,000?

If you multiply each element of the set of whole numbers by 5, you obtain a subset of the set of whole numbers called the **multiples** of 5. You can represent such a set as follows: $\{0, 5, 10, 15, \cdots\}$.

■ **P-7** How could you describe the set {0, 3, 6, 9, 12, · · ·}?

A subset of whole numbers with which you are familiar is the set of **even** numbers, the multiples of 2, or {0, 2, 4, 6, · · ·}. The whole numbers that are not even numbers make up the set of **odd** numbers.

■ **P-8** How can the set of odd numbers be obtained from the set of even numbers?

ORAL EXERCISES 1.4

1. What is meant by equal sets?
2. Describe two sets that are equal.
3. What is meant by equivalent sets?
4. Describe two sets that are equivalent.
5. If you pair each of your courses with each of your textbooks, is the pairing a one-to-one correspondence?
6. Does each counting number have a successor?
7. What number can be added to each whole number to obtain its successor?
8. Can you name a whole number that is not the successor of any whole number?
9. Can you name a counting number that is not the successor of any counting number?
10. Is the set of whole numbers finite or infinite? Why?
11. Are the set of whole numbers and the set of counting numbers equal?
12. Can you say that the set of counting numbers is a subset of the set of whole numbers? Explain.

WRITTEN EXERCISES 1.4

A Indicate whether the sets in each of the following pairs of sets are *Equal, Equivalent, Both equal and equivalent,* or *Neither.*

1. {counting numbers between 3 and 5} and {0}
2. {least counting number} and {1}
3. {whole numbers less than 9}
   and
   {counting numbers less than 10}
4. {counting numbers less than 10}
   and
   {whole numbers less than 10}

5. $\{\phi\}$ and $\{0\}$

6. ϕ and {counting numbers less than 1}

7. $\{\frac{3}{12}, 0, 5, \frac{1}{2}\}$ and $\{\frac{2}{3} - \frac{4}{6}, 10 \div 2, 0.25, \frac{5}{4} - \frac{3}{4}\}$

8. $\{\frac{5}{6}, \frac{15}{8}, \frac{7}{8}\}$ and $\{\frac{2}{3}, \frac{3}{4}\}$

9. {months having 31 days} and {months having 30 days}

10. $\{2, 3, 5, 7, 11\}$ and $\{5, 2, 7, 11, 3\}$

Demonstrate a one-to-one correspondence between the sets in each of the following pairs.

11. {first five whole numbers} and {first five counting numbers}

12. {even whole numbers less than 10}
and
{odd counting numbers less than 10}

13. {first five whole numbers}
and
{numbers that are doubles of the first five whole numbers}

14. {first five even counting numbers}
and
{successors of the first five even counting numbers}

15. {counting numbers} and {even counting numbers}

16. {whole numbers} and {counting numbers}

In each of the following, a correspondence is indicated between a subset of the counting numbers and another set. Name the second set by the roster method, and indicate whether the correspondence is one-to-one.

17.
1	2	3	4	5
↕	↕	↕	↕	↕
A	B	C	D	E

18.
1	2	3	4	5
↕	↕	↕	↕	↕
Tom	Don	Tom	Don	Tom

19.
1	2	3	4
↕	↕	↕	↕
2	3	4	5

20.
1	2	3	4	5
↕	↕	↕	↕	↕
5	10	15	20	25

21.
1	2	3	4	5	6
↕	↕	↕	↕	↕	↕
$\frac{1}{1}$	$\frac{1}{2}$	$\frac{2}{1}$	$\frac{3}{1}$	$\frac{2}{2}$	$\frac{1}{3}$

22.
1	2	3	4	5	6	7	8
↕	↕	↕	↕	↕	↕	↕	↕
$\frac{1}{1}$	$\frac{1}{2}$	$\frac{1}{3}$	$\frac{2}{3}$	$\frac{1}{4}$	$\frac{3}{4}$	$\frac{1}{5}$	$\frac{2}{5}$

Name the following subsets of the set of whole numbers by the roster method.

23. {multiples of 3 between 2 and 10}

24. {multiples of 11 that are less than 51}

25. {successors of the even multiples of whole numbers between 7 and 12}

26. {successors of odd counting numbers less than 6}
27. {multiples of 5 that are less than 22}
28. {multiples of 4 that are greater than 5 and less than 25}
29. {multiples of 3 that are even numbers and less than 30}
30. {multiples of 5 that are odd numbers and less than 50}

C The square of a number is the result obtained when the number is multiplied by itself. Let A = {0, 1, 2, 3, 4}.

31. Form set S whose elements are the squares of the elements of A.
32. Is S a subset of A? Are S and A equal? Are they equivalent?
33. Form the set B of elements that are in A *and* S.
34. Is B a subset of A? Is B a subset of S?

Let E = {0, 1, 2, 3} and F = {0, 2, 4, 6}.

35. Form set K whose elements are in E *or* in F. (If an element is in E, put it in K. If an element is in F, put it in K.)
36. How many elements are in E? in F? in K?
37. Is E a subset of K? Is F a subset of K?
38. What are the elements of K that are in E *and* F?

1.5 Sets and the Number Line

The **number line** is a handy device in mathematics for picturing many relationships. You can construct a number line in the following way. First draw a line and locate two points on it, matching the point to the left with 0 and the point to the right with 1.

Next, use the length of the segment between these two points as a unit of measure and locate more points to the right of 1. The distance between any two adjacent points that you have located will then be the same as the distance between the points marked 0 and 1. Match the successive points to the right of 1 with the whole numbers as follows.

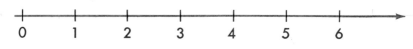

Put an arrowhead at the right to indicate that the marked points extend indefinitely far in that direction. The number line demonstrates a correspondence between certain points on the line and the set of whole numbers. The number paired with a point on the number line is called the **coordinate** of the point.

■ **P-1** Is this correspondence between points of the line and the whole numbers a one-to-one correspondence?

Now, locate a point on the number line halfway between the points whose coordinates are 0 and 1.

■ **P-2** What coordinate would you give to this point?

■ **P-3** What coordinate would you give to a point halfway between the points whose coordinates are 2 and 3?

If you mark off all points halfway between the points whose coordinates are whole numbers, you can set up the following correspondence.

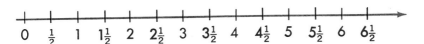

If you mark off a point one third of the way between 0 and 1 and then mark off segments of the same length to the right, you can set up the following correspondence.

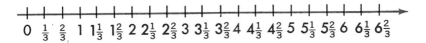

By continuing this argument, you can form a correspondence between a set of points on the number line and the set of numbers named by fractions.

The number line can also be used as another way of representing a set of numbers. The set of points on a number line associated with the elements of a particular set is the **graph** of that set. It is common practice to indicate the points that are in the graph of a set by marking them with heavy dots.

The graph of $\{1, 2\frac{1}{2}, 3, 5\frac{1}{3}\}$ is shown as follows.

■ **P-4** What set of numbers is represented by the following graph?

You can see that it is best to show the coordinates of all the points of the graph in order to avoid any errors in reading it. For example, there might be some disagreement in listing the elements of the set that is pictured by this graph:

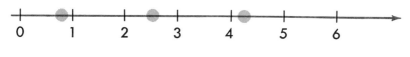

ORAL EXERCISES 1.5

1. In constructing a number line, how is the distance between the first two points determined?
2. Are the points that are associated with the whole numbers on a number line equally spaced?
3. What do you call the number that is paired with a point on the number line?
4. What coordinate would you match with the point halfway between the points whose coordinates are 5 and 6?
5. What number would you assign to the point that is $\frac{2}{3}$ of a unit to the left of the point with coordinate 3?

What is wrong with the following number lines?

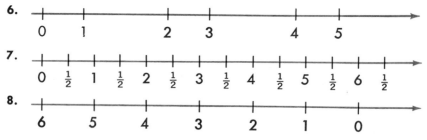

9. What is meant by the graph of a set?
10. How are points of a graph distinguished from other points on the line?

A Construct a number line in the following way. Locate the points with coordinates 0 and 1 so that they are 1 inch apart. Now mark points whose coordinates are 2, 3, 4, 5, and 6 and label these points accordingly.

Now use $\frac{1}{2}$ inch as a unit of measure, and successively mark points to the right of 0. Make a second line of coordinates below the whole number coordinates, naming all the points that you have marked on the line thus far. Each of these coordinates should be expressed as the quotient of two whole numbers, all having 2 as the denominator.

Next use $\frac{1}{4}$ inch as a unit of measure, and successively mark points to the right of 0. Make a third line of coordinates. This time name all the points by using fractions, each having 4 as the denominator.

1. How many names do you have for the first point on the line? How many names could it possibly have?

2. How many names do you have for the second point marked? Could it have more names?

3. If you located a point halfway between the points with coordinates $\frac{6}{4}$ and $\frac{7}{4}$, how could you name its coordinates?

4. What name could you give to a point located at a distance equal to $\frac{1}{3}$ inch to the left of the point whose coordinate is 5?

Draw graphs of the following sets.

5. $\{0, 1, 2, 3\}$

6. $\{\frac{1}{2}, \frac{3}{2}, \frac{5}{2}\}$

7. $\{0, 1, \frac{7}{3}\}$

8. $\{1, 0.5, 2.75\}$

9. $\{\frac{1}{3}, \frac{4}{3}, \frac{7}{3}\}$

10. $\{\frac{1}{4}, 2, \pi, 5\}$

11. $\{2, \frac{9}{3}, \frac{0}{3}\}$

12. $\{\ \}$

13. $\{\frac{8}{3}, \frac{9}{4}, \frac{29}{8}\}$

14. $\{\frac{3}{3}, \frac{6}{3}, \frac{9}{3}\}$

Use the roster method to name the sets that are graphed below.

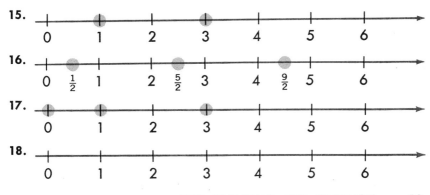

15.

16.

17.

18.

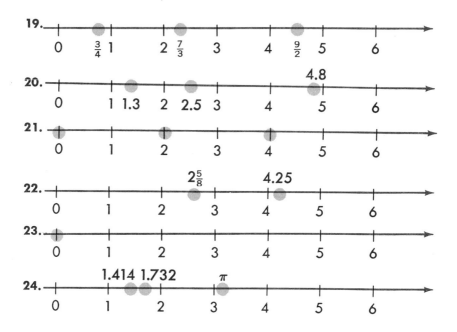

1.6 Rational Numbers of Arithmetic

The coordinates of one of the number lines in the preceding lesson could have been represented as follows.

Notice that each coordinate is now expressed as the quotient of two whole numbers.

> The set of numbers each of which can be represented as the quotient of two whole numbers is called the set of **rational numbers of arithmetic.**

You cannot name the set of rational numbers of arithmetic by the modified roster method because you cannot establish the pattern for the set by just listing a few of its elements. Some examples of rational numbers are $\frac{3}{4}$, $\frac{15}{16}$, $\frac{21}{55}$, $\frac{101}{95}$, $\frac{3152}{5}$.

■ **P-1** Can you represent 5 as the quotient of two whole numbers? What about $3\frac{1}{8}$? 2.56?

You have seen that it is possible to set up a correspondence on the number line so that there is a point of the line for each rational number of arithmetic.

■ **P-2** Do you think there is a rational number of arithmetic that can be paired with each point of the line?

There is a point of the line whose coordinate is the number π which you have used in arithmetic. You should recall that π is the number obtained when the circumference of any circle is divided by the length of one of its diameters. Many students have the mistaken notion that π equals $\frac{22}{7}$. However, $\frac{22}{7}$ is only an approximate value for π. The number π cannot be expressed as a quotient of two whole numbers and therefore is not a rational number. The number π expressed in decimal form correct to ten decimal places is 3.1415926536, but even this is only an approximation!

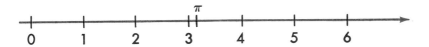

Later, you will learn about many more numbers that are not rational that can serve as coordinates of points on the number line. Every point to the right of 0 on the number line has a coordinate that is a number.

> The set consisting of 0 and the coordinates of points to the right of 0 is the set of **numbers of arithmetic.**

You will be working exclusively with these numbers in the next few chapters.

■ **P-3** If two points on a number line are one inch apart, do you think there is a point halfway between them?

■ **P-4** Is there a point halfway between two points that are 0.001 inch apart? between two points that are 0.00000001 inch apart?

■ **P-5** Suppose the coordinates of two points are $\frac{5}{8}$ and $\frac{6}{8}$. What do you think is the coordinate of the point halfway between them on the number line?

Perhaps you have reached the conclusion that you can always find a number of arithmetic between any two given numbers of arithmetic. This is true, and it is a very important fact in mathematics.

■ **P-6** Can you find a number between $3\frac{5}{16}$ and $3\frac{7}{16}$? between $\frac{3}{4}$ and $\frac{1}{2}$? between 2.6 and 2.62?

■ **P-7** Can you suggest a way of always finding a number of arithmetic between two given numbers?

ORAL EXERCISES 1.6

1. What is meant by a rational number of arithmetic?

Express each of the following as a quotient of two whole numbers in two different ways.

2. 0	**3.** 1	**4.** 1000
5. $5\frac{1}{2}$	**6.** $3\frac{7}{8}$	**7.** 5.2
8. 1.35	**9.** $\dfrac{1\frac{1}{2}}{4\frac{1}{2}}$	**10.** $\dfrac{2.3}{6.9}$

11. Is there exactly one point on a number line for each rational number of arithmetic?

12. Can you name a number of arithmetic that is not rational?

13. Are there any points on a number line whose coordinates are not rational numbers?

14. What is meant by the numbers of arithmetic?

Find a number between each of the following pairs of numbers.

15. 2 and 5	**16.** $\frac{1}{2}$ and $\frac{2}{3}$	**17.** $\frac{3}{8}$ and $\frac{5}{8}$
18. $\frac{1}{2}$ and $\frac{5}{6}$	**19.** 4 and $3\frac{4}{8}$	**20.** $2\frac{1}{3}$ and $2\frac{1}{2}$

WRITTEN EXERCISES 1.6

A Express each of the following numbers as the quotient of two whole numbers in two ways.

1. 15	**2.** 1	**3.** 100	**4.** 55
5. $3\frac{1}{5}$	**6.** $7\frac{1}{3}$	**7.** 2.3	**8.** 5.7
9. $2\frac{3}{100}$	**10.** $5\frac{7}{1000}$		

For each of the following, find a number that is between the two given numbers.

11. 5 and 6	**12.** 13 and 14	**13.** $5\frac{1}{2}$ and $5\frac{3}{4}$
14. $2\frac{3}{4}$ and 3	**15.** $\frac{3}{8}$ and $\frac{5}{8}$	**16.** $\frac{13}{16}$ and $\frac{15}{16}$

17. $\frac{3}{5}$ and $\frac{4}{5}$ 18. $\frac{2}{7}$ and $\frac{3}{7}$ 19. 4.2 and 4.3

20. 5.7 and 5.8   21. 4.01 and 4.02   22. 3.15 and 3.16

23. 0.01 and 0.009   24. 2.1 and 2.09

B   The rational number $\frac{22}{7}$ is sometimes used as an approximation for π. Expressed in decimal form, an approximation for π correct to 5 decimal places would be 3.14159.

25. Express $\frac{22}{7}$ as a decimal rounded to the nearest thousandth.
26. Which is a closer approximation of π, $\frac{22}{7}$ or 3.14?

1.7   Numerals and Numerical Phrases

A young child probably first learns about numbers when he senses a difference between a set consisting of one element and a set consisting of two elements. For example, he may see one block by itself and two blocks, one on top of the other, and realize in what sense the sets are different. This is his first experience with the ideas of oneness and twoness. For the child, the blocks probably serve as symbols for these ideas. Later he learns to write the symbols 1 and 2.

Symbols that are used as names for numbers are called **numerals.** Numbers themselves are abstract ideas, but numerals are names or labels for these ideas. Most people in their everyday talk refer to numerals as numbers and make no distinction between them. Usually it is easy to understand what they mean. You should realize, however, that it is impossible to write the number five on the chalkboard. You can only write a name for the idea of fiveness — that is, you can write a numeral representing five.

Occasionally it will be convenient to enclose numerals in single quotation marks to indicate clearly that the symbol is meant and not the number itself. Thus, the statement that ' 3 ' is greater than ' 5 ' is true when referring to the numerals. On the other hand, the statement that 3 is greater than 5 is false when referring to numbers. If the symbol is not shown between single quotation marks, or if it does not specifically say "the numeral 3," for example, you can assume that the number is meant.

■ **P-1**   Can you explain why the following statement is true?

Half of '8' is '3'.

Most persons that you know have many names. For example, the name of a basketball coach may be George Smith. This is his common name. To his players, however, he is Coach Smith, to his students he is Mr. Smith, to his wife he is George, and to his close friends he is Smitty.

Just as a person has many names, so too does each number. For example, some of the names for the number five are as follows.

$$5; \quad V; \quad 4+1; \quad \cancel{||||}; \quad 8-3; \quad 10 \div 2; \quad 1 \times 5; \quad \frac{11+4}{3}$$

You may call the numeral 5 the common name for the number five. In general, think of the common name of a number as being its simplest name.

■ **P-2**   What are the common names for the numbers that are named by the following numerals?

$$6+2; \quad 0+10; \quad 5-5; \quad \tfrac{0}{7}; \quad 3 \times 5; \quad \tfrac{2}{4}; \quad \tfrac{1}{2}+\tfrac{1}{4}; \quad \tfrac{25}{100}; \quad \tfrac{3}{8}+\tfrac{1}{8}$$

■ **P-3**   Would you consider '$\tfrac{1}{2}$' or '0.5' as the common name for one-half? Discuss.

One problem that you face quite often in mathematics is that of finding a common name for a number that is named in some other form. In arithmetic, you learned that 144 is a common name for the number named by 12×12 and that 667 is a common name for $756 - 89$. Although a number may have several common names, in this course *the* common name for a whole number will mean one of the elements of the set $\{$'0', '1', '2', '3', '4', $\cdots\}$.

You have noticed that many of the examples of numerals in this section involve one or more symbols of operation, such as $\dfrac{11+4}{3}$. These are **numerical phrases.**

A **numerical phrase** is itself a numeral, and it involves other numerals and one or more signs of operation.

The following are some special numerical phrases.

$2 + 3$ is an example of an **indicated sum.**
$7 - 4$ is an example of an **indicated difference.**
5×4 is an example of an **indicated product.**
$10 \div 3$ is an example of an **indicated quotient.**

ORAL EXERCISES 1.7

1. What is a numeral?

2. Give five different names for the number ten.

What are the common names for the numbers represented as follows?

3. VII **4.** 𝟕𝟭𝟭𝟭𝟭 **5.** $\frac{1}{2} \times \frac{1}{3}$

6. $\frac{1}{3} + \frac{1}{2}$ **7.** $0.02 + 0.15$ **8.** $1.7 - 0.9$

9. 0.1×0.1 **10.** $\frac{1}{2} \times \frac{1}{2}$

11. What do you call a numeral such as $2 + 3 - 4$?

Name the special type for each of the following numerical phrases.

12. 3×5 **13.** $8 \div 5$ **14.** $1.3 + 0.7$

15. $\frac{3}{4} - \frac{1}{8}$ **16.** $\frac{5}{2}$ **17.** $\frac{1}{4} \times \frac{1}{3}$

18. Explain why a number cannot be written down.

Are the following statements *True* or *False?*

19. 'Eight' is larger than 'nine'.

20. '3' is on this page, but 3 is not on this page.

WRITTEN EXERCISES 1.7

A Applying your understanding of the difference in meaning between number and numeral, tell whether each of the following statements is *True* or *False.*

1. 2 is greater than 3.

2. '45' consists of two numbers.

3. '5' is smaller than ' 5 '.

4. 100 is made up of '1', '0', and '0'.

5. '0.00005' is larger than '0.5'.

6. Numbers can be found on this page.

Indicate which of the following are just numerals and which are also numerical phrases.

 7. 215.3   **8.** 2×7 **9.** $\frac{1}{2}$
 10. $2 + 5$ **11.** $15.0 + 2.3$ **12.** 56
 13. $15 \div 15$ **14.** XLVI   **15.** $2 + 5 \div 3 - 1 + 3 \times 5$

What type of numerical phrase is each of the following?

 16. 2.3×1.5 **17.** $17\frac{1}{2} - 15\frac{3}{4}$ **18.** $54 \div 2.7$
 19. $18 + 17$ **20.** $\frac{1}{4} \times \frac{3}{8}$ **21.** $13.50 - 8.65$
 22. $\frac{1}{4} \div \frac{3}{5}$

C State whether each of the following is *True* or *False* if single quotes indicate the symbol and not the idea.

 23. Carl can erase the '6' in 46.
 24. 'Six' has three letters.
 25. 'Numbers' can be found on this page.

1.8   Order of Operations

■ **P-1**   What number do you think is named by each of the following numerical phrases?

$$2 \times 3 + 4; \quad 2 + 3 \times 4; \quad 5 - 4 \div 2; \quad 8 \div 2 - 3$$

To make sure that each numerical phrase names only one number, you must agree on the order of operations for finding the common name for the number named by the phrase.

Mathematicians agree to multiply or divide before adding or subtracting in finding a common name.

For the examples in **P-1**, note the following.

10 is the common name for $2 \times 3 + 4$.
 The multiplication is done before the addition. 2×3 is 6, and $6 + 4$ is 10.

14 is the common name for $2 + 3 \times 4$.
 3×4 is 12, and $2 + 12$ is 14.

3 is the common name for $5 - 4 \div 2$.
 The division is done before the subtraction. $4 \div 2$ is 2, and $5 - 2$ is 3.

1 is the common name for $8 \div 2 - 3$.
 $8 \div 2$ is 4, and $4 - 3$ is 1.

In case several operations are indicated in the numerical phrase, first perform the multiplication and division from left to right as they are indicated in the phrase. The addition and subtraction will then be performed from left to right in the resulting phrase.

18 is the common name for $8 \times 2 + 6 \div 3$.	8×2 is 16, $6 \div 3$ is 2, and $16 + 2$ is 18.
17 is the common name for $16 - 8 \div 2 + 5$.	$8 \div 2$ is 4, $16 - 4$ is 12, and $12 + 5$ is 17.

■ **P-2** What number is named by $20 - 3 \times 5 + 8 \div 2$? Explain.

■ **P-3** What number is named by $18 - 2 + 3 - 15$? Explain.

■ **P-4** What number is named by $32 \div 8 \times 2$? by $5 \times 8 \div 4$?

ORAL EXERCISES 1.8

1. Why is it necessary to perform operations in a certain order to find the number named by a numerical phrase?
2. What is the agreement for the order of performing operations?

Give the common name for the number named by each of the following numerical phrases.

3. $8 - 3 + 5$	**4.** $\frac{1}{2} \times 6 + 2$
5. $\frac{1}{2} + 6 \times 2$	**6.** $2 - 6 \div 3$
7. $5 + 3 \times 2 - 8$	**8.** $12 \div 3 - 2$
9. $3 \times \frac{5}{3} - 4$	**10.** $\frac{3}{8} + \frac{1}{8} \times 4$
11. $13 - 10 \div 2 + 1$	**12.** $1 - 1 + 1 \times 1 - 1 \div 1 + 1$
13. $8 + 2 \times 3 - 6 + 12 \div 4 - 7$	**14.** $28 - 14 \div 7 + 2 \times 10 - 40$

WRITTEN EXERCISES 1.8

A Give a common name for the number named by each of the following numerical phrases.

1. $4 + 8 \times 3$	**2.** $3 \times 5 + 10$
3. $21 \div 7 - 2$	**4.** $21 - 7 \div 2$
5. $27 - 3 \times 4$	**6.** $27 \times 3 - 4$
7. $\frac{5}{4} + \frac{1}{2} - \frac{3}{8}$	**8.** $\frac{15}{8} - \frac{3}{8} + \frac{1}{4}$
9. $7 + 8 \div 3$	**10.** $8 \div 7 + 3$
11. $3 \times 5 \div 2$	**12.** $5 \div 3 \times 2$
13. $8 + 12 \div 3 - 2 \times 5$	**14.** $22 - 3 \times 6 + 5 \div 2$
15. $0 - 0 \div 7 \div 15 + 0$	**16.** $1 \times 7 \div 7 + 1 - 8 \div 8$

B In general, the operation that is performed last is used to name the specific type of numerical phrase that is given. With this in mind, name each of the following phrases.

Example: $10 + 3 \times 5$ is an indicated sum.

17. $8 - 2 \times 3$

18. $16 \div 2 - 3$

19. $5 \times 6 + 2$

20. $\frac{1}{4} + 7 \div 4$

21. $17.3 - 52.7 \div 8.3$

22. $55 \div 8 + 17$

23. $8 + 2 - 5$

24. $23 - 17 + 2$

25. $2 \times 5 + 8 \div 3$

26. $27 \div 3 \div 2 - 1$

C Find the common name for the number named by each of the following.

27. $\frac{3}{8} \times \frac{2}{5} - \frac{1}{20}$

28. $19 \div 4 - \frac{7}{8}$

29. $\frac{1}{2} + 14 - 5\frac{3}{4}$

30. $7\frac{1}{8} - 7 \div 4 + \frac{1}{4} \times 5$

31. $2 \times 5 \div 3 \times 15 \div 10$

32. $21 \div 7 \times 4 \div 8 \times 14 \div 2$

1.9 Punctuation of Numerical Phrases

While it is necessary to have an agreement on the order of operations in a numerical phrase, another device is also needed. Sometimes you wish a different order for the operations to be performed in finding a common name for the number named by a phrase. Most often, you will use symbols of inclusion called **parentheses,** ( ).

Numerals and signs of operation that are enclosed in parentheses will be considered as naming a single number. Thus $(7 + 2) \times 3$ can be thought of as the product of 9 and 3 because $(7 + 2)$ is considered to name the number 9. Likewise, $8 \div (4 - 2)$ can be thought of as $8 \div 2$ because $(4 - 2)$ is a name for 2.

Notice that this understanding about parentheses suggests that you should perform the operations indicated within the parentheses first. Then proceed with the other operations according to the rule of order stated previously.

■ **P-1** What number is named by $21 + 9 \div 3$? by $(21 + 9) \div 3$?

Thus, the phrases $21 + 9 \div 3$ and $(21 + 9) \div 3$ name different numbers while the phrases $21 + 9 \div 3$ and $21 + (9 \div 3)$ name the same number.

■ **P-2** What is a common name for $(2 + 3) \times 5$? for $(15 - 3) \div 2$?

The symbols called fractions have the double role of serving as names for rational numbers and also as indicated quotients. You can think of the fraction $\frac{2}{5}$ as being a name for a certain rational number of arithmetic and also as indicating that 2 is to be divided by 5. In this latter sense, $\frac{2}{5}$ and $2 \div 5$ convey the same notion.

A fraction is often used to represent division in a numerical phrase involving other operations. Thus, the phrases $(3 + 5) \div (8 - 2)$ and $\frac{(3 + 5)}{(8 - 2)}$ name the same number. It is common practice to let the fraction bar serve the role as a symbol of inclusion in phrases involving division. Therefore, $\frac{(3 + 5)}{(8 - 2)}$ and $\frac{3 + 5}{8 - 2}$ name the same number, but the second is certainly easier to write. Of course, you should always use parentheses in a phrase if the meaning will not be clear otherwise.

■ **P-3** What is a common name for $\frac{21 - 3}{4 + 2}$? for $21 - 3 \div 4 + 2$?

■ **P-4** How could you name $(2 + 3 \times 4) \div (5 \times 8)$ by using a fraction?

ORAL EXERCISES 1.9

1. What do you call the symbols of inclusion indicated by ( )?
2. What operation would be performed first in finding a common name for the number named by $(4 + 5) \div 2$?
3. What is a common name for $8 - 3 \times 2$?
4. How would you rewrite the phrase $8 - 3 \times 2$ if you want the subtraction to be performed first? What number would be named then?
5. What other well-known symbol sometimes serves as a symbol of inclusion?
6. What is a common name for $\frac{24 - 3 \times 6}{2} - \frac{8 - 6}{2}$?

Read the following phrases, inserting parentheses so that each phrase will name the greatest possible number.

7. $2 \times 3 + 5$
8. $18 - 5 \times 3$
9. $15 + 8 \div 2$
10. $2 \times 10 - 3$
11. $24 \div 8 - 2$
12. $5 \times 1 - 1$
13. $\frac{1}{2} \times \frac{1}{3} + \frac{2}{3}$
14. $\frac{1}{2} \times \frac{1}{2} + \frac{1}{2}$
15. $\frac{2}{3} \times \frac{3}{2} + 1$

A Find a common name for each number named by the following numerical phrases.

1. $(2 + 3) \times 5$
2. $8 \times (5 - 2)$
3. $(7 \times 5) + 3$
4. $12 - (14 \div 2)$
5. $7 \times 5 + 3$
6. $12 - 14 \div 2$
7. $\frac{1}{2} \times (3 + 12)$
8. $(9 - 2) \times \frac{1}{3}$
9. $(8 - 2) \times (10 - 3)$
10. $(17 - 5) \div (9 - 5)$
11. $(8.2 - 1.2) \div 2$
12. $8.2 - 1.2 \div 2$
13. $4 \times (3 \times 5)$
14. $(4 \times 3) \times 5$
15. $(\frac{1}{2} \times \frac{1}{2}) \times \frac{1}{2}$
16. $\frac{1}{2} \times \frac{1}{2} \times \frac{1}{2}$

Rewrite the following numerical phrases by using a fraction bar to indicate division. Then find a common name for the number named by the phrase.

17. $(35 - 27) \div (14 - 9)$
18. $(2 \times 9 - 5) \div 6$
19. $2 \times (15 - 7) \div (13 - 4)$
20. $(25 + 4) \times 2 \div (30 - 1)$
21. $(2 \times 3 + 2 \times 5) \div 2 \times (3 + 5)$
22. $8 \times (13 - 5) \div 8 \times 13 - 8 \times 5$
23. $8 \div (12 - 7) + 2$
24. $(75 - 63) \div 10 - 0.3$

Copy the following numerical phrases and use parentheses so that the resulting phrase will name the same number as the common name following it.

25. $2 \times 7 - 5;$ 4
26. $19 + 3 \times \frac{1}{2};$ 11
27. $8 - 3 \times 2 + 5;$ 35
28. $2 \times 3 + 2 \times 7;$ 70
29. $2 + 3 \times 5 + 2 + 3 \times 4;$ 45
30. $8 + 7 \div 3 + 8 - 3;$ 10

B Which of the following pairs of numerical phrases are names for the same number?

31. $2 \times 3;$ 3×2
32. $8 + 3;$ $3 + 8$
33. $8 \div 4;$ $4 \div 8$
34. $8 - 12;$ $12 - 8$
35. $2 \times (3 \times 4);$ $(2 \times 3) \times 4$
36. $(5 + 7) + 3;$ $5 + (7 + 3)$
37. $5 + (3 \times 4);$ $(5 + 3) \times (5 + 4)$
38. $5 \times (3 + 4);$ $5 \times 3 + 5 \times 4$
39. $\frac{1}{2} \times (\frac{5}{4} - \frac{3}{4});$ $\frac{1}{2} \times \frac{5}{4} - \frac{1}{2} \times \frac{3}{4}$
40. $13 - 12 \div 4;$ $(13 - 12) \div (13 - 4)$

1.10 Multiplication Symbols

There are special symbols that are useful in algebra for indicating the operation of multiplication.

> The **raised dot,** · , placed between two numerals indicates that the numbers named are to be multiplied.

Thus, 2 · 5 is the indicated product of 2 and 5. In using this symbol for multiplication, you must take care to raise the dot so that it will not be confused with the decimal point.

Parentheses can also be used to indicate multiplication in the following ways.

(2)(5) is the indicated product of 2 and 5.

2(5) is the indicated product of 2 and 5.

(2 + 7)(3 + 4) is the indicated product of 9 and 7.

(2 + 7)3 is the indicated product of 9 and 3.

> Two pairs of parentheses placed next to each other with no symbol between the pairs indicates multiplication. A numeral placed next to a parenthesis with no symbol between the numeral and the parenthesis indicates multiplication.

It is also permissible to use the raised dot between parentheses to indicate multiplication, but this is really unnecessary. For example, (14) · (15) is the indicated product of 14 and 15. You know, however, that (14)(15) and 14 · 15 name the same product.

■ **P-1** What is a common name for 2(3 + 5)?

■ **P-2** What is a common name for 3 + 2 · 5?

From this point on, the multiplication symbol, ×, as used in arithmetic will no longer be used. This is done to avoid confusing the symbol × with the letter x. The letter x will be used extensively in later work for a different purpose.

ORAL EXERCISES 1.10

1. What symbols can now be used to indicate multiplication?

Find the common name for each number named below.

2. $2 \cdot 2 \cdot 2$

3. $2(2 \cdot 3)$

4. $3(4 + 2)$

5. $(5)(8)$

6. $3(\frac{2}{7})$

7. $(5)\frac{3}{5}$

8. $(\frac{2}{3} + 1\frac{1}{3})(\frac{1}{8} + 2\frac{7}{8})$

9. $(\frac{1}{5} + 4\frac{4}{5})5$

10. 78

11. $7 \cdot 8$

12. $7 \cdot 10 + 8$

13. $2 \cdot 3 \cdot 5$

14. $(2)(3)(5)$

15. $2(3)(5)$

16. $2 \cdot 3(5)$

17. $23(5)$

18. $(2 \cdot 3)5$

19. $2(3 \cdot 5)$

20. $2 \cdot (3 \cdot 5)$

21. $2(35)$

22. 235

23. $(2.5)(3.0)$

24. $(1.8)(0.2)$

WRITTEN EXERCISES 1.10

A Write the common name for each number named below.

1. $2 \cdot 3 \cdot 4$

2. $3 \cdot 2 \cdot 4$

3. $3 \cdot 3 \cdot 3$

4. $4 \cdot 4 \cdot 4$

5. $(\frac{1}{2})(\frac{1}{2})$

6. $(\frac{1}{2})(\frac{1}{4})$

7. $3(\frac{2}{3})$

8. $5(\frac{4}{5})$

9. $7 \cdot \frac{2}{3}$

10. $6 \cdot \frac{3}{5}$

11. $(\frac{1}{3})\frac{3}{5}$

12. $(\frac{1}{5})\frac{5}{8}$

13. $(\frac{1}{5} + \frac{4}{5})5$

14. $(\frac{1}{3} + 1\frac{2}{3})4$

15. $(\frac{1}{4} + 1\frac{3}{4})(2\frac{3}{4} - \frac{3}{4})$

16. $(\frac{2}{5} + 1\frac{3}{5})(\frac{1}{8} + 2\frac{7}{8})$

17. $3(25)$

18. $4(22)$

19. $3(2 \cdot 5)$

20. $4(2 \cdot 2)$

21. $(3.2)(2.5)$

22. $(3.7)(8.3)$

23. $(0.18)(0.03)$

24. $(0.09)(0.27)$

25. $0.7(1.3 + 2.8)$

26. $(3.5 + 7.2)(0.6)$

27. $(1.06 + 0.51)(0.3)$

28. $0.5(0.78 + 2.01)$

29. $\frac{2}{100}(0.78)$

30. $\frac{5}{1000}(3.1)$

C Write the common name for each number named below.

31. $(\frac{1}{4} + \frac{1}{2}) \cdot \frac{2}{5}$

32. $\frac{1}{4} \cdot \frac{2}{5} + \frac{1}{2} \cdot \frac{2}{5}$

33. $1.3(8.7 - 6.9)$

34. $(16.02 - 1.80)(0.050 + 1.113)$

35. $(2 \cdot 2 \cdot 2 \cdot 3 \cdot 3) \div (3 \cdot 2 \cdot 2 \cdot 3)$

36. $(\frac{1}{4} \cdot 4)(\frac{2}{3} \cdot \frac{3}{2})$

37. $(3 \cdot \frac{5}{2})(\frac{1}{3} \cdot \frac{2}{5})$

38. $2(\frac{2}{3}) + 2(\frac{1}{3})$

39. $2 \div 3.5 \div 4.8 \div 5$

40. $\dfrac{2 \cdot 5 \cdot 8}{3 \cdot 4 \cdot 5}$

1.11 Sentences

In your study of grammar, you learned what a sentence is and how to write good sentences. Sentences are also used in mathematics. Sentences that can be labeled true or false are called **statements.**

The sentence "5 + 3 equals 8" is a true statement.
The sentence "2 + 3 is greater than 10" is a false statement.

On the other hand, 10 − 3 is not a sentence. Recall that 10 − 3 is a numerical phrase. You know that phrases studied in grammar are not sentences either.

■ **P-1** Is "5 + 2 is not equal to 8" a true sentence?

■ **P-2** Is "2 + 8 − 4 ÷ 3" a false sentence?

A very useful and common symbol used in mathematics is the symbol for equality, = (read "is equal to"). You could have written the true sentence above as $5 + 3 = 8$. Whenever the equality symbol is used to form a sentence and the sentence is true, then the numerals or numerical phrases on each side of the equals sign name the same number.

> You may use the symbol for equality, =, to indicate that two symbols name the same thing.

The sentence $2 + 3 \cdot 6 = 20$ is a true statement.
The sentence $\{3, 5, 6\} = \{5, 3, 6\}$ is a true statement.
The sentence $2 + 3 \cdot 6 = 30$ is a false statement.

In the last sentence the symbols on each side of the equals sign do not name the same number. You can show that this is the case by the sentence $2 + 3 \cdot 6 \neq 30$.

> The symbol ≠ (read "is not equal to") indicates that the symbols on each side of it name two different things.

■ **P-3** With what symbol can you replace the question mark in $(8 − 3)5 \underline{\ ?\ } 32 − 8$ to form a true sentence?

■ **P-4** Is the sentence $5(3 + 4) = 5 \cdot 3 + 5 \cdot 4$ true or false?

Two other common mathematical symbols used in forming sentences are the inequality symbols $>$ and $<$.

> The symbol $>$ is read "is greater than," and the symbol $<$ is read "is less than."

Perhaps it will help you to remember that both $>$ and $<$ open toward the symbol for the greater quantity.

■ **P-5** Is each of the following sentences true or is it false?

$$2 + 8 > 5 + 4; \qquad 8 - 3 < 1 + 3; \qquad (2 \cdot 3) + 5 > (25 - 3) \div 2;$$
$$8 > 5; \qquad 5 < 8$$

You can see that the same relationship can be expressed in two different ways by use of these inequality symbols. Thus the sentences $7 + 3 \cdot 4 > 12$ and $12 < 7 + 3 \cdot 4$ express the same idea. This is an important fact to remember for future work.

■ **P-6** How can you rewrite the sentence $8 - 3 < 12 + 7$ by using the symbol for "is greater than"?

ORAL EXERCISES 1.11

1. What is a statement in mathematics?
2. Is $2 + 7 = 8$ a sentence?
3. What does the equality symbol, $=$, mean as used in mathematics?

For each of the following that is a sentence, indicate whether it is *True* or *False*.

4. $7 \div 5 \neq 5 \div 7$
5. $2 + 5 \cdot 10 - 3$
6. $\{A, B, C\} = \{1, 2, 3\}$
7. $\frac{1}{4} = \frac{2}{8}$
8. $(5 + 2) + 3 \neq 5 + (2 + 3)$
9. $\phi = \{\ \}$
10. $2 + 5 \neq 5 + 2$
11. What does the symbol $<$ mean? the symbol $>$?
12. How can you remember the meaning of the symbols $>$ and $<$?

Tell whether each of the following sentences is *True* or *False*.

13. $15 < 21$
14. $21 > 15$
15. $\frac{1}{4} > \frac{1}{8}$
16. $\frac{15}{8} < \frac{15}{9}$
17. $8 - 3 + 2 > 8 - (3 + 2)$
18. $9 \cdot 3 \div 7 > 3 \div 7 \cdot 9$

Rewrite each of the following in another way as a true sentence.

19. $24 < 35$ **20.** $15\frac{1}{2} > 10$

21. A and B are names for two different sets.

22. $\{\phi\}$ is not the empty set.

23. π is not equal to $\frac{22}{7}$, and π is not greater than $\frac{22}{7}$.

24. $\frac{3}{4}$ is not less than $\frac{717}{956}$, and $\frac{3}{4}$ is not greater than $\frac{717}{956}$.

WRITTEN EXERCISES 1.11

A Indicate whether each of the following is a *Sentence* or a *Numerical Phrase*. If it is a sentence, indicate whether it is *True* or *False*.

1. $2 \cdot 5 + 3$ **2.** $18 > 21$

3. $5 \cdot 3 \neq 3 \cdot 5$ **4.** $18 - 10 \div 3$

5. $2(5 + 3) = 2 \cdot 5 + 2 \cdot 3$ **6.** $3(4 \cdot 5) = (3 \cdot 4) \cdot 5$

7. $(12 \cdot 3) + 2 = (12 + 2) \cdot (3 + 2)$ **8.** $0 < 13$

9. $\frac{2}{3} < \frac{2}{4}$ **10.** $0.5 > 0.48$

Copy each sentence, and replace ⬤ with $>$, $<$, or $=$ to make the sentence true.

11. $12 \cdot 13$ ⬤ $13 \cdot 12$ **12.** $3(21)$ ⬤ $21(3)$

13. $14 + 15$ ⬤ $15 + 16$ **14.** $7(5 \cdot 8)$ ⬤ $(7 \cdot 5)8$

15. $\frac{3}{53}$ ⬤ $\frac{2}{53}$ **16.** $\frac{82}{87}$ ⬤ $\frac{83}{87}$

17. $5(8 + 3)$ ⬤ $5 \cdot 8 + 5 \cdot 3$ **18.** $(17 + 4) \cdot 3$ ⬤ $17 \cdot 3 + 4 \cdot 3$

19. $\frac{15}{16}$ ⬤ $\frac{16}{17}$ **20.** $\frac{12}{13}$ ⬤ $\frac{11}{12}$

21. $\frac{2}{3}$ ⬤ 0.66 **22.** $\frac{3}{8}$ ⬤ 0.375

23. $\frac{2}{7}$ ⬤ 0.285

24. $(12 \cdot 3) + 2$ ⬤ $(12 + 2) \cdot (3 + 2)$

25. $30 - (14 \div 2)$ ⬤ $(30 - 14) \div (30 - 2)$

26. $11 + (13 + 15) + 17$ ⬤ $(11 + 13) + (15 + 17)$

27. $(256 + 198) + 114$ ⬤ $256 + (198 + 114)$

28. $(2 \cdot 2)(3 \cdot 3 \cdot 3)$ ⬤ $(3 \cdot 3)(2 \cdot 2 \cdot 2)$

B Copy each of the following and place a numeral in the frame, $\square$, in order to represent a number that makes the sentence true. If more than one number makes it true, try to give a word description of the set of such numbers.

29. $3 + \square = 15$ **30.** $21 - \square = 12$ **31.** $15 \div \square = 2\frac{1}{7}$

32. $3 \cdot \square = 13$ **33.** $3 + \square < 12$ **34.** $\square - 10 < 1$

35. $15 - \square < 3$ **36.** $\square + 6 \neq 5$ **37.** $\square + 0 = 10$

38. $\square \cdot \frac{3}{7} = 1$

CHAPTER SUMMARY

Important Terms

1. A **set** is a collection of objects.
2. The **elements** of a set are the objects that make up the set.
3. **Braces,** { }, are symbols used in naming sets.
4. Set A is a **subset** of set B if every element of A is also an element of B.
5. The **empty,** or **null, set** is the set with no elements.
6. A **finite set** is either empty or its elements can be counted and the counting comes to an end.
7. An **infinite set** is a set that is not finite.
8. **Equal sets** contain exactly the same elements.
9. **Equivalent sets** contain the same number of elements.
10. The **counting numbers** form the set {1, 2, 3, 4, · · ·}.
11. The **whole numbers** form the set {0, 1, 2, 3, 4, · · ·}.
12. The **successor** of a whole number is the next greater whole number.
13. A **coordinate** is a number that is associated with a point on the number line.
14. A **rational number of arithmetic** is a number that can be represented as the quotient of two whole numbers.
15. The set of **numbers of arithmetic** consists of 0 and the coordinates of points to the right of 0 on the number line.
16. A **numeral** is a symbol used as a name for a number.
17. A **numerical phrase** is a phrase consisting of numerals and one or more symbols of operation.
18. An **indicated sum** is a phrase showing addition.
19. An **indicated difference** is a phrase showing subtraction.
20. An **indicated product** is a phrase showing multiplication.
21. An **indicated quotient** is a phrase showing division.
22. A **sentence** that is true or false is called a **statement.**

Important Ideas

1. Every set is a subset of itself.
2. There is only one empty set, and it is designated by ϕ or { }, but not {ϕ}.
3. The empty set is considered a subset of every set.

4. In a numerical phrase, it is agreed to multiply and divide before adding or subtracting unless parentheses indicate otherwise.
5. The equality symbol, $=$, between two symbols or groups of symbols means that they are names for the same thing.
6. The symbol $>$ means "is greater than."
7. The symbol $<$ means "is less than."
8. The symbol $\neq$ means "is not equal to."
9. The simplest name for a number is its common name.

CHAPTER REVIEW

Use the roster method to name the following sets.
1. The set of whole numbers less than 6
2. The set of even numbers greater than 3
3. The set consisting of the two largest cities in California
4. The set consisting of the two largest states in the United States
5. The set of elements common to

$$A = \{\tfrac{1}{2}, \tfrac{1}{3}, \tfrac{1}{4}, \tfrac{1}{5}, \tfrac{1}{6}\} \text{ and } B = \{\tfrac{1}{4}, \tfrac{2}{4}, \tfrac{3}{4}, \tfrac{4}{4}\}$$

6. The set of elements belonging to either or both of the sets

$$\{a, b, c\} \quad \text{and} \quad \{c, d, e\}$$

Use any convenient method for naming each of the following sets in a different way.
7. The set of even numbers
8. The set of odd numbers
9. $\{3, 6, 9, \cdots, 90\}$
10. $\{25, 30, 35, \cdots, 95\}$
11. The set of counting numbers less than 1
12. The set of whole numbers between $5\tfrac{1}{3}$ and $5\tfrac{7}{8}$

Indicate whether each of the following sets is *Finite* or *Infinite*.
13. The set of whole numbers greater than 53
14. The set of counting numbers greater than 105
15. The set of counting numbers less than 5000
16. The set of whole numbers less than 1,000,000
17. The set of rational numbers of arithmetic
18. The set of numbers of arithmetic

19. What is the successor of 21?
20. What is the successor of 106?
21. Of what whole number is 1 the successor?
22. Is there a number of arithmetic of which 0 is the successor?

23. Demonstrate a one-to-one correspondence between the first five counting numbers and the first five whole numbers.

24. Demonstrate a one-to-one correspondence between the sets {Mays, McCovey, Marichal} and {pitcher, outfielder, infielder}.

Draw graphs of the following sets.

25. {1, 2, 4, 5} **26.** {0, 2, 4, 6}

27. {whole numbers less than 5}

28. {counting numbers between 1 and 7}

29. $\{\frac{5}{5}, \frac{6}{5}, \frac{7}{5}, \frac{8}{5}, \frac{9}{5}, \frac{10}{5}\}$ **30.** $\{\frac{3}{4}, \frac{4}{4}, \frac{5}{4}, \frac{6}{4}, \frac{7}{4}, \frac{8}{4}\}$

Give a common name for each of the following phrases.

31. $5 + 7 \cdot 2$ **32.** $18 - 5 \cdot 2$

33. $11 + 2 \cdot 3 - 5$ **34.** $26 - 8 \div 2 + 1$

35. $(6 + 2) \cdot 3$ **36.** $(8 - 5) \cdot 7$

37. $2(\frac{1}{2} + 2\frac{1}{2})$ **38.** $5 \cdot (2\frac{7}{8} - \frac{7}{8})$

39. $12 - (4 + 3)$ **40.** $12 - (\frac{1}{8} + \frac{7}{8})$

41. $\dfrac{2(15 + 3)}{8 - 2}$ **42.** $\dfrac{3(17 - 3)}{5 + 2}$

Indicate whether each of the following is a phrase or a sentence. If it is a sentence, tell whether it is *True* or *False*.

43. $2 + 13 < 15$ **44.** $17 > 14 + 3$

45. $(5)(3) = 3 \cdot 5$ **46.** $(5 \cdot 3) \cdot 2 = 5 \cdot (3 \cdot 2)$

47. $2 \cdot 4 + 3$ **48.** $5 \cdot (7 + 2)$

49. $10 + 20 \cdot 3 = 10 + (20 \cdot 3)$ **50.** $15 + 25 \cdot 2 = (15 + 25) \cdot 2$

REVIEW OF ARITHMETIC

Recall that a fraction is a symbol that names a rational number by indicating the quotient of two whole numbers. The fraction $\frac{3}{4}$ has the number 3 as its **numerator** and the number 4 as its **denominator**. When you think of $\frac{3}{4}$ as an indicated quotient, then 3 is the **dividend** and 4 is the **divisor**.

1. In the fraction $\frac{5}{6}$, _?_ is the denominator and _?_ is the numerator.

2. The fraction $\frac{7}{8}$ indicates the quotient of _?_ divided by _?_ .

3. In the quotient $21 \div 15$, _?_ is the divisor and _?_ is the dividend.

4. In the quotient $\frac{256}{178}$, _?_ is the divisor and _?_ is the dividend.

5. In the example $17\overline{)256}$, _?_ is the divisor and _?_ is the dividend.

6. The fractions $\frac{7}{25}$ and $\frac{7}{30}$ show the same _?_ .

7. The fractions $\frac{3}{8}$ and $\frac{7}{8}$ show a common _?_ .

The **sum** of two numbers named by fractions showing the same denominator is a number named by a fraction whose numerator is the sum of the numerators of the given fractions and whose denominator is their common denominator.

Example: $\frac{2}{3} + \frac{5}{3} = \frac{2+5}{3} = \frac{7}{3}$

8. $\frac{3}{4} + \frac{10}{4} = \frac{?}{4}$ **9.** $\frac{2}{5} + \frac{11}{5} = \frac{13}{?}$

10. $\frac{10}{8} + \frac{17}{8} = \frac{?}{?}$ **11.** $\frac{3}{7} + \frac{4}{7} = \frac{?}{?}$

12. $\frac{1}{15} + \frac{1}{15} = \frac{?}{?}$ **13.** $\frac{3}{100} + \frac{12}{100} = \frac{?}{?}$

The **product** of two numbers named by fractions is named by the fraction whose numerator is the product of the numerators and whose denominator is the product of the denominators of the given fractions.

Example: $\frac{2}{3} \cdot \frac{5}{8} = \frac{2 \cdot 5}{3 \cdot 8} = \frac{10}{24}$

14. $\frac{5}{6} \cdot \frac{3}{10} = \frac{15}{?}$ **15.** $\frac{3}{7} \cdot \frac{4}{9} = \frac{?}{63}$

16. $\frac{5}{8} \cdot \frac{3}{8} = \frac{?}{?}$ **17.** $\frac{5}{100} \cdot \frac{2}{100} = \frac{?}{?}$

18. $\frac{7}{8} \cdot \frac{8}{7} = \frac{?}{?} = \frac{?}{}$ **19.** $\frac{10}{7} \cdot \frac{7}{10} = \frac{?}{?} = \frac{?}{}$

20. $\frac{5}{6} \cdot 5 = \frac{5}{6} \cdot \frac{5}{1} = \frac{?}{?}$ **21.** $\frac{7}{12} \cdot 7 = \frac{7}{12} \cdot \frac{7}{1} = \frac{?}{?}$

Numbers named by fractions that show 100 as their denominators can also be named by using the symbol for per cent, %. For example, $12\% = \frac{12}{100} = 0.12$. Express each of the following per cents first as a fraction and then as a decimal.

22. $15\% = \frac{?}{100} = \underline{\ ?\ }$ **23.** 32%

24. 78% **25.** 115%

26. 235% **27.** 0.4%

To compute a certain per cent of a given number, find the product of the number named by the per cent and the given number.

Example: 15% of 25 means $\frac{15}{100}(25)$, or $0.15(25)$.

28. 10% of 50 means $\frac{10}{100}(50) = \frac{10}{100} \cdot \frac{50}{1} = \frac{?}{?} = \underline{\ ?\ }$

29. 12% of 42 means $0.12(42) = \underline{\ ?\ }$

30. 5% of $22 = \underline{\ ?\ }$

31. 28% of $53 = \underline{\ ?\ }$

32. 14% of $100 = \underline{\ ?\ }$

33. 72% of $56 = \underline{\ ?\ }$

```
00100    1*   C      FORTRAN 1V TEST 14 - OUTPUT OF DOUBLE PRECISION VALUES UNDER
00100    2*   C      CONTROL OF  DW.D FORMAT FIELD DESCRIPTORS.
00101    3*          DOUBLE PRECISION A,B,C,D,E,F,G,H,O,Z
00103    4*          INTEGER P
00104    5*          P=6
00104                    000000    1017 00 00 0 000006                LA,XM      A0.6
00105    6*          WRITE ( P,1 )
00105                    000001    0100 00 00 0 000024    0000         SA         A0,P
00105                    000002    7413 13 00 0 000000    0003         LMJ        B11,N
00105                    000003    0000 00 01 0 000024    0000         +          00001
00105                    000004    0000 00 00 0 000025    0000         +          1F
00105                    000005           000105000000                           (W.B.
00107    7*   1      FORMAT ( 85H FORTRAN IV TEST 14 -  OUTPUT OF DOUBLE PRECISION VALU
00107    8*          1ES UNDER CONTROL OF DW.D FORMAT //81H VALUES: A= 0.45063D-4, B= -0
00107    9*          2.73849D-3, C= 0.15260D-2, D= -0.73645, E= 0.12345D+1 /
00107   10*          377H F= -0.67890D+2, G= 0.19082D+3, H= -0.73645D+4, O= 0.15260D+5,
00107   11*          4Z= -0.72819D+8 / )
00110   12*          A= 4.5063D-5
00110                    000006    7201 00 00 0 000000    0004         SLJ        NI02$
```

The language in which a computer is addressed must be mathematically precise. One such language used for programing computers is FOR–TRAN. The word "FORTRAN" is based on the phrase "formula translation." The FORTRAN language identifies the positions of variables within a machine. It also instructs the machine as to which operations should be performed in solving a particular program. Information for the computer shown here is stored on magnetic tape. The FOR–TRAN program locates positions in the magnetic tape where particular information is to be found.

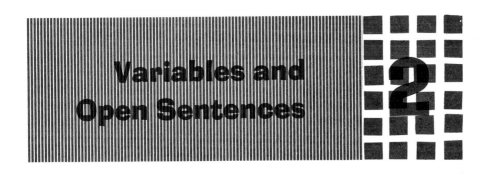

2.1 Variables and Open Phrases

You will remember that the perimeter of a square is the sum of the lengths of the four sides. The perimeter of the square in Figure 1 can be found as follows.

$$5 + 5 + 5 + 5 = 20$$

Figure 1

■ **P-1** What is the perimeter of a square whose sides are each 10 inches long? 15 centimeters long? $2\frac{1}{2}$ feet long?

■ **P-2** What is a simpler phrase that names the same number as the phrase $5 + 5 + 5 + 5$?

Since $5 + 5 + 5 + 5$ is equal to $4(5)$, this suggests that you can find the perimeter of a square by multiplying the length of one side by four. Let n represent the length of a side of a square as in Figure 2. Then the phrase $4(n)$ will represent the perimeter of the square. In fact, if n represents the length of a side of *any* square, then $4(n)$ represents its perimeter.

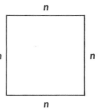

Figure 2

■ **P-3** If x stands for the length of a side of a square, what phrase stands for its perimeter? Can you name two such phrases?

Letters such as n and x used in this way are called **variables.**

> A **variable** is a symbol that may be replaced by any element of a specified set.

You might wish to find the perimeters of several squares whose sides have the lengths represented by the members of the following set.

$$L = \{1, 3, 3\tfrac{3}{4}, 5, 6.2, 10\tfrac{1}{3}\}$$

The phrase $4(n)$ can represent the perimeter of each of these squares, and all the perimeters can be found by replacing the variable n by each of the elements of set L.

A set such as L from which the replacements of the variable may be chosen is called the **domain** of the variable.

■ **P-4** What is the perimeter of a square if the variable is replaced by 3 in the phrase $4(n)$?

■ **P-5** What is the perimeter when 6.2 is the replacement for the variable?

Phrases such as $4(n)$ and $x + x + x + x$, which contain a variable, are called **open phrases.** The **value** of an open phrase is the number that is named by the open phrase when the variable is replaced by an element of the domain.

■ **P-6** What are all the values of $x + 2$ if the domain is $\{0, \tfrac{1}{2}, 3\}$?

■ **P-7** What are the values of $5 + 2(x)$ if the domain is $\{\tfrac{1}{2}, 1, 5\}$?

ORAL EXERCISES 2.1

1. What is the perimeter of a square?
2. Give two phrases that represent the perimeter of any square.
3. What is the perimeter of a square whose sides are each 99 inches long?
4. If $4(y)$ represents the perimeter of a square, what does y stand for?
5. If s represents the length of the side of a square, what does $s + s + s + s$ represent?
6. What name is given to the special set from which replacements for a variable are chosen?
7. What is an open phrase?
8. Give some examples of open phrases.

Give all the values of each of the following open phrases, using $\{0, 1, 2\}$ as the domain of the variable.

9. $x + 3$

10. $5(x) + 1$

11. $8 - 3(n)$

12. $x + x$

13. $4(y) \div 2$

14. $7 - y + 2$

15. $3(a) + a$

16. $4 + y \cdot 2$

17. $8 - t \div 2$

18. $6 + b \div 2$

WRITTEN EXERCISES 2.1

A Find all the values of each of the following open phrases, using $\{\frac{1}{2}, 1, 3\}$ as the domain of the variable.

1. $x + 2$

2. $3 + t$

3. $2(y) + 1$

4. $4(r) + 3$

5. $2(a) - 1$

6. $4(n) - 2$

7. $2 + 2(y)$

8. $1 + 4(c)$

9. $2 + g - 1$

10. $5 - k - \frac{1}{2}$

11. $3 + 2 \div x$

12. $1 + 1 \div x$

13. $8 \div 2(k)$

14. $2(s) \div 3$

15. $2(a + 1)$

16. $2(3 - x)$

Indicate, using *Yes* or *No*, whether each of the following pairs of phrases name the same number when the variable in each is replaced by 5.

17. $x + 2$ and $2 + x$

18. $3(x) + 2$ and $2 + 3(x)$

19. $2(3 + x)$ and $2(3) + x$

20. $(x + 2)3$ and $x \cdot 3 + 2(3)$

21. $(x+3)+2(x)$ and $x+(3+2\cdot x)$

22. $(5 \cdot x)3$ and $5(x \cdot 3)$

23. $x + x$ and $x \cdot x$

24. $x \cdot x$ and $2(x)$

25. $3(a) + a$ and $4(a)$

26. $3(a) - a$ and $2(a)$

27. $3(x) + 2(x)$ and $5(x \cdot x)$

28. $3(x) + 2(x)$ and $5(x)$

29. $2(y \cdot y)$ and $(2 \cdot y)(2 \cdot y)$

30. $2(y \cdot y)$ and $(2 \cdot y) \cdot y$

B Find the values of each of the following open phrases, using $\{0, 1, 2\}$ as the domain.

31. $x + 3 - x$

32. $x + 0$

33. $2(x + 3)$

34. $2(x) + 2(3)$

35. $2 \cdot a \div 2$

36. $4(y) \div 4$

37. $a \left(\dfrac{1}{a}\right)$

38. $(1x)x$

39. $x + (x + 1)$

40. $(x + x) + 1$

Suppose a set of rectangles all have lengths of 10 inches. One such rectangle is shown in Figure 3.

41. Choose a variable to represent its width.

42. What open phrase represents the perimeter?

43. Using your phrase of Exercise 42, find the perimeters of rectangles whose widths are elements of the domain {5, 8, 9}.

44. What are the values of the phrase $2(w) + 20$ for the domain {5, 8, 12}?

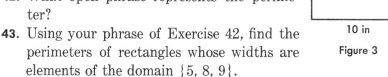

10 in

Figure 3

C If a baseball is dropped from a certain height, the phrase $16(t \cdot t)$ represents the approximate distance in feet that it will fall in t seconds of time. This means that the elements of the domain of t are numbers of seconds.

45. Find the values of the phrase $16(t \cdot t)$ for the domain {1, 2, 3, 4, 5, 6}.

46. How far would a baseball fall in 4 seconds?

47. About how many seconds would it take a baseball to fall from the observation deck of the Washington Monument 500 feet above the ground?

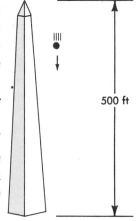

500 ft

2.2 Open Phrases and Word Phrases

You have just learned that an open phrase is a phrase that contains a variable.

■ **P-1** Which of the following are open phrases?

$x + 3$; $2(3) - t$; $5(3)$; $2(5) + 7$; $5 \cdot y$

In mathematics, you usually write an open phrase such as $5 \cdot y$ as $5y$. That is, whenever an open phrase is the indicated product of a number and a variable, you can write the numeral in front of the variable, and the raised dot or parentheses will not be needed. Thus, $3a$, $3 \cdot a$, and $3(a)$ all mean the same thing. Note, however, that $5 \cdot 3$ and 53 do not name the same number.

■ **P-2** What is the simplest way of writing the phrase $(n)(15) + 2$?

One of the important skills to learn in algebra is to change word phrases into open phrases. The table below shows some examples.

Word Phrase	Open Phrase
three more than a number	$n + 3$
five times the width of the rectangle	$5w$
one year less than the man's age	$a - 1$
the number of dollars divided by five	$d \div 5$, or $\dfrac{d}{5}$
one more than twice a certain number	$2x + 1$

Notice in these examples that a variable is chosen to represent a number of the word phrase and that the meaning of the phrase is shown by the use of other numerals and symbols of operation.

■ **P-3** What open phrase can be used to describe the word phrase "ten more than the product of three times a number"?

There are many key expressions that are used in word descriptions of problems to suggest operations. This table shows some of them.

Operation	Expressions
addition	sum, plus, increased by, more than
subtraction	less, less than, minus, difference, decreased by
multiplication	product, multiplied by, times, twice, tripled
division	quotient, divided by

■ **P-4** Can you give several word phrases for each of the following open phrases?

$$a - 3; \qquad 2 + x; \qquad 100n; \qquad 3 \div a; \qquad \frac{5}{y}$$

ORAL EXERCISES 2.2

Tell by *Yes* or *No* whether each of the following word phrases has been correctly changed to an open phrase. Then tell what the variable represents.

Word Phrase	Open Phrase
1. Three more than the number of players	$n + 3$
2. Five less than twice the number of surfers	$2x - 5$
3. Seven times as many students	$7 + s$
4. The number of jets increased by ten	$10x$
5. The number of tigers less eight	$8 - t$

6. Fifty divided by the number of teams $\dfrac{50}{n}$

7. The sum of 75 and the number of pilots $p + 75$

8. The sum of three and twice the number of records $3 + 2r$

9. Twenty more than the number of people at the game $20p$

10. The product of seven and the number of weeks $7w$

11. The number of footballs less three $3 - b$

12. Three less the number of footballs $3 - b$

13. Three less than the number of footballs $b - 3$

14. The number of miles divided by five $5 \div m$

15. One more than twice the number of teachers $2(t + 1)$

16. Three less than five times the number of yards $3 - 5y$

17. Twice the number of touchdowns less one $2t - 1$

18. The number of race cars decreased by six $6 - n$

19. Five times the sum of three and the number of ships $5(3) + s$

WRITTEN EXERCISES 2.2

A Write an open phrase for each of the following, using the variable that is suggested.

1. The sum of x and 1

2. The sum of 5 and $2n$

3. $3x$ less 16

4. $10y$ less 7

5. The product of 8 and t

6. The product of w and 9

7. a divided by 10

8. y divided by 16

9. $7x$ increased by 2

10. 2 more than $3y$

11. $4q$ decreased by 7

12. 18 decreased by w

13. 5 less than k

14. 2 less than $3v$

15. Twice the sum of x and 5

16. Twice the difference of y and 2

In each of the following, choose a variable and write an open phrase describing the word phrase.

17. The number of soldiers increased by fifty

18. Five more than the number of horses

19. The number of planes decreased by seven

20. The number of basketball players minus two

21. Thirty-three less the number of all-star players

22. Twenty-seven less the number of high jumpers

23. The number of inches divided by twelve

24. The number of meters multiplied by 1000

C Write an open phrase for each of the following.

25. The number of inches in x feet

26. The number of feet in y yards

27. The number of days in w weeks

28. The number of months in y years

29. The number of cents in d dollars

30. The number of cents in n nickels

31. The number of ounces in p pounds

32. The number of dimes in x dollars

33. The number of yards in x feet

34. The number of feet in y inches

2.3 Variables and Number Patterns

You have probably seen number puzzles of the following kind. You consider a **sequence** of numbers and note the rule that is used to name each number of the sequence in order. The challenge will be to find missing numbers of the sequence.

■ **P-1** What number is missing in the following sequence?

$$2, 5, 8, \underline{?}, 14, 17$$

You probably saw here that the rule is to add 3 to any number of the sequence to find the next number.

■ **P-2** What is the last number in the following sequence?

$$27, 23, 19, 15, \underline{?}$$

■ **P-3** What rule is used to find the missing number in **P-2**?

You can often use variables to state the rule that is used in number puzzles like these. Consider the sequence of numbers 2, 5, 11, $\underline{?}$, 47. It might be hard for you to find a rule that will give the missing number.

■ **P-4** What is the value of the phrase $2n + 1$ when n is replaced by 11?

■ **P-5** What is the missing number in the following sequence?

$$2, 5, 11, \underline{?}, 47$$

■ **P-6** What open phrase could you use as the rule to find a missing number in the following sequence if t stands for any number in the sequence?

$$19, 17, 15, 13, 11, 9$$

You may get the idea that a sequence of numbers is the same as a set of numbers. You will recall, however, that in a finite set the elements may be written in any order. In a sequence the order is very important.

In algebra, you are interested in discovering patterns in numbers. Here you have seen how the variable can be used to show such patterns.

ORAL EXERCISES 2.3

Using $2n - 1$ as the rule, find the next three numbers of each of the following sequences.

1. 2, ?, ?, ?   **2.** 3, ?, ?, ?
3. 1, ?, ?, ?   **4.** 4, ?, ?, ?

Find the missing numbers in each of the following sequences.

5. 9, ?, 19, 24, 29   **6.** 21, 24, ?, 30, 33
7. 30, 26, 22, ?, 14   **8.** 5, $7\frac{1}{2}$, 10, $12\frac{1}{2}$, ?

Can you find an open phrase for the rule of the following sequences?

9. 1, 3, 5, 7, 9, 11   **10.** 2, 4, 8, 16, 32, 64
11. 19, 18, 17, 16, 15, 14   **12.** 1, 3, 9, 27, 81
13. 35, 33, 31, 29, 27, 25   **14.** 64, 32, 16, 8, 4, 2
15. 4, 12, 36, 108, 324   **16.** 1, 10, 100, 1000, 10,000

WRITTEN EXERCISES 2.3

A Find the missing number in each of the following sequences.

1. 5, 11, 17, ?, 29   **2.** ?, 3, 6, 9, 12
3. ?, 3, 9, 27, 81   **4.** $1\frac{1}{2}$, 3, 6, ?, 24
5. 0.5, 0.8, 1.1, 1.4, ?   **6.** 0.2, 0.7, 1.2, 1.7, ?

Use the open phrase $2n + 3$ as the rule for finding the next three numbers of each sequence.

7. 1, ?, ?, ?   **8.** 2, ?, ?, ?
9. 3, ?, ?, ?   **10.** 4, ?, ?, ?
11. $\frac{1}{2}$, ?, ?, ?   **12.** $1\frac{1}{2}$, ?, ?, ?

Find an open phrase for the rule of each of the following.

13. 8, 14, 20, 26, 32

14. 2, 12, 22, 32, 42

15. 5, 10, 20, 40, 80

16. 2, 6, 18, 54, 162

17. $\frac{1}{2}, \frac{1}{4}, \frac{1}{8}, \frac{1}{16}, \frac{1}{32}$

18. $\frac{1}{3}, \frac{1}{6}, \frac{1}{12}, \frac{1}{24}, \frac{1}{48}$

19. $\frac{1}{32}, \frac{1}{16}, \frac{1}{8}, \frac{1}{4}, \frac{1}{2}$

20. $\frac{1}{48}, \frac{1}{24}, \frac{1}{12}, \frac{1}{6}, \frac{1}{3}$

Use the phrase $n(n) + 1$ as the rule for finding the next three numbers of each sequence.

21. 1, ?, ?, ?

22. 2, ?, ?, ?

Use the phrase $n(n + 1)$ as the rule for finding the next three numbers of each sequence.

23. 1, ?, ?, ?

24. 2, ?, ?, ?

In each of the following, indicate by writing *Yes* or *No* whether the given phrase describes the rule for the sequence. If it does not, find the correct open phrase for the rule.

25. $\frac{1}{2}, \frac{1}{3}, \frac{1}{4}, \frac{1}{5}, \frac{1}{6}$ $\frac{1}{n} + 1$

26. $\frac{1}{8}, \frac{1}{7}, \frac{1}{6}, \frac{1}{5}, \frac{1}{4}$ $\frac{1}{n} - 1$

27. $2, \frac{1}{2}, 2, \frac{1}{2}, 2$ $\frac{1}{n}$

28. $1, \frac{1}{2}, 1, \frac{1}{2}, 1$ $\frac{1}{2n}$

29. 3, 3, 3, 3, 3 $2n - 3$

30. 1, 2, 3, 4, 5 n

B The following are some sequences that are not easily described by an open phrase. Can you discover the pattern and fill in the missing numbers?

31. 2, 2, 3, 3, 8, 8, 9, 9, 14, 14, ?, ?, ?, ?

32. 1, 5, 4, 8, 7, 11, ?, ?, ?

33. 1, 0, 1, 0, 0, 1, 0, 0, 0, 1, ?, ?, ?, ?, ?

34. 4, 3, 6, 5, 10, 9, 18, 17, ?, ?, ?

35. 1, 1, 2, 3, 5, 8, 13, 21, ?, ?, ?

36. 1, 2, 6, 24, 120, ?, ?, ?

C There is another way that you can find the numbers of a sequence by the use of an open phrase. Suppose you put down in order all the values of the open phrase $2n - 1$ by using $\{1, 2, 3, 4, 5\}$ as the domain of the variable. You would get the following sequence.

$$1, 3, 5, 7, 9$$

37. What sequence of numbers do you get by writing down in order the values of the phrase $\frac{1}{n}$ for the domain $\{1, 2, 3, 4, 5\}$?

38. What are the next three terms of the following sequence whose rule is the phrase $2(n + 1)$ with the domain $\{1, 2, 3, 4, 5\}$?

$$4, 6, \underline{\ ?\ }, \underline{\ ?\ }, \underline{\ ?\ }$$

In each of the following, write down five terms of the sequence by using the given open phrase and the domain $\{1, 2, 3, 4, 5\}$.

39. $n \cdot n$

40. $\dfrac{1}{n \cdot n}$

41. $3(n + 1)$

42. $3n + 1$

2.4 Open Sentences and Truth Numbers

In the first chapter, you learned about sentences in algebra. You found that some sentences are always either true or false. These sentences can be called statements. You also saw that sentences in algebra are much like sentences in grammar.

■ **P-1** Is the following sentence true or false? "He is captain of our football team."

Of course you cannot tell whether this sentence is true or false unless you know to whom the pronoun "he" refers. If you replace the word "he" with the name of your captain, it will be true. If you replace it with any other name, the sentence is false.

Sentences such as this one in algebra are called *open sentences*. **Open sentences,** like open phrases, contain one or more variables.

$$\boxed{1} \quad x + 3 = 5$$
$$\boxed{2} \quad 2x - 5 < 3$$
$$\boxed{3} \quad x + 2x \neq 10$$

Notice that you cannot decide whether these sentences are true or false unless you replace the variable in each by a number.

> An **open sentence** is a sentence containing a variable that becomes true or false when the variable is replaced by an element from its domain.

■ **P-2** Is sentence $\boxed{1}$ true or false when x is replaced by 5?

■ **P-3** Is sentence $\boxed{2}$ true or false when x is replaced by 3?

■ **P-4** Is sentence $\boxed{3}$ true or false when x is replaced by 4?

■ **P-5** Can you find a number that will make sentence $\boxed{1}$ true when it is used to replace the variable x?

> Any number that will make an open sentence true when it replaces the variable is called a **truth number.**

■ **P-6** Can you name three truth numbers for the sentence

$$x < 8?$$

■ **P-7** Can you find a truth number for the sentence

$$x + 5 = 11?$$

■ **P-8** What is a truth number for the sentence

$$2x + 3 = 15?$$

ORAL EXERCISES 2.4

Tell whether each of the following is an open phrase or an open sentence.

1. $a + 3$
2. $a + 3 = 5$
3. $x + 1 < 2$
4. $y \neq 2$
5. $a + 2a - 3$
6. $2x - 1 = 5$

Tell whether each of the following is an open sentence or a statement.

7. $2 \cdot 5 + 1 = 13$
8. $2 \cdot x + 1 = 13$
9. $5 + 3 < 10$
10. $2 + 5x > 3$
11. $1 + 1 + 1 = 1$
12. $x + x + x = x$

Find a truth number for each of the following sentences.

13. $x + 1 = 4$
14. $x - 1 = 7$
15. $x + 2 = 5$
16. $8 - x = 3$
17. $5 + a = 9$
18. $11 - 6 = y$
19. $2x = 16$
20. $3x = 21$
21. $4 = \dfrac{8}{x}$
22. $x - 5 = 10$
23. $r - 2 = 13$
24. $t + t = 10$

25. What is meant by an open sentence?
26. What is meant by a truth number of an open sentence?

WRITTEN EXERCISES 2.4

A   Write *Open phrase* or *Open sentence* to identify correctly each of the following.

1. $2x + 3 = 5$ 2. $a + 5 = 10$
3. $3 - 2x$ 4. $3a - 7$
5. $2 + 3 < y$ 6. $8 - 5 > r$
7. $x + 3 \neq 2x$ 8. $t \neq 2t + 5$

Indicate whether each of the following is a *True statement*, a *False statement*, or an *Open sentence*.

9. $2 \cdot 5 + 1 = 12$ 10. $3 + 2 \cdot 5 = 30$
11. $2 \cdot x + 1 = 12$ 12. $3 + 2 \cdot x = 30$
13. $x + x = x + 1$ 14. $a + 2a = a + 1$
15. $2(3 \cdot 4) = (2 \cdot 3) \cdot 4$ 16. $2(5 + 3) = 2 \cdot 5 + 2 \cdot 3$
17. $2 + 1 \cdot 4 < 10$ 18. $14 - 6 \div 2 > 10$

Find a truth number for each of the following sentences.

19. $2 + x = 10$ 20. $a + 3 = 9$
21. $y - 3 = 15$ 22. $r - 2 = 19$
23. $t \div 2 = 4$ 24. $w \div 5 = 6$
25. $15 + 2 = v$ 26. $16 - 5 = x$
27. $10 - x = 3$ 28. $13 - y = 1$
29. $x + \frac{1}{2} = 3$ 30. $y + \frac{1}{3} = 1$
31. $x + x = 12$ 32. $y + y = 16$
33. $2x = 6$ 34. $3x = 36$
35. $2a = 7$ 36. $3b = 10$

B   Find three truth numbers for each of the following.

37. $x < 5\frac{1}{2}$ 38. $y > 17\frac{1}{3}$
39. $2x < 10$ 40. $3x < 10$
41. $x < 2$ 42. $2x < 3$

Can you find any truth numbers for each of the following sentences?

43. $x - x = 1$ 44. $x = x + 3$

45. $x > x + 1$ 46. $x \left(\dfrac{1}{x}\right) = 1$

C   Find a truth number for each of the following.

47. $2x + 3 = 15$ 48. $1 + 2x = 10$
49. $2x + 1 < 3$ 50. $y + 2 = 2y$

2.5 Truth Sets of Open Sentences

You have just learned what is meant by a truth number of an open sentence. You saw that some sentences have only one truth number and that other sentences have many truth numbers.

For example, 3 is the only truth number for the sentence $x + 2 = 5$. There are infinitely many truth numbers for the sentence $x + 1 > 10$. The numbers 11, $11\frac{1}{2}$, 12, $12\frac{1}{3}$, 15, 100.7 are just a few of them.

You can think of the truth numbers of an open sentence as forming a set of numbers called the **truth set** of the sentence. The set $\{2\}$ is the truth set of the open sentence $x + 5 = 7$.

> The **truth set** of an open sentence is the subset of the domain whose members make the sentence true when they replace the variable in the sentence.

■ **P-1** What is the truth set of the sentence $x + 3 = 3\frac{1}{2}$?

■ **P-2** What is the truth set of the sentence $2 + x = 2$?

■ **P-3** Can you find a truth number for the sentence $x + 1 = x$?

■ **P-4** How would you represent the truth set of the sentence in **P-3**?

You will recall that the set with no elements is the empty set, or the null set. Either $\{\ \}$ or ϕ represents the empty set.

When you are trying to find the truth set of an open sentence, you must know what the domain of the variable is. Remember that the domain is the set of numbers that are used to replace the variable in open phrases or open sentences.

■ **P-5** If the domain is $\{0, 1, 2, 3, 4, 5\}$, what is the truth set of each of the following sentences?

$\boxed{1}$ $2x + 5 = 13$ $\boxed{2}$ $2x < 5$ $\boxed{3}$ $x + 1 > 4$

When you list the elements of the truth set, you list *all* the numbers that make the sentence true. Also, the truth set contains no elements that make the sentence false.

■ **P-6** Why is T $= \{1, 2\}$ not the truth set of sentence $\boxed{2}$ in **P-5**?

■ **P-7** Why is T $= \{3, 4, 5\}$ not the truth set of sentence $\boxed{3}$?

Often you are shown what the domain of the variable is when you are to find a truth set. If, however, you are not told what the domain is, use all the numbers of arithmetic that give the sentence meaning.

The following table shows some open sentences and their truth sets.

Open Sentence	Truth Set
$x + 2 = 5$	$\{3\}$
$2x + 1 = 11$	$\{5\}$
$x + 1 > 10$	$\{$numbers of arithmetic greater than $9\}$
$x + 1 > x$	$\{$all numbers of arithmetic$\}$
$x \cdot x + 2 - 3 \cdot x = 0$	$\{1, 2\}$

■ **P-8** What is the truth set of the sentence $2x < 6$?

■ **P-9** What did you use for the domain in **P-8**?

■ **P-10** Can you list all the elements of the truth set of the sentence in **P-8**?

ORAL EXERCISES 2.5

1. What is the set of numbers called that make a sentence true?
2. What is the name of the set from which all the truth numbers are chosen?

Using $\{0, 1, 2, 3, 4, 5\}$ as the domain of the variable, find the truth numbers of each of the following sentences.

3. $x + 2 = 7$
4. $x > 3$
5. $x < 1$
6. $x + 1 = 3$
7. $x + 1 < 3$
8. $2x < 1$
9. $x + 2 > 8$
10. $2x + 1 = 11$
11. $2x < 12$
12. $2x + 1 > 0$
13. $x + \frac{1}{2} = 4$
14. $x - 2 = 1$
15. $\dfrac{x}{2} = 3$
16. $\dfrac{4}{x} = 2$

Describe the truth set of each of the following sentences.

17. $x + 1 > 15$
18. $2x > 10$
19. $x + 1 < 5$
20. $x + 2 > x$
21. $x + 3 = x$
22. $x + 0 = 0$
23. $2 < 2x$
24. $\dfrac{x}{2} > 10$

WRITTEN EXERCISES 2.5

A Using $\{0, 1, 2, 3, 4, 5\}$ as the domain, find the truth set of each of the following.

1. $x + 7 = 11$
2. $x + 9 = 14$
3. $a + 1 > 4$
4. $a + 3 > 5$
5. $2r + 1 = 7$
6. $2r + 3 = 11$
7. $2x < 2$
8. $3x < 4$
9. $2x + 1 > 12$
10. $2 + 2x < 1$
11. $\frac{x}{2} = 2.5$
12. $\frac{x}{3} = 1\frac{1}{3}$
13. $3c + 1 < 20$
14. $2m + 1 < 15$
15. $y + 3 \neq 7$
16. $t + \frac{1}{2} \neq 2\frac{1}{2}$

Find the truth set of each of the following.

17. $x - 5 = 17$
18. $x - 7 = 30$
19. $2s > 18$
20. $2t < 22$
21. $3t + 1 = 19$
22. $3 + 3y = 33$
23. $2x + 1 = 8$
24. $3 + 2x = 10$

An open sentence separates its domain into two sets, its truth set and the set of numbers that make the sentence false. Using $\{2, 4, 6, 8, 10\}$ as the domain, find for each sentence both its truth set, T, and the set F whose elements make the sentence false.

25. $2x + 1 = 3x$
26. $y + 4 = 3y$
27. $2a - 1 = a + 3$
28. $3d - 2 = d + 4$
29. $3x - 1 > 13$
30. $2x - 3 < 7$
31. $7 < 2x + 5$
32. $5x - 1 < 9$

C Show by the modified roster method or by word description the truth set of the sentence $2x + 1 > 15$ for each domain that is indicated.

33. $\{2, 4, 6, 8, 10, \cdots\}$
34. $\{1, 3, 5, 7, 9, \cdots\}$
35. $\{3, 6, 9, 12, 15, \cdots\}$
36. $\{5, 10, 15, 20, \cdots\}$
37. $\{\frac{1}{2}, 1, 1\frac{1}{2}, 2, 2\frac{1}{2}, 3, \cdots\}$
38. $\{$numbers of arithmetic$\}$
39. $\{$whole numbers$\}$
40. $\{$rational numbers of arithmetic$\}$

2.6 Open Sentences and Exponents

You probably remember that you can find the area of a square by multiplying the length of one side by itself.

Thus, the area of the square in Figure 1 is $5 \cdot 5$, or 25, square inches.

5 in

Figure 1

> When you multiply a number by itself, the product that you get is the **square** of that number.

The number 25 is the square of 5.

■ **P-1** What is the square of each of the numbers 6, 10, 12, $\frac{1}{2}$, $\frac{3}{4}$?

A number called an *exponent* is used to show a product that is a square of a number. The numeral for the exponent is written small and is raised. For example, $6 \cdot 6$ can be shown as 6^2, and $(12)(12)$ can be shown as 12^2. It is common practice to read 6^2 as "six squared" and 12^2 as "twelve squared." The small 2 used in this way is called an **exponent.**

■ **P-2** What is a common name for each of the following?

$$4^2; \quad 7^2; \quad (8)^2; \quad (3 + 2)^2; \quad 3^2 + 2^2$$

■ **P-3** What are all the values of the phrase y^2 if the domain is $\{3, 4, 5\}$?

Other numbers besides 2 can be used as exponents, but you will not make use of any until later in this course.

■ **P-4** Using the domain $\{1, 2, 3, 4, 5, 6\}$, what is the truth number of the sentence $x^2 + 1 = 37$?

When exponents are used in a phrase, there must be an agreement about the order of operations. In the phrase $2 \cdot 3^2$, square 3 first and then multiply by 2. A common name for $2 \cdot 3^2$ is 18.

■ **P-5** What is a common name for $2 \cdot 5^2$?

By this agreement, you see that a number is squared first and then multiplied by another number. When you want to indicate a different order of operation from this, use parentheses. Thus, $(2 \cdot 3)^2$ represents the square of 6, and its common name is 36.

■ **P-6** What is a common name for $(2 \cdot 5)^2$?

In finding a common name for a phrase that has a square, you square first and then multiply, divide, add, and subtract, unless parentheses indicate a different order of operations.

$2 + 3^2$ has the common name 11.
$18 - 4^2$ has the common name 2.
$2 \cdot 3^2$ has the common name 18.
$36 \div 3^2$ has the common name 4.

■ **P-7** What is a common name for $5 + 4^2$? for $100 \div 5^2$?

ORAL EXERCISES 2.6

Give a common name for each of the following.
1. 3^2
2. $(8)^2$
3. $(7 - 1)^2$
4. $(\frac{1}{3})^2$
5. $(0.5)^2$
6. $(2 + 7)^2$
7. $(3 \cdot 2)^2$
8. $3 \cdot 2^2$
9. $5 \cdot 3^2$
10. $5 + 3^2$
11. $20 - 4^2$
12. $(1 + \frac{1}{4})^2$
13. $20 \div 2^2$
14. $(20 \div 2)^2$
15. $1^2 + 1^2$
16. $5 \cdot 1^2$

Using $\{0, 1, 2\}$ as the domain of the variable, find all the values of each of the following.
17. x^2
18. $2x^2$
19. $1 + x^2$
20. $(1 + x)^2$
21. $3^2 \cdot x$
22. $5 - x^2$

Find the truth set of each of the following open sentences.
23. $x^2 = 81$
24. $a^2 = 121$
25. $y^2 = 144$
26. $t^2 = \frac{1}{4}$
27. $c^2 = \frac{1}{9}$
28. $w^2 = .01$
29. $x^2 + 1 = 26$
30. $y^2 - 2 = 47$

WRITTEN EXERCISES 2.6

A Find a common name for each of the following.
1. 13^2
2. 14^2
3. $5 \cdot 10^2$
4. $8 \cdot 5^2$
5. $(8 - 3)^2$
6. $(15 - 11)^2$
7. $8 + 7^2$
8. $11 + 8^2$
9. $(\frac{1}{5})^2$
10. $(\frac{1}{7})^2$
11. $(\frac{2}{3})^2$
12. $(\frac{4}{5})^2$
13. $(1.2)^2$
14. $(1.3)^2$
15. $(0.6)^2$
16. $(0.9)^2$
17. $(11 + 3)^2$
18. $(15 + 1)^2$
19. $72 \div 6^2$
20. $98 \div 7^2$

Using $\{1, \frac{1}{2}, 3\}$ as the domain of the variable, find all the values of each of the following.

21. x^2 **22.** $y^2 + 1$ **23.** $4x^2$ **24.** $8t^2$

25. $(x + 1)^2$ **26.** $(a + 2)^2$ **27.** $3 + 2x^2$ **28.** $2 + 3w^2$

Find the truth set of each of the following sentences.

29. $x^2 = 16$ **30.** $t^2 = 1$ **31.** $r^2 = \frac{1}{16}$

32. $s^2 = \frac{1}{81}$ **33.** $a^2 = \frac{4}{9}$ **34.** $d^2 = \frac{9}{25}$

35. $2x^2 = 18$ **36.** $3x^2 = 12$ **37.** $y^2 + 1 = 101$

38. $r^2 + 3 = 124$ **39.** $\frac{1}{4}x^2 = 9$ **40.** $\frac{1}{3}x^2 = 27$

B   For each of the following phrases, find the common name if $10^3 = 10 \cdot 10 \cdot 10$.

41. $2 \cdot 10^3 + 3 \cdot 10^2 + 4 \cdot 10 + 5$

42. $1 \cdot 10^3 + 0 \cdot 10^2 + 1 \cdot 10 + 0$

43. $4 \cdot 10^3 + 1 \cdot 10^2 + 0 \cdot 10 + 3$

44. $9 \cdot 10^3 + 9 \cdot 10^2 + 9 \cdot 10 + 9$

If $2^4 = 2 \cdot 2 \cdot 2 \cdot 2 = 16$ and $2^3 = 2 \cdot 2 \cdot 2 = 8$, find the common name for each of the following.

45. $1 \cdot 2^4 + 1 \cdot 2^3 + 1 \cdot 2^2 + 1 \cdot 2 + 1$

46. $1 \cdot 2^4 + 0 \cdot 2^3 + 0 \cdot 2^2 + 0$

47. $1 \cdot 2^4 + 0 \cdot 2^3 + 1 \cdot 2^2 + 0 \cdot 2 + 1$

48. $1 \cdot 2^3 + 0 \cdot 2^2 + 1 \cdot 2 + 1$

What do you think is the common name for each of the following?

49. $2.56(10^5)$ **50.** $1.01(10^{10})$

2.7 Truth Sets of Sentences Using $\leq$ and $\geq$

You have worked with sentences whose verbs are represented by the symbols $=$, $\neq$, $<$, and $>$. These symbols should be meaningful to you. Now consider open sentences such as the following.

$$\boxed{1} \quad x \leq 5$$
$$\boxed{2} \quad n \geq 10$$

Sentence $\boxed{1}$ is read "x is less than or equal to 5." Sentence $\boxed{2}$ is read "n is greater than or equal to 10."

Consider the set of numbers of arithmetic as the domain. The first sentence will be true if x is replaced by 5 or any number less than 5.

■ **P-1** What is the truth set of the sentence $n \geq 10$?

■ **P-2** Is $10\frac{1}{4}$ in the truth set of the sentence in **P-1**?

■ **P-3** Is $9\frac{7}{8}$ one of the truth numbers of the sentence in **P-1**?

You have probably noticed that the symbol $\leq$ is a combination of the symbols $<$ and $=$.

Suppose the domain of the variable x is {whole numbers}.

■ **P-4** What is the truth set of the sentence $x \leq 5$?

■ **P-5** What is the truth set of $2x \geq 10$?

■ **P-6** Are the truth sets named in **P-4** and **P-5** finite or infinite?

Sometimes the sentences shown here are stated in a different way. For example, the sentence $a \leq 3$ might be read "a is not greater than 3."

■ **P-7** Can you think of a different way of expressing $y \geq 6$ rather than "y is greater than or equal to 6"?

Often the same mathematical idea can be expressed in different ways. You will see more examples of this fact as you progress in this course.

ORAL EXERCISES 2.7

Indicate whether each of the following is *True* or *False*.

1. $3 < 5$	**2.** $7 > 10$	**3.** $3 \leq 15$
4. $\frac{1}{2} \geq 1$	**5.** $8 \leq 8$	**6.** $12 \geq 12$

Find the truth sets of the following, using $\{0, 1, 2, 3, 4, 5\}$ as the domain of the variable.

7. $x \leq 3$	**8.** $x \leq 1$	**9.** $x \geq 2$
10. $x \geq 5$	**11.** $x \leq 0$	**12.** $x \geq 6$
13. $x \leq 100$	**14.** $x \geq 100$	**15.** $2x \leq 3$
16. $2x \leq 8$	**17.** $2x \geq 6$	**18.** $2x \geq 10$
19. $x + 1 \leq 5$	**20.** $x + 1 \geq 3$	

Using {numbers of arithmetic} as the domain, indicate whether each of the following has a *Finite* or an *Infinite* truth set.

21. $x \leq 2$	**22.** $x \geq 15$	**23.** $x \neq 5$
24. $x = 2\frac{1}{2}$	**25.** $x < 0$	

VARIABLES AND OPEN SENTENCES   59

A   Using $\{0, 1, 2, 3, 4, \cdots\}$ as the domain of the variable, find the truth sets of the following.

1. $x \le 6$ **2.** $x \le 3$ **3.** $x \ge 10$

4. $x \ge 50$ **5.** $x \le 35$ **6.** $x \le 75$

Indicate whether each of the following sentences is *True* or *False*.

7. $10\tfrac{1}{2} \le 10\tfrac{3}{4}$ **8.** $\tfrac{7}{8} \ge \tfrac{15}{16}$ **9.** $\tfrac{3}{4} \le \tfrac{6}{8}$

10. $\tfrac{2}{3} \ge \tfrac{6}{9}$ **11.** $\tfrac{3}{5} < \tfrac{4}{5}$ **12.** $\tfrac{13}{15} > \tfrac{14}{15}$

13. $\tfrac{3}{7} > \tfrac{3}{8}$ **14.** $\tfrac{5}{11} < \tfrac{5}{12}$

Using $\{0, 2, 4, 6, 8, 10\}$ as the domain of the variable, find the truth sets of the following.

15. $2x \ge 3$ **16.** $2x \le 12$ **17.** $3x \le 15$ **18.** $3x \ge 21$

19. $x + 1 \le 7$ **20.** $x + 1 \ge 3$ **21.** $2x + 1 \ge 12$

22. $2x + 1 \le 11$ **23.** $2x + 3 \ge 25$ **24.** $2x + 3 \le 2$

Using the domain $\{$numbers of arithmetic$\}$ for the variable, indicate the truth sets of the following.

25. $a \le a$ **26.** $2x \ge 2x$ **27.** $b < b$ **28.** $x > x$

29. $x + 1 = x + 1$ **30.** $x + 1 = x$ **31.** $x + 1 > x$ **32.** $3x \le x$

B   The symbol $\subseteq$ is used to show the subset relation. The sentence $R \subseteq S$ means R is a subset of S. Let $A = \{1, 2, 3\}$, $B = \{1, 2, 3, 4\}$, and $C = \{1, 2, 3, 5\}$. Indicate whether each of the following is *True* or *False*.

33. $A \subseteq B$ **34.** $B \subseteq B$ **35.** $C \subseteq A$ **36.** $B \subseteq C$

37. $A \subseteq C$ **38.** $B = C$ **39.** $\phi \subseteq A$ **40.** $\{ \quad \} \subseteq \phi$

2.8   Graphs of Truth Sets

You have learned that the graph of a set A is the set of all points on the number line that correspond to the elements of A.

■ **P-1**   What set of numbers is represented by the following graph?

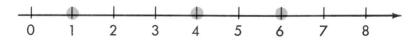

This, of course, illustrates the graph of a finite set. Each point of the graph is marked with a heavy dot.

As you noted in the preceding section, sentences using $<$ and $>$ often have infinite truth sets when the domain of the variable is the set of numbers of arithmetic. To show the graphs of such sets, you must darken not only separate points but also the number line itself.

The graph of the truth set of the open sentence $x > 4$ is as follows.

Notice that a circle is drawn at the point with coordinate 4 to show that this point is not in the truth set. The coordinates of all points to the right of 4 are in the truth set.

■ **P-2** Is $4\frac{1}{2}$ in the graph of the truth set? Is 100? Is $57\frac{1}{3}$?

■ **P-3** What is the open sentence whose truth set is graphed below?

Notice that you darken the point at 0 just so that it will be clear that 0 is included in the truth set.

In the last section you worked with sentences using $\leq$ and $\geq$. Graphs of these sentences are easy to show. The graph of $a \geq 3$ is as follows.

The point at 3 is darkened because 3 is in the truth set.

■ **P-4** What is the open sentence whose truth set is graphed below?

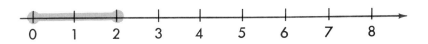

■ **P-5** What set of numbers is the domain of the variables in the sentences graphed in this section?

If you let the domain be {whole numbers}, then the graph of the sentence $x \geq 3$ will be as follows.

Note that "etc." is used here to show that infinitely many whole numbers are included as the number line is extended to the right.

You can see that it is very important to know what the domain is.

The graph of the empty set is the number line with no point darkened. The graph of the set of numbers of arithmetic is as shown below.

ORAL EXERCISES 2.8

Describe an open sentence whose truth set is shown by each graph. Give its domain.

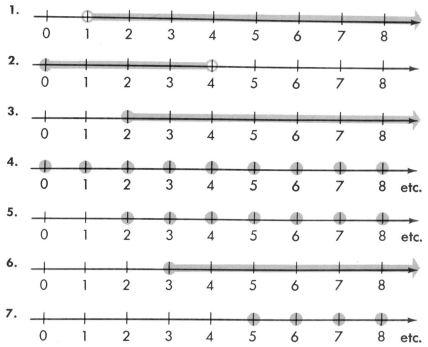

8. What is meant by the graph of the truth set of an open sentence?
9. How do you think a graph is useful?

Tell whether each graph shown is the graph of the truth set of the given open sentence. Use {numbers of arithmetic} as the domain for the variable unless otherwise indicated.

10. $2x \geq 8$

11. $x < 6$; the domain is {counting numbers}.

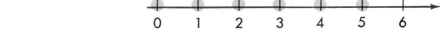

12. $n + 1 < 5$

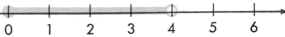

13. $a > 3$

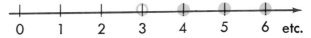
etc.

14. $2x + 1 = 4$

15. $t \leq 3$

16. $r \geq 3\frac{2}{3}$

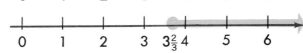

WRITTEN EXERCISES 2.8

A Write an open sentence whose truth set is shown by each graph. Give its domain.

1.

2.

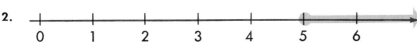

3.

4.

5.

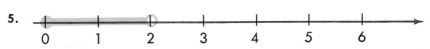

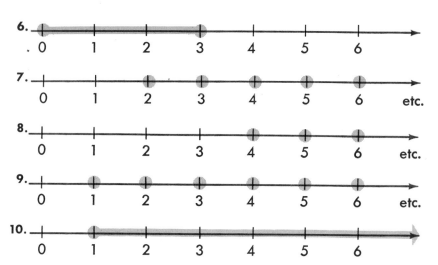

6.

7. etc.

8. etc.

9. etc.

10.

Draw the graph of the truth set of each of the following sentences, using {numbers of arithmetic} as the domain.

11. $x \geq 2$ **12.** $m \geq 5$ **13.** $y < 6$ **14.** $a < 2$ **15.** $x > 3\frac{1}{2}$
16. $y > 4\frac{3}{5}$ **17.** $w \neq 5$ **18.** $g \neq 0$ **19.** $x + 1 = x$ **20.** $x \geq 0$

Draw graphs of the truth sets of the following sentences, using {whole numbers} as the domain.

21. $x \leq 7$ **22.** $x > 5$ **23.** $y > 2$ **24.** $y \leq 5$

B   Give a word description of the sets that are graphed.

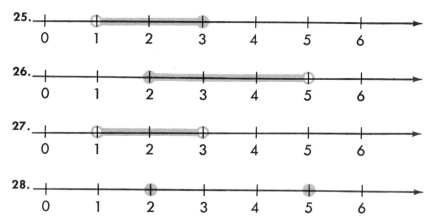

25.

26.

27.

28.

C   The symbol $\not>$ means "is not greater than." With similar meanings attached to $\not<$, $\not\leq$, and $\not\geq$, make graphs of the truth sets of the following, using {numbers of arithmetic} as the domain for the variables.

29. $x \not> 5$ **30.** $x \not< 3$ **31.** $a \not\leq 6$ **32.** $y \not\geq 4$

2.9 *And* Sentences and Their Truth Sets

Suppose your friend makes this statement: "I am going to the game tonight, *and* I am going to the dance." It should be clear:

1. If your friend does not go to the game, his statement is false.
2. If your friend does not go to the dance, his statement is false.
3. If your friend goes to neither the game nor the dance, his statement is false.
4. His statement is true only if he goes to both the game and the dance.

Sentences such as the one in the first paragraph above are called **compound sentences.** They are useful in mathematics.

Consider the sentence

$$5 + 2 = 7 \quad and \quad 8 + 1 = 10.$$

This sentence is false because $8 + 1 \neq 10$. You know from your daily usage of English that the following is true.

> A compound sentence in which the clauses are connected by *and* is true only when both clauses are true.

The clauses are the separate sentences that make up a compound sentence.

P-1 Is the following compound sentence true or false?

$$5 + 7 = 13 \quad and \quad 25 - 11 = 14$$

P-2 Is the following compound sentence true or false?

$$\tfrac{1}{4} + \tfrac{3}{4} = 1 \quad and \quad \tfrac{5}{8} + \tfrac{3}{8} = 1$$

Now consider a compound sentence whose clauses are both open sentences.

$$x \geq 3 \quad and \quad x < 7$$

Restrict the domain of x to {whole numbers}.

P-3 What is the truth set of the left clause, $x \geq 3$? You could express it as L = $\{3, 4, 5, 6, \cdots\}$.

■ **P-4** What is the truth set of the right clause, $x < 7$? It could be expressed as R $= \{0, 1, 2, 3, 4, 5, 6\}$.

■ **P-5** What whole numbers make the compound sentence true?

The set $\{3, 4, 5, 6\}$ is the truth set of the compound sentence $x \geq 3 \ and \ x < 7$.

Note that the truth set of a compound *and* sentence is the set of numbers that are in the truth sets of both the open clauses.

You may have learned that the set of elements that two sets have in common is called their **intersection**. If A $= \{1, 2, 3\}$ and B $= \{2, 4, 6\}$, then $\{2\}$ is their intersection. In the above example, $\{3, 4, 5, 6\}$ is the intersection of R $= \{0, 1, 2, 3, 4, 5, 6\}$ and L $= \{3, 4, 5, 6, \cdots\}$. The elements 3, 4, 5, and 6 are in both sets R and L, and they are the only elements of both. You may also know the symbol $\cap$, which is used to represent the intersection of sets. Thus, R $\cap$ L $= \{3, 4, 5, 6\}$ is a true sentence.

Consider the open sentence $x \leq 3 \ and \ x > 0$ with $\{$whole numbers$\}$ as the domain.

■ **P-6** If A is the truth set of $x \leq 3$, what are its elements?

■ **P-7** If B is the truth set of $x > 0$, what are its elements?

■ **P-8** What elements are in A $\cap$ B?

■ **P-9** What is the truth set of the compound sentence $x \leq 3 \ and \ x > 0$?

In finding the truth set of a compound sentence with the connective *and*, first list the elements of the truth set of each clause. Then find the intersection of the two truth sets.

ORAL EXERCISES 2.9

Tell whether each of the following compound sentences is *True* or *False*.

1. $10 - 6 = 3 \ and \ 2 + 3 = 6$
2. $8 + 7 = 15 \ and \ 20 - 2 = 17$
3. $13 + 28 = 31 \ and \ 18 + 4 = 22$
4. $15 + 16 = 31 \ and \ 13 + 19 = 32$
5. $\frac{1}{2} + \frac{1}{3} = \frac{1}{5} \ and \ \frac{1}{4} + \frac{2}{4} = \frac{3}{4}$
6. $(\frac{1}{2})(\frac{1}{3}) = 16 \ and \ (\frac{1}{4})(\frac{1}{5}) = \frac{1}{20}$

7. When is a compound sentence with the connective *and* true?
8. When is a compound sentence with the connective *and* false?

Let the domain of the variable be {whole numbers}. (a) Find L, the truth set of the left clause; (b) find R, the truth set of the right clause; and (c) find L ∩ R, the truth set of the compound sentence.

9. $x + 1 = 3$ *and* $x \leq 5$ 10. $x < 5$ *and* $x > 1$

11. $x \leq 4$ *and* $x < 2$ 12. $x = 2$ *and* $x > 3$

13. $x \geq 3$ *and* $x > 5$ 14. $x \geq 3$ *and* $x \leq 4$

15. $x \leq 5$ *and* $x \geq 5$ 16. $x > 0$ *and* $x < 3$

WRITTEN EXERCISES 2.9

A   Indicate whether each of the following compound sentences is *True* or *False*.

1. $2 + 8 = 10$ *and* $13 - 9 = 4$
2. $2(25) = 50$ *and* $24 \div 8 = 3$
3. $50 + 30 = 70$ *and* $80 + 20 = 100$
4. $35 + 15 = 50$ *and* $37 + 23 = 50$
5. $13 > 12 + 2$ *and* $15 < 8 + 9$
6. $5\frac{3}{8} + 2\frac{5}{8} > 8$ *and* $8 + 13 \leq 22$
7. $13 + 2 \leq 15$ *and* $2 + 9 = 12$
8. $23 - 5 \geq 18$ *and* $53 + 17 \neq 60$
9. $5.6 + 2.3 > 7.9$ *and* $\frac{121}{256} > \frac{120}{257}$
10. $\frac{315}{508} < \frac{314}{509}$ *and* $0.2 + 0.3 = 0.5$

Let the domain of the variable be {whole numbers}. (a) Find L, the truth set of the left clause; (b) find R, the truth set of the right clause; and (c) find L ∩ R, the truth set of the compound sentence.

11. $x < 3$ *and* $x \geq 0$ 12. $x \leq 5$ *and* $x > 3$

13. $x < 7$ *and* $x < 12$ 14. $x > 3$ *and* $x > 7$

15. $x \leq 5$ *and* $x \geq 1$ 16. $x \leq 0$ *and* $x \leq 6$

17. $x = 5$ *and* $x \leq 10$ 18. $x > 3$ *and* $x + 1 = 8$

19. $x \neq 3$ *and* $x \leq 4$ 20. $x < 6$ *and* $x \neq 0$

21. $x \leq 5$ *and* $x > 8$ 22. $x > 3$ *and* $x \leq 2$

B   Using the variable x, form a compound *and* sentence whose left and right clauses have truth sets as given. Let the domain be {whole numbers}.

23. L = {0, 1, 2, 3};   R = {5}
24. L = {3};   R = {0, 1, 2}
25. L = {7, 8, 9, 10, · · ·};   R = {0, · · ·, 8, 9, 10}
26. L = {0, · · ·, 25, 26, 27};   R = {1, 2, 3, 4, · · ·}

27. L = {0, 1, 2}; R = {0, 1, 2, 3}
28. L = {11, 12, 13, · · ·}; R = {15, 16, 17, · · ·}

29. List the truth sets of the compound sentences formed in Exercises 23, 25, and 27.
30. List the truth sets of the compound sentences formed in Exercises 24, 26, and 28.

2.10 Graphs of *and* Sentences

In the preceding section, you learned about the truth sets of compound sentences that use the connective *and*. Now you will study the graphs of the truth sets of such compound sentences. From now on, the graph of an open sentence means the graph of its truth set.

Look at the following compound sentence for which the domain of the variable is {numbers of arithmetic}.

$$x < 5 \quad and \quad x > 2$$

The graph of the left clause, $x < 5$, is as follows.

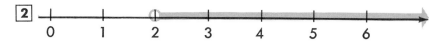

The graph of the right clause, $x > 2$, is shown below.

You will recall that the truth set of an *and* sentence is the set of numbers that are elements of the truth sets of both the left and right clauses; that is, its truth set is the intersection of the truth sets of the left and right clauses. Thus, the graph of the compound sentence $x < 5$ *and* $x > 2$ will be the set of points that are common to the graphs labeled ① and ②. This is shown in the graph below.

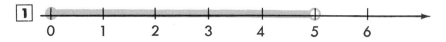

■ **P-1** Why is the point at 2 not included in graph ③?

■ **P-2** Why is the point at $3\frac{1}{2}$ included in graph ③?

Now consider the graph of the following sentence.

$$x \leq 3 \quad and \quad x > 5$$

The graph of the left clause is labeled $\boxed{4}$,

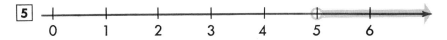

and the graph of the right clause is labeled $\boxed{5}$.

■ **P-3** What points do graphs $\boxed{4}$ and $\boxed{5}$ have in common?

You can see that the truth set is empty, and the graph of the compound sentence is as shown below.

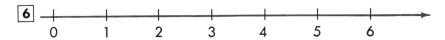

It may help you with graphs of *and* sentences to imagine pushing the two number lines together so that their zero points match up. Then you can easily tell where the graphs overlap.

Another example may be helpful. Consider $x \geq 3$ *and* $x < 5$. For this sentence, restrict the domain to {whole numbers}. The graph of the left clause is labeled $\boxed{7}$, and the graph of the right clause is labeled $\boxed{8}$.

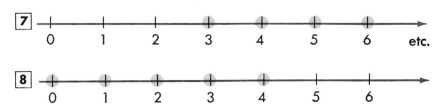

■ **P-4** What points lie on both graphs?

You can probably see that the graph of the compound sentence is as follows.

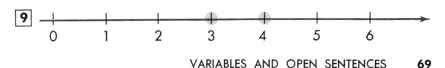

■ **P-5** What would graph ⑨ look like if the domain were the set of numbers of arithmetic?

Again you can see the importance of knowing what domain is being used for the variable.

ORAL EXERCISES 2.10

Let {numbers of arithmetic} be the domain. Tell whether each graph is the correct graph of the given compound sentence.

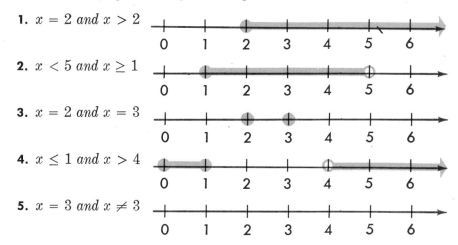

1. $x = 2$ *and* $x > 2$

2. $x < 5$ *and* $x \geq 1$

3. $x = 2$ *and* $x = 3$

4. $x \leq 1$ *and* $x > 4$

5. $x = 3$ *and* $x \neq 3$

Let {whole numbers} be the domain. Make a compound open sentence whose clauses have graphs that are shown, using the connective *and*.

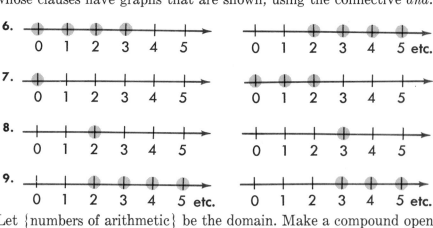

6.

7.

8.

9.

Let {numbers of arithmetic} be the domain. Make a compound open sentence to fit each graph shown.

10.

11.

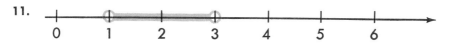

12.

WRITTEN EXERCISES 2.10

A For each of the following compound sentences, first draw the graph of each clause, and then draw the graph of the compound sentence. Let {numbers of arithmetic} be the domain for each variable.

1. $x > 2$ *and* $x < 7$
2. $x < 5$ *and* $x > 0$
3. $a \le 5$ *and* $a > 3$
4. $r > 4$ *and* $r \le 5$
5. $t \le 3$ *and* $t \ge 5$
6. $w > 8$ *and* $w \le 5$
7. $x = 5$ *and* $x \le 6$
8. $y \ge 2$ *and* $y = 4$
9. $x \le 5\frac{1}{2}$ *and* $x > 2\frac{1}{2}$
10. $p > 3\frac{1}{3}$ *and* $p \le 5\frac{1}{5}$
11. $x \ne 5$ *and* $x \ge 4$
12. $y < 6$ *and* $y \ne 2$

Follow the same directions as given for Exercises 1–12 for the following compound sentences, except use {whole numbers} as the domain.

13. $x \le 6$ *and* $x < 3$
14. $y > 2$ *and* $y \ge 5$
15. $a < 5$ *and* $a > 3$
16. $b \ge 2$ *and* $b < 3$

For each of the following, state a compound open sentence to fit the graph. Let {numbers of arithmetic} be the domain for the variable.

17.

18.

19.

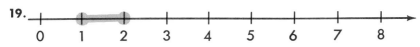

20.

2.11 *Or* Sentences and Their Truth Sets

You have just learned how to find the truth sets of compound open sentences that use *and* as the connective. Now you are going to work with compound sentences in which the connective is *or*.

Suppose your friend makes this statement: "I am going to the game tonight, *or* I am going to the dance."

1 If your friend goes to the game and does not go to the dance, his statement is true.

2 If he does not go to the game but goes to the dance, his statement is true.

3 If he goes to the game and also goes to the dance, his statement will be considered true.

4 If he goes to neither the game nor the dance, his statement is false.

Such compound sentences are also useful in mathematics. Consider the sentence

$$15 - 8 = 6 \quad or \quad 8 + 3 = 11.$$

This compound sentence is true because the right clause is true even though the left clause is false.

> A compound sentence with connective *or* is true if the left clause is true, or the right clause is true, or both clauses are true.

Now look at the sentence

$$20 - 8 = 12 \quad or \quad 2 + 3 \cdot 4 = 20.$$

■ **P-1** Is the left clause true or false?

■ **P-2** Is the right clause true or false?

■ **P-3** Is the compound sentence true or false? Why?

■ **P-4** Is the sentence $8 - 3 \cdot 2 = 10$ *or* $2 \cdot 3 + 4 = 14$ true or false?

■ **P-5** Is the sentence $8 - 3 + 2 = 7$ *or* $2 \cdot 8 \div 4 = 4$ true or false?

You can also say that such sentences are true when at least one of the clauses is true.

You remember how to determine the truth sets of *and* sentences. Now look at a compound open sentence whose connective is *or*, and let {whole numbers} be the domain.

$$x + 1 = 8 \quad or \quad x \leq 3$$

■ **P-6** What is the truth number of the left clause?

■ **P-7** What are the truth numbers of the right clause?

■ **P-8** What set of numbers will make the compound sentence true?

Since {7} is the truth set of the left clause, 7 will make the compound sentence true. Since {0, 1, 2, 3} is the truth set of the right clause, any of the numbers 0, 1, 2, or 3 will also make the compound sentence true. The truth set of the compound sentence must be {0, 1, 2, 3, 7}.

You may also have learned about the union of two sets. The union of A = {1, 5} and B = {2, 3, 4, 5} is the set {1, 2, 3, 4, 5}. The symbol for set union is $\cup$. Thus, A $\cup$ B = {1, 2, 3, 4, 5}. The **union** of two sets is the set of elements that are members of at least one of the two sets; that is, an element that is in the union of two sets may be in either one or both of the two given sets.

You saw that the truth set of the compound sentence $x + 1 = 8$ *or* $x \leq 3$ is {0, 1, 2, 3, 7}. This set is actually the union of {7} and {0, 1, 2, 3}.

Consider another compound sentence for which the domain is {whole numbers}.

$$x < 2 \quad or \quad x \leq 5$$

■ **P-9** If L is the truth set of $x < 2$, what are its elements?

■ **P-10** If R is the truth set of $x \leq 5$, what are its elements?

■ **P-11** What elements are in L $\cup$ R?

■ **P-12** What is the truth set of the compound sentence $x < 2$ *or* $x \leq 5$?

Remember not to repeat any elements in a set!

> The truth set of an *or* sentence is the union of the truth sets of the clauses.

Again it is wise to find the truth set of each clause first before writing down the truth set of the compound sentence.

ORAL EXERCISES 2.11

Tell whether each of the following is *True* or *False*.

1. $2 + 8 = 10$ *or* $5 + 2 = 6$
2. $12 - 5 = 8$ *or* $18 \div 9 = 2$
3. $17 + 3 = 21$ *or* $25 - 7 = 19$
4. $13 + 12 = 25$ *or* $21 + 8 = 29$
5. $2 + 3(5) = 30$ *or* $2 + 3(5) = 17$
6. $3(4) - 2 = 6$ *or* $8 - 3 + 2 = 3$
7. $30 \div 5(2) = 12$ *or* $3(5 + 2) = 21$
8. $15 \leq 15$ *or* $10 < 10$
9. $\frac{5}{8} < \frac{4}{9}$ *or* $0.3 \geq 0.1$
10. $0.03 > 0.1$ *or* $0.2 \geq \frac{1}{5}$

11. When is a compound sentence with the connective *or* true?
12. When is a compound sentence with the connective *or* false?

Let the domain of the variable be {whole numbers}. (a) Find L, the truth set of the left clause; (b) find R, the truth set of the right clause; and (c) find L $\cup$ R, the truth set of the compound sentence.

13. $x = 2$ *or* $x + 1 = 5$
14. $x < 3$ *or* $x = 0$
15. $x \leq 5$ *or* $x < 3$
16. $x + 2 = 10$ *or* $x \leq 4$
17. $x = 5$ *or* $x \leq 2$
18. $x = 0$ *or* $x \geq 1$
19. $x > 5$ *or* $x \geq 4$
20. $x + 1 = 6$ *or* $2x = 10$

WRITTEN EXERCISES 2.11

A Indicate whether each of the following compound sentences is *True* or *False*.

1. $1 + 2 = 3$ *or* $8 - 5 = 4$
2. $3 + 7 = 11$ *or* $13 + 12 = 25$
3. $\frac{1}{8} + \frac{7}{8} = 1$ *or* $\frac{1}{4} + \frac{3}{4} = 1$
4. $\frac{1}{3} + \frac{2}{3} = 1$ *or* $\frac{3}{5} + \frac{2}{5} = 1$
5. $0.2 + 0.3 = 0.05$ *or* $0.1 + 0.8 = 0.09$
6. $0.5 + 0.2 = 0.05$ *or* $0.3 + 0.6 = 0.09$
7. $3 < 5$ *or* $\frac{1}{3} \neq \frac{2}{6}$
8. $\frac{2}{5} \neq 0.4$ *or* $10 \leq 10$
9. $15 + 17 = 32$ *or* $\frac{19}{37} > \frac{20}{36}$
10. $\frac{153}{167} < \frac{154}{168}$ *or* $28 + 13 = 41$

Let the domain of the variable be {whole numbers}. (a) Find L, the truth set of the left clause; (b) find R, the truth set of the right clause; and (c) find $L \cup R$, the truth set of the compound sentence.

11. $x = 2 \ or \ x \leq 5$ 12. $x < 7 \ or \ x + 1 = 4$

13. $a \leq 4 \ or \ a < 3$ 14. $r < 7 \ or \ r \leq 1$

15. $y < 2 \ or \ y + 1 = 10$ 16. $t - 2 = 6 \ or \ t \leq 5$

17. $w \geq 8 \ or \ w - 1 = 11$ 18. $x + 5 = 15 \ or \ x > 5$

19. $m \neq 5 \ or \ m > 3$ 20. $n \leq 6 \ or \ n \neq 1$

Using the variable x, form a compound *or* sentence whose left and right clauses have truth sets as given. Let the domain of the variable be {whole numbers}.

21. $L = \{1, 2, 3, \cdots\}; \quad R = \{5\}$

22. $L = \{10\}; \quad R = \{5, 6, 7, \cdots\}$

23. $L = \{1\}; \quad R = \{0\}$

24. $L = \{1\}; \quad R = \{10\}$

25. $L = \{0, 1, 2, 3, 4, 5\}; \quad R = \{0, 1, 2, 3\}$

26. $L = \{5, 6, 7, \cdots\}; \quad R = \{10, 11, 12, \cdots\}$

Find the truth sets of the compound sentences formed in the following lists of exercises.

27. in Exercises 21, 23, and 25   28. in Exercises 22, 24, and 26

2.12 Graphs of *or* Sentences

You learned about the truth sets of compound sentences that use the connective *or*. Now look at the problem of making their graphs.

Consider the sentence

$$x < 2 \quad or \quad x \geq 5,$$

for which the domain is {numbers of arithmetic}. The graph of the left clause, $x < 2$, is labeled $\boxed{1}$, and the graph of the right clause, $x \geq 5$, is labeled $\boxed{2}$.

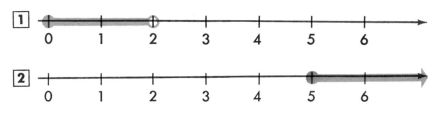

You remember that the truth set of an *or* sentence is the set of numbers that are in the truth sets of at least one of the clauses; that is, its truth set is the union of the truth sets of the left and right clauses. Thus, the graph of the compound sentence $x < 2$ *or* $x \geq 5$ is as shown below.

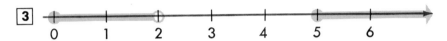

■ **P-1** Why is the point at 1, for example, included in the graph of the compound sentence?

■ **P-2** Why is the point at 6, for example, included in the graph of the compound sentence?

■ **P-3** Why is the point at 4 not included in the graph labeled ③?

The compound sentence

$$x < 6 \quad or \quad x \leq 3$$

has the following graphs for its left and right clauses, respectively, with {numbers of arithmetic} again as the domain.

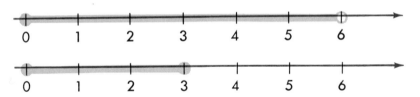

■ **P-4** Is the point at 2 in the graph of the compound sentence? Why?

■ **P-5** Is the point at 5 in the graph of the compound sentence? the point at 6?

You can probably see that the graph is as follows.

Again it may be helpful for you to imagine pushing the graphs of the two clauses together. Any point on the combined number lines that appears darkened will be in the graph of the *or* sentence.

One more example may be helpful. This time, the domain is restricted to {whole numbers}.

$$x = 5 \quad or \quad x + 1 \neq 6$$

The graph of the left clause is labeled $\boxed{4}$,

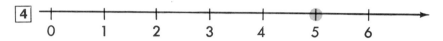

and the graph of the right clause is labeled $\boxed{5}$.

The graph of the compound sentence is the graph labeled $\boxed{6}$.

Notice that graph $\boxed{6}$ represents the set of whole numbers.

ORAL EXERCISES 2.12

For each of the following, tell whether the graph of the given compound sentence is correct. Let {numbers of arithmetic} be the domain.

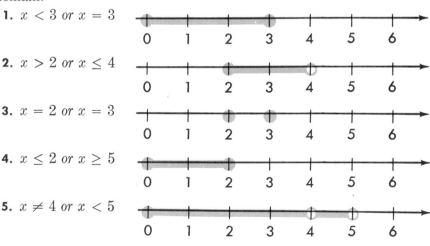

1. $x < 3$ *or* $x = 3$

2. $x > 2$ *or* $x \leq 4$

3. $x = 2$ *or* $x = 3$

4. $x \leq 2$ *or* $x \geq 5$

5. $x \neq 4$ *or* $x < 5$

Let {whole numbers} be the domain. Make a compound open sentence whose clauses have graphs that are shown, using the connective *or*.

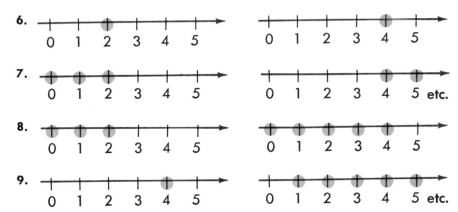

Let {numbers of arithmetic} be the domain. Make a compound open sentence to fit each graph shown.

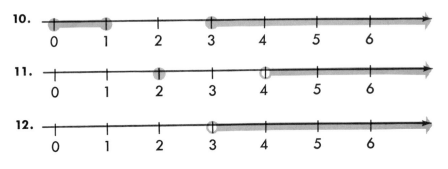

WRITTEN EXERCISES 2.12

A For each of the following compound sentences, first draw the graph of each clause, and then draw the graph of the compound sentence. Let {numbers of arithmetic} be the domain of the variable.

1. $x = 5$ *or* $x \leq 3$ 2. $x > 4$ *or* $x = 0$

3. $x = 1$ *or* $x = 5$ 4. $x = 3$ *or* $x = 0$

5. $x \geq 3$ *or* $x > 6$ 6. $x > 3$ *or* $x \geq 5$

7. $x \leq 2\frac{1}{2}$ *or* $x > 5\frac{1}{2}$ 8. $x < 3\frac{1}{3}$ *or* $x \geq 6\frac{3}{5}$

9. $x \neq 3$ *or* $x \leq 5$ 10. $x > 3$ *or* $x \neq 6$

11. $x \neq 3$ *and* $x \leq 5$ 12. $x > 3$ *and* $x \neq 6$

Follow the same directions for the following compound sentences as for Exercises 1–12, except use {whole numbers} as the domain.

13. $x < 5$ *or* $x = 6$

14. $x = 1$ *or* $x \geq 4$

15. $x \leq 5$ *or* $x < 3$

16. $x \geq 1$ *or* $x > 5$

State a compound open sentence to fit each graph shown. Let {numbers of arithmetic} be the domain of the variable.

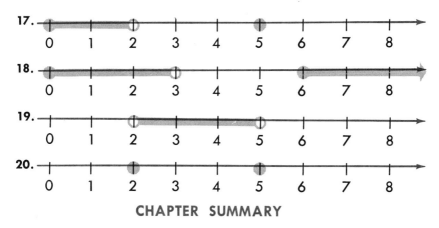

17.

18.

19.

20.

CHAPTER SUMMARY

Important Terms

1. A **variable** is a symbol that may be replaced by any element of a specified set.
2. A **domain** of a variable is a set from which replacements for the variable may be chosen.
3. An **open phrase** is a phrase that contains a variable.
4. The **value** of an open phrase is the number it names when the variable is replaced by an element of its domain.
5. An **open sentence** is a sentence that contains a variable.
6. A **truth number** of an open sentence is any number that will make the sentence true when it replaces the variable.
7. The **truth set** of an open sentence is the set of its truth numbers.
8. The **graph of a set** is the set of points on the number line that correspond to the elements of the given set.
9. The **graph of a sentence** is the graph of its truth set.
10. The **intersection** of two sets is the set of elements that are in both of the given sets.
11. The **union** of two sets is the set of elements that are in at least one of the given sets.

Important Ideas

1. The truth set of an open sentence must contain all the elements for which the sentence is true.
2. The symbol $\leq$ means "is less than or equal to."
3. The symbol $\geq$ means "is greater than or equal to."
4. In graphing truth sets of open sentences, it is important to consider the domain of the variable.
5. A compound sentence with connective *and* is true only when both clauses are true.
6. A compound sentence with connective *or* is true when either clause is true or when both clauses are true.
7. The graph of an *and* sentence contains a point if that point is in the graph of each clause.
8. The graph of an *or* sentence contains a point if that point is in the graph of either clause or in both.

CHAPTER REVIEW

Find all the values of the following open phrases, using $\{3, 5\}$ as the domain.

1. $2x + 8$
2. $5x - 10$
3. $4 + 3x$
4. $20 - 3x$
5. $3(x - 2)$
6. $(x + 3)2$

Translate each of the following word phrases to open phrases. Tell what the variable represents.

7. Thirteen more than the unknown number
8. Three less than the number of players
9. The number of addresses divided by 15
10. The product of 5 and the number of candy bars
11. The number of quarts in x gallons
12. The number of cents in d dollars

Using $\{$whole numbers$\}$ as the domain, find the truth set of each of the following.

13. $x - 3 = 21$
14. $2x = 7$
15. $x + 2 = 2 + x$
16. $2x < 10$

Using $\{1, 2, 3\}$ as the domain, find all values of each of the following.

17. $x^2 + 3$
18. $2 + 3x^2$
19. $x^2 - 1$
20. $25 - 2x^2$

Draw graphs of the following sentences, using {numbers of arithmetic} as the domain.

21. $x \leq 5$ **22.** $x > 3$

23. $y \neq 2\frac{2}{3}$ **24.** $y \geq 0$

25. $y - 1 \leq 2\frac{4}{5}$ **26.** $x + 1 > 4\frac{1}{2}$

Let {whole numbers} be the domain. (a) Find L, the truth set of the left clause; (b) find R, the truth set of the right clause; and (c) find either L $\cap$ R or L $\cup$ R, whichever is the truth set of the compound sentence.

27. $x \leq 7$ *and* $x > 3\frac{1}{4}$ **28.** $x \geq 2$ *and* $x < 6\frac{1}{2}$

29. $x \leq 7$ *or* $x > 3\frac{1}{4}$ **30.** $x \geq 2$ *or* $x < 6\frac{1}{2}$

31. $x = 5$ *and* $x \leq 6$ **32.** $x > 5$ *and* $x + 1 = 10$

33. $x = 5$ *or* $x \leq 6$ **34.** $x > 5$ *or* $x + 1 = 10$

Let {numbers of arithmetic} be the domain. Draw a graph of the truth set of each compound sentence. (First sketch the graph of each clause.)

35. $x \leq 5\frac{1}{2}$ *and* $x > 1\frac{2}{3}$ **36.** $x < 8\frac{2}{3}$ *and* $x \geq 1\frac{3}{4}$

37. $x \leq 5\frac{1}{2}$ *or* $x > 1\frac{2}{3}$ **38.** $x < 8\frac{2}{3}$ *or* $x \geq 1\frac{3}{4}$

39. $x = 5$ *and* $x \leq 3$ **40.** $x = \frac{3}{4}$ *and* $x = 5\frac{1}{2}$

41. $x = 5$ *or* $x \leq 3$ **42.** $x = \frac{3}{4}$ *or* $x = 5\frac{1}{2}$

A view of Lower California, or Baja California, photographed from a manned satellite also shows a portion of the satellite. Algebra is one of the mathematical techniques used in locating the position of such a satellite several hundred miles above the surface of the earth.

Number Properties and Operations

3

3.1 Identity Elements

Zero is a very special number in mathematics. You can probably see what property of zero is suggested by these examples:

[1] $5 + 0 = 5$ [2] $\frac{1}{2} + 0 = \frac{1}{2}$

[3] $0 + 0.7 = 0.7$ [4] $x + 0 = x$

■ **P-1** What special property in addition does zero have that is not shared by any other number?

You may call this property the **Addition Property of Zero.** It can be stated as follows.

> **The sum of zero and any number is equal to that given number.**

■ **P-2** Are the following sentences true or false?

[1] $0 + 1\frac{3}{4} = 1\frac{3}{4}$ [2] $22 + 0 = 0$ [3] $0 + 0 = 0$

■ **P-3** What are the truth sets of the following sentences if the domain of the variables is {numbers of arithmetic}?

[1] $x + \frac{2}{3} = \frac{2}{3}$ [2] $a + 0 = \frac{5}{6}$

The number 1 is also a special number in mathematics. The following examples should tell you what property 1 has in multiplication.

[1] $5(1) = 5$ [2] $1(\frac{3}{4}) = \frac{3}{4}$

[3] $27(\frac{3}{3}) = 27$ [4] $1(x) = x$

■ **P-4** What special property in multiplication does 1 have that is not shared by any other number?

You may refer to the property shown here as the **Multiplication Property of One.** It can be stated as follows.

> The product of 1 and any given number is that given number.

■ **P-5** Are the following sentences true or false?

| 1 | $1(2\frac{1}{4}) = 2\frac{1}{4}$ | 2 | $356(1) = 356$ |
| 3 | $\frac{5}{5}(13) = 13$ | 4 | $1 \cdot 1 = 1$ |

■ **P-6** What are the truth sets of the following sentences?

| 1 | $1(x) = 15$ | 2 | $x(\frac{2}{3}) = \frac{2}{3}$ |

The two properties in this section can be stated formally as follows.

> If a is any number, then both of the following are true.
>
> $a + 0 = a$ and $1(a) = a$

Since the given numbers are left unchanged in these operations, 0 and 1 are called **identity elements.** The number 0 is the identity element for addition. The number 1 is the identity element for multiplication.

ORAL EXERCISES 3.1

Tell whether each of these is *True* or *False*.

1. $0 + \frac{3}{5} = \frac{3}{5}$ **2.** $1(15) = 1$
3. $\frac{2}{3} + 0 = 0$ **4.** $(\frac{5}{5})16 = 16$
5. $3 + 0 = 0 + 3$ **6.** $1(\frac{3}{4}) = \frac{3}{4}(1)$

Find the truth sets of the following. Let {numbers of arithmetic} be the domain.

7. $x + \frac{1}{4} = \frac{1}{4}$ **8.** $0 + x = \frac{5}{6}$
9. $y(15) = 15$ **10.** $1(a) = 1$
11. $x + 0 = x$ **12.** $x + 0 = 0$
13. $a(1) = a$ **14.** $a(1) = 1$
15. $n \cdot 0 = n$ **16.** $x + 1 = x$

17. What is the Addition Property of Zero?

18. What is the Multiplication Property of One?

19. What is the Identity Element for Addition?

20. What is the Identity Element for Multiplication?

WRITTEN EXERCISES 3.1

A Identify each of these sentences as *True* or *False*.

1. $0 + \frac{2}{3} = 0$

2. $0.15 + 0 = 0$

3. $1(\frac{5}{8}) = \frac{5}{8}$

4. $\frac{3}{4}(1) = \frac{3}{4}$

5. $(\frac{3}{3})17 = 17$

6. $(\frac{7}{7})5 = 1$

7. $\frac{5}{5} \cdot 0 = \frac{5}{5}$

8. $0 \cdot \frac{2}{2} = 0$

9. $3 + 0(5) = 15$

10. $15(0 + 3) = 3$

Find the truth sets of the following. Let {numbers of arithmetic} be the domain.

11. $x + \frac{3}{7} = \frac{3}{7}$

12. $0.08 + y = 0.08$

13. $0 + x = 23$

14. $a + 0 = 29\frac{1}{2}$

15. $1(y) = 11\frac{1}{3}$

16. $x(1) = \frac{7}{9}$

17. $x(\frac{3}{3}) = 13$

18. $y(\frac{10}{10}) = 15$

19. $t + 0 = 0$

20. $s(1) = 1$

21. $x + 0 = x + 1$

22. $y(\frac{2}{2}) = y + 1$

23. $a + 0 = 0 + a$

24. $0 + n = n + 0$

25. $y(1) = 1(y)$

26. $(\frac{4}{4})p = p(\frac{5}{5})$

27. $0.3a = 0.3$

28. $0.7x = 0.7$

29. $1 \cdot x = x$

30. $0 + n = n$

B Find the truth sets of the following sentences of which the domain is {numbers of arithmetic}.

31. $x(0) = 0$

32. $x + 1 = x$

33. Do you think 0 has a special property in multiplication?

34. Do you think 1 has a special property in addition?

35. What is the whole number called that is obtained by adding 1 to any whole number?

3.2 Binary Operations and Closure

You have been using the numbers of arithmetic for a long time. You know that you can add any two numbers of arithmetic and the sum is a number of arithmetic. For example, $5 + 7$ names the sum of two numbers of arithmetic. This sum is also a number of arithmetic named by 12.

■ **P-1**   What number is named by the sum

$$2 + 3 + 4?$$

You probably found the sum in this way. First you noted that the sum of 2 and 3 is 5. Then you added 5 and 4 to get the sum 9. A phrase such as $2 + 3 + 4$ means $(2 + 3) + 4$. Since numbers are actually added in pairs, addition is sometimes called a **binary** operation. The prefix "bi" means "two."

■ **P-2**   How could you pair numbers in finding the sum

$$3 + 1 + 5 + 4?$$

Multiplication is also called a binary operation because, in finding a product, you use two numbers at a time.

■ **P-3**   What number do you get for the product

$$2 \cdot 3 \cdot 4?$$

Again you probably found the product of 2 and 3 first. Then you multiplied 6 and 4 to obtain the product 24. A phrase such as $2 \cdot 3 \cdot 4$ means $(2 \cdot 3) \cdot 4$.

■ **P-4**   If two numbers of arithmetic are multiplied, is their product a number of arithmetic?

Consider the set A = $\{0, 1, 2, 3, 4\}$.

■ **P-5**   If any two elements of A are added, is their sum also an element of A? Explain.

■ **P-6**   If any two elements of A are multiplied, is their product also an element of A? Explain.

Consider the set B = $\{1, 3, 5, 7, \cdots\}$.

■ **P-7**   If any two elements of B are added, is their sum also an element of B?

■ **P-8**   If any two elements of B are multiplied, is their product also an element of B?

> A certain set is said to be **closed under addition** if the sum of any two of its elements is also an element of that set.

For example, the set of whole numbers, $\{0, 1, 2, 3, 4, 5, \cdots\}$, is closed under addition.

■ **P-9** Do you think the set of whole numbers is closed under multiplication?

> A set is **closed under multiplication** if the product of any two of its elements is also an element of that set.

For example, the set of even whole numbers, $\{0, 2, 4, 6, \cdots\}$, is closed under multiplication.

Consider the set $R = \{0, 1\}$. Keep in mind that a number may be added to itself or multiplied by itself.

■ **P-10** Is set R closed under addition? Why?

■ **P-11** Is set R closed under multiplication? Why?

You may refer to the property of sets in this section as the **Closure Property.** It should be evident that the following is true.

> The set of numbers of arithmetic is closed under both addition and multiplication.

ORAL EXERCISES 3.2

Find the following sums and products.

1. $\frac{1}{3} + \frac{2}{3} + \frac{1}{5}$ **2.** $2 + \frac{1}{2} + 3 + 1\frac{1}{2}$

3. $2 \cdot 5 \cdot 7$ **4.** $2 \cdot 2 \cdot 2 \cdot 2$

5. Why are addition and multiplication called binary operations?

6. Can you name some other binary operations in mathematics?

Give one example showing why each of the given sets is not closed.

7. $\{0, 1, 2\}$ under addition   **8.** $\{0, 1, 2\}$ under multiplication

9. $\{1, 3, 5, 7, \cdots\}$ under addition   **10.** $\{\frac{1}{2}, \frac{1}{4}\}$ under addition

11. $\{\frac{1}{2}, \frac{1}{3}\}$ under multiplication

Is each of the following sets closed under division? Explain.

12. $\{2, 4\}$ **13.** $\{1, \frac{1}{2}\}$

14. $\{1, 2, 3, 4, 5, \cdots\}$ **15.** $\{$whole numbers$\}$

16. $\{$numbers of arithmetic$\}$

WRITTEN EXERCISES 3.2

A Find the following sums and products.

1. $0.3 + 0.7 + 3.0$ 2. $1.2 + 0.8 + 5.0$
3. $\frac{2}{5} + \frac{3}{5} + \frac{1}{2}$ 4. $\frac{3}{7} + \frac{4}{7} + \frac{3}{4}$
5. $5 \cdot 4 \cdot 3 \cdot 2$ 6. $6 \cdot 5 \cdot 4 \cdot 3$
7. $3 \cdot 3 \cdot 3 \cdot 3$ 8. $2 \cdot 2 \cdot 3 \cdot 3$

Give an example to show why each of the following sets is not closed under the operation indicated.

9. $\{1, 2, 3, 4, 5\}$ under multiplication
10. $\{1, 2, 3, 4, 5\}$ under addition
11. $\{0, 2\}$ under addition
12. $\{0, 2\}$ under multiplication
13. $\{$odd whole numbers$\}$ under addition
14. $\{0, 1, 2, 4, 6, 8, 10, \cdots\}$ under addition

State whether each of the following sets is *Closed* under the operation indicated.

15. $\{$whole numbers$\}$ under addition
16. $\{$whole numbers$\}$ under multiplication
17. $\{$counting numbers$\}$ under multiplication
18. $\{$counting numbers$\}$ under addition
19. $\{0, 2, 4, 6, 8, \cdots\}$ under addition
20. $\{1, 3, 5, 7, 9, \cdots\}$ under multiplication
21. $\{1, 2, 3, 4, 5, \cdots\}$ under division
22. $\{0, 2, 4, 6, \cdots\}$ under division
23. $\{$rational numbers of arithmetic$\}$ under division
24. $\{$numbers of arithmetic$\}$ under division
25. $\{10, 100, 1000, \cdots\}$ under addition
26. $\{10, 100, 1000, \cdots\}$ under multiplication

C Let * represent the operation of "finding the average of two numbers." For example, $4 * 6 = 5$ because the average of 4 and 6 is 5; that is,

$$\left(\frac{4 + 6}{2}\right) = 5.$$

Indicate which of the following sets are *Closed* under the operation *.

27. $\{0, 1, 2, 3, 4, \cdots\}$ 28. $\{1, 3, 5, 7, 9, \cdots\}$
29. $\{$numbers of arithmetic$\}$ 30. $\{0, \frac{1}{2}, 1\}$

Suppose the following table shows the meaning of ⊕ on the set {0, 1, 2, 3, 4}. The first number will be taken from the left column and the second number from the top row of the table. For example, 2 ⊕ 4 is equal to 1.

⊕	0	1	2	3	4
0	0	1	2	3	4
1	1	2	3	4	0
2	2	3	4	0	1
3	3	4	0	1	2
4	4	0	1	2	3

31. What is 2 ⊕ 3?
32. What is 3 ⊕ 2?
33. What is 4 ⊕ 4?
34. What is 2 ⊕ 1?
35. Is the set closed under ⊕?

3.3 Commutative Property of Addition

You know that $3 + 2$ is a symbol for the number that is obtained by adding 2 to 3. The number line can be used to show addition of numbers. The sum $3 + 2$ can be thought of as first a move from 0 to 3 on the number line followed by a move of 2 more units to the right. The motion ends at the point whose coordinate is 5.

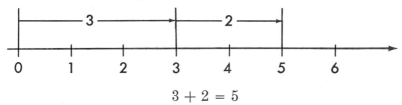

$$3 + 2 = 5$$

Now see what the sum $2 + 3$ looks like by the number line method.

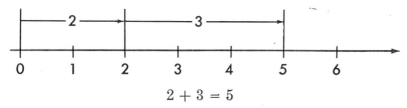

$$2 + 3 = 5$$

You can see that the first step is a move of 2 units to the right of 0 and that the second step is a move of 3 more units to the right. The steps for $2 + 3$ are not the same as those for $3 + 2$, but the result is still 5.

The diagrams show that the following is a true sentence.

$$3 + 2 = 2 + 3$$

Now consider the sum $4\frac{1}{2} + 3$, using the number line.

■ **P-1** What motion is made as the first step?

■ **P-2** At what number does the second step end?

Now try the sum $3 + 4\frac{1}{2}$.

■ **P-3** What step is taken first, using the number line?

■ **P-4** Where does the second motion stop?

■ **P-5** Is the following sentence true?

$$4\frac{1}{2} + 3 = 3 + 4\frac{1}{2}$$

You should have imagined these two problems as follows.

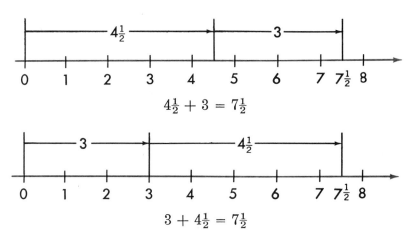

$$4\frac{1}{2} + 3 = 7\frac{1}{2}$$

$$3 + 4\frac{1}{2} = 7\frac{1}{2}$$

These examples show that addition of two numbers can be performed in either order. The sum is the same in each case. This property is called the **Commutative Property of Addition.**

> If *a* and *b* are any two numbers of arithmetic, then it is true that
>
> $$a + b = b + a.$$

You have used the Commutative Property in checking addition problems. In adding a long column of numbers, you can first add from bottom to top. Then adding from top to bottom will help you catch any errors. The sums should be the same.

ORAL EXERCISES 3.3

Is each of the following sentences *True* or *False*? Why?

1. $12 + 13 = 13 + 12$
2. $\frac{1}{2} + \frac{1}{3} = \frac{1}{3} + \frac{1}{2}$
3. $\frac{13}{17} + \frac{15}{97} = \frac{15}{97} + \frac{13}{17}$
4. $0.08 + 0.29 = 0.29 + 0.08$
5. $8 \div 4 = 4 \div 8$
6. $3 \div 9 = 9 \div 3$
7. $7.6 + 2.9 = 6.7 + 9.2$
8. $13(45 + 3) = 13(3 + 45)$

9. What is meant when you say that addition is commutative?

10. Do you think that subtraction of numbers of arithmetic is commutative?

Find the truth sets of the following. Let {numbers of arithmetic} be the domain.

11. $x + 1 = 1 + x$
12. $a + 3 = 3 + 5\frac{1}{2}$
13. $\frac{1}{2} + \frac{1}{3} = \frac{1}{3} + y$
14. $t + 13\frac{1}{2} = 13\frac{1}{2} + t$
15. $a + 0 = 0 + \frac{1}{5}$
16. $x + 2 = \frac{3}{3}(2 + 5)$
17. $2 + (x + 3) = 2 + (3 + 8)$
18. $(y + 6) + 2 = 2 + (6 + 10)$
19. $3(x + 1) = 3(1 + 5)$
20. $(t + 8)5 = (8 + \frac{1}{2})5$

WRITTEN EXERCISES 3.3

A Indicate whether each of the following sentences is *True* or *False*.

1. $25 + 28 = 28 + 25$
2. $56 + 12 = 12 + 56$
3. $2\frac{1}{3} + 5\frac{1}{8} = 5\frac{1}{8} + 2\frac{1}{3}$
4. $3\frac{2}{3} + 1\frac{1}{5} = 1\frac{1}{5} + 3\frac{2}{3}$
5. $5.3 + 8.7 = 3.5 + 7.8$
6. $9.2 + 3.7 = 2.9 + 7.3$
7. $2 \cdot 3 + 5 = 5 + 2 \cdot 3$
8. $4 \cdot 7 + 1 = 1 + 4 \cdot 7$
9. $3 \cdot 7 + 2 = 3 \cdot 2 + 7$
10. $5 \cdot 6 + 3 = 5 \cdot 3 + 6$
11. $2(8 + 5) = 2(5 + 8)$
12. $5(9 + 2) = 5(2 + 9)$

Find the truth sets of the following sentences. Let the domain be {numbers of arithmetic}.

13. $3 + s = s + 3$
14. $x + 10 = 10 + x$
15. $y + 5 = 5 + \frac{2}{3}$
16. $8 + t = \frac{15}{16} + 8$
17. $(x + 2) + 5 = (2 + 9) + 5$
18. $(y + 3) + 1 = (3 + 11) + 1$
19. $(11 + 12) + x = 5 + (12 + 11)$
20. $a + (20 + 10) = (10 + 20) + 5$
21. $5(x + 2) = 5(2 + 7)$
22. $(3 + y)8 = (10 + 3)8$
23. $a + 3 = \frac{5}{5}(3 + 7)$
24. $8 + x = (19 + 8)\frac{2}{2}$

C Let $\boxed{+}$ mean that the first number is multiplied by 3 and the second number added. Thus, $4 \boxed{+} 1 = 13$ is true because $3(4) + 1$ equals 13. Find the value of each of the following:

25. $1 \boxed{+} 4$ **26.** $5 \boxed{+} 3$ **27.** $3 \boxed{+} 5$

28. $\frac{1}{3} \boxed{+} 5$ **29.** $5 \boxed{+} \frac{1}{3}$

30. Is the operation $\boxed{+}$ as described here commutative?

Now use the set $\{a, b, c, d\}$ and a table to define the operation $*$ on this set. The first element is obtained from the left column and the second element from the top row of the table. For example, $c * b$ is equal to a.

*	a	b	c	d
a	a	c	d	b
b	b	d	c	a
c	c	a	b	d
d	d	b	a	c

31. What is b * c?

32. What is c * b?

33. What is d * c?

34. What is c * d?

35. Is * a commutative operation?

3.4 Associative Property of Addition

In the last section, you learned about the Commutative Property of Addition. It means that it makes no difference in what order you add two numbers.

Consider the phrase $(3 + 8) + 5$. The symbol $(3 + 8)$ is read "the quantity three plus eight." In finding the value of this phrase, you would first find a common name for the number named by $(3 + 8)$, which is 11. Then you would find the common name for the sum $11 + 5$, which is 16. Thus, $(3 + 8) + 5 = 16$ is true.

Now find the value of the phrase $3 + (8 + 5)$. You can think of this as the sum of the numbers named by the numerals 3 and $(8 + 5)$. First find the common name for $(8 + 5)$, which is 13. Then the sum $3 + 13$ is 16. Thus, $3 + (8 + 5) = 16$.

You have shown that the following sentence is true.

$$(3 + 8) + 5 = 3 + (8 + 5)$$

Try another example in which you will find the value of $(7 + 9) + 4$.

■ **P-1** What two numbers are to be added first? What is their sum?

■ **P-2** What two numbers are added next?

■ **P-3** What is the value of $(7 + 9) + 4$?

Now you will find the value of $7 + (9 + 4)$.

■ **P-4** What two numbers are added first in this phrase? What is their sum?

■ **P-5** What two numbers are added next?

■ **P-6** What is the value of the phrase $7 + (9 + 4)$?

You have shown that the following sentence is true.

$$(7 + 9) + 4 = 7 + (9 + 4)$$

These two examples show that, when you find the sum of three numbers, it does not make any difference how you group them, or pair them off. This property is called the **Associative Property of Addition.** It can be stated as follows.

> If a, b, and c are any three numbers of arithmetic, then it is true that
>
> $$(a + b) + c = a + (b + c).$$

Notice that, in the statement of this property, the order of the three numbers is not changed — only the grouping is changed. Changing the order in addition involves the Commutative Property!

The true sentence $(\frac{1}{2} + \frac{1}{3}) + \frac{1}{4} = \frac{1}{2} + (\frac{1}{3} + \frac{1}{4})$ is an example of the Associative Property of Addition.

The sentence $(\frac{1}{2} + \frac{1}{3}) + \frac{1}{4} = \frac{1}{2} + (\frac{1}{4} + \frac{1}{3})$ is also true, but it uses both the Commutative and Associative Properties of Addition.

Now consider the phrase $(\frac{1}{5} + \frac{3}{4}) + \frac{1}{4}$.

■ **P-7** What phrase do you get by applying the Associative Property of Addition?

■ **P-8** What is the value of $\frac{1}{5} + (\frac{3}{4} + \frac{1}{4})$?

You can see that the Associative Property sometimes makes addition easier.

ORAL EXERCISES 3.4

Tell whether each of the following sentences is an example of the *Commutative Property of Addition*, the *Associative Property of Addition*, or *Both*.

1. $10 + (15 + 20) = (10 + 15) + 20$
2. $(3 + 4) + 5 = 5 + (3 + 4)$
3. $7 + (9 + 11) = (9 + 7) + 11$
4. $(13 + 16) + 19 = (16 + 19) + 13$
5. $(50 + 100) + 25 = 50 + (100 + 25)$
6. $(\frac{1}{2} + \frac{1}{3}) + \frac{1}{4} = (\frac{1}{4} + \frac{1}{3}) + \frac{1}{2}$
7. $0.5 + (0.3 + 0.2) = (0.3 + 0.2) + 0.5$
8. $(1 + 2) + 3 = (2 + 1) + 3$
9. $(20 + 40) + 30 = (30 + 40) + 20$
10. $\frac{2}{5} + (\frac{2}{7} + \frac{2}{3}) = \frac{2}{5} + (\frac{2}{3} + \frac{2}{7})$

Find a common name for each phrase. Use the Associative Property of Addition to make the work easier.

11. $(16 + 19) + 1$
12. $3 + (37 + 18)$
13. $(3.9 + 1.7) + 0.3$
14. $1.4 + (0.6 + 3.7)$
15. $(\frac{1}{3} + \frac{3}{4}) + \frac{1}{4}$
16. $\frac{7}{8} + (\frac{1}{8} + \frac{3}{5})$
17. $(\frac{9}{16} + \frac{3}{8}) + \frac{5}{8}$
18. $\frac{5}{13} + (\frac{8}{13} + \frac{5}{6})$
19. $(8.3 + 9.8) + 0.2$
20. $6.3 + (3.7 + 13.9)$

Find the truth sets of the following, letting {numbers of arithmetic} be the domain.

21. $(x + 2) + 5 = 8 + (2 + 5)$
22. $(10 + a) + 7 = 10 + (15 + 7)$
23. $(\frac{2}{5} + \frac{1}{2}) + \frac{1}{3} = y + (\frac{1}{2} + \frac{1}{3})$
24. $(t + \frac{5}{6}) + \frac{1}{8} = \frac{1}{3} + (\frac{5}{6} + \frac{1}{8})$
25. $(y + 18) + 23 = (23 + 16) + 18$

WRITTEN EXERCISES 3.4

A Copy each of the following sentences and show parentheses in the right-hand phrase to illustrate the Associative Property of Addition.

1. $(15 + 4) + 7 = 15 + 4 + 7$
2. $(3 + 9) + 1 = 3 + 9 + 1$
3. $17 + (0 + 8) = 17 + 0 + 8$
4. $23 + (89 + 13) = 23 + 89 + 13$
5. $(\frac{2}{3} + \frac{1}{8}) + \frac{5}{7} = \frac{2}{3} + \frac{1}{8} + \frac{5}{7}$
6. $0.50 + (0.80 + 0.07) = 0.50 + 0.80 + 0.07$

Indicate whether each of the following is an example of the *Commutative Property of Addition,* the *Associative Property of Addition,* or *Both.*

7. $35 + (16 + 23) = (23 + 35) + 16$

8. $(50 + 20) + 70 = 20 + (50 + 70)$

9. $\frac{2}{3} + (\frac{3}{4} + \frac{4}{5}) = (\frac{2}{3} + \frac{3}{4}) + \frac{4}{5}$

10. $(\frac{1}{5} + \frac{1}{3}) + \frac{1}{4} = \frac{1}{5} + (\frac{1}{3} + \frac{1}{4})$

11. $(0.5 + 0.3) + 0.7 = 0.7 + (0.5 + 0.3)$

12. $0.01 + (0.90 + 0.53) = 0.01 + (0.53 + 0.90)$

13. $86 + (91 + 53) = (91 + 86) + 53$

14. $(36 + 58) + 19 = 19 + (58 + 36)$

Use the Associative Property of Addition to rewrite each phrase. Then find a common name.

15. $(\frac{1}{3} + \frac{1}{4}) + \frac{3}{4}$

16. $(\frac{1}{6} + \frac{3}{8}) + \frac{5}{8}$

17. $\frac{5}{9} + (\frac{4}{9} + \frac{5}{6})$

18. $\frac{3}{8} + (\frac{5}{8} + \frac{5}{16})$

19. $(3.9 + 1.8) + 3.2$

20. $5.3 + (2.7 + 12.8)$

21. $(1\frac{1}{4} + 2\frac{3}{7}) + 1\frac{4}{7}$

22. $1\frac{5}{13} + (2\frac{8}{13} + 3\frac{2}{3})$

Find the truth sets of the following, letting the domain be {numbers of arithmetic}.

23. $(x + 12) + 15 = 9 + (12 + 15)$

24. $23 + (5 + y) = (23 + 5) + 17$

25. $(n + 5) + 7 = 7 + (5 + 13)$

26. $1 + (x + 5) = (5 + x) + 1$

27. $\frac{3}{5} + (a + \frac{1}{3}) = (\frac{3}{5} + \frac{1}{6}) + \frac{1}{3}$

28. $(\frac{5}{8} + t) + \frac{1}{7} = \frac{1}{7} + (\frac{2}{9} + \frac{5}{8})$

29. $(x^2 + 5) + 3 = 4 + (5 + 3)$

30. $10 + (y^2 + 2) = (2 + 9) + 10$

C Let $\otimes$ mean that the second number is multiplied by 2 and then added to the first number. Thus, $4 \otimes 3$ is equal to $4 + 2 \cdot 3$, or 10.

31. Find the value of $(2 \otimes 3) \otimes 4$.

32. Find the value of $2 \otimes (3 \otimes 4)$.

33. Is the operation $\otimes$ as described here associative?

Let * mean "take the average of the two numbers." Thus, $5 * 3$ is equal to 4.

34. Find $(6 * 8) * 10$.

35. Find $6 * (8 * 10)$.

36. Is * an associative operation?

3.5 Commutative Property of Multiplication

You know that the product $2 \cdot 3$ can be expressed as the sum $3 + 3$. Therefore, you can show multiplication of these two numbers on the number line as you did for addition.

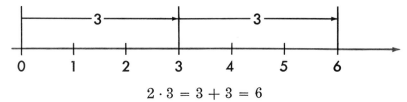

$$2 \cdot 3 = 3 + 3 = 6$$

Likewise, the product $3 \cdot 2$ can be expressed as the sum $2 + 2 + 2$. With the use of the number line, the product $3 \cdot 2$ can be shown as follows.

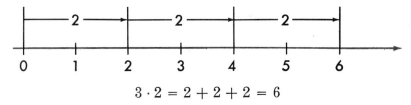

$$3 \cdot 2 = 2 + 2 + 2 = 6$$

You can see from the two number-line examples that the two problems do not look alike; yet the result is the same in each case. The example shows that the following is a true sentence.

$$2 \cdot 3 = 3 \cdot 2$$

Now work another problem using the number line. Consider the product $3 \cdot 4$.

■ **P-1** How can you write $3 \cdot 4$ as a sum?

This can be shown on the number line as follows.

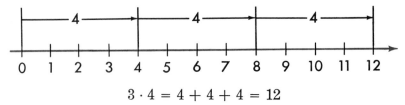

$$3 \cdot 4 = 4 + 4 + 4 = 12$$

■ **P-2** How can you express $4 \cdot 3$ as a sum?

This can be shown on the number line as follows.

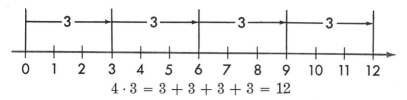

$$4 \cdot 3 = 3 + 3 + 3 + 3 = 12$$

Again the two ways of getting the answer do not look alike, but the answer is 12 in each case. This shows that the following sentence is true.

$$3 \cdot 4 = 4 \cdot 3$$

By now you realize that the order in which two numbers are multiplied does not affect the product. This property is called the **Commutative Property of Multiplication** and can be stated as follows.

> If a and b are any two numbers of arithmetic, then it is true that
> $$a \cdot b = b \cdot a.$$

You have now learned about two commutative properties of numbers of arithmetic, one for addition, the other for multiplication. Remember that the commutative properties refer to the order of performing the operations.

■ **P-3** What product is represented by the following number-line example?

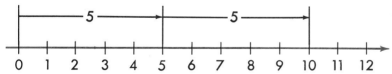

■ **P-4** What product is represented by the following number-line example?

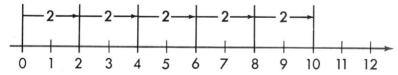

■ **P-5** Is the following a true sentence?

$$(13\tfrac{12}{29})(17\tfrac{15}{73}) = (17\tfrac{15}{73})(13\tfrac{12}{29})$$

ORAL EXERCISES 3.5

Is each of the following sentences *True* or *False?* Why?

1. $(17)(39) = (39)(17)$

2. $\frac{2}{3}(\frac{5}{8}) = \frac{5}{8}(\frac{2}{3})$

3. $3 + 2(8) = 3 + (8)2$

4. $(3 + 2)8 = (3 + 8)2$

5. $(2.3)(5.6) = (3.2)(6.5)$

6. $2(3 \cdot 4) = 2(4 \cdot 3)$

7. $(\frac{2}{7} \cdot \frac{3}{5}) \cdot \frac{1}{2} = (\frac{3}{5} \cdot \frac{2}{7}) \cdot \frac{1}{2}$

8. $(17 \cdot 32)(15 \cdot 19) = (32 \cdot 17)(19 \cdot 15)$

9. What does it mean to say that multiplication is commutative?

10. Is division a commutative operation?

Find the truth sets of the following. Let {numbers of arithmetic} be the domain.

11. $3 \cdot y = y \cdot 3$

12. $8 \cdot x = 10 \cdot 8$

13. $a \cdot (\frac{3}{4}) = (\frac{3}{4})(\frac{9}{13})$

14. $0.05t = (0.17)(0.05)$

15. $3(4x) = 3(8 \cdot 4)$

16. $x(12 + 13) = (12 + 13)5$

17. $(q + 20)\frac{1}{2} = \frac{1}{2}(20 + 36)$

18. $\frac{2}{3}(p + 12) = (25 + 12)\frac{2}{3}$

19. $(2x + 3) + 5 = 10 \cdot 2 + (3 + 5)$

20. $8y + 12y = 7 \cdot 8 + 7 \cdot 12$

WRITTEN EXERCISES 3.5

A   Indicate whether each of the following sentences is *True* or *False*.

1. $(56)(78) = (78)(56)$

2. $92 \cdot 134 = 134 \cdot 92$

3. $(\frac{7}{8})(\frac{3}{5}) = (\frac{3}{5})(\frac{7}{8})$

4. $(\frac{2}{9})(\frac{7}{13}) = (\frac{7}{13})(\frac{2}{9})$

5. $(3.8)(5.6) = (8.3)(6.5)$

6. $(7.3)(0.37) = (0.37)(0.73)$

7. $5(8 + 3) = (8 + 3)5$

8. $(18 + 15)3 = 3(18 + 15)$

9. $(\frac{1}{2} \cdot \frac{1}{3})\frac{1}{4} = (\frac{1}{3} \cdot \frac{1}{2})\frac{1}{4}$

10. $\frac{5}{6}(\frac{2}{5} \cdot \frac{1}{8}) = \frac{5}{6}(\frac{1}{8} \cdot \frac{2}{5})$

11. $3(10) + 5 = 10(3) + 5$

12. $5(10) + 7 = 7 + 10(5)$

Find the truth sets of the following sentences. Let the domain be {numbers of arithmetic}.

13. $3x = 8(3)$

14. $17 \cdot 5 = 5y$

15. $a(12 + 17) = (12 + 17)9$

16. $(52 + 47)13 = b(52 + 47)$

17. $t(\frac{1}{2} + \frac{1}{3}) = (\frac{1}{3} + \frac{1}{2})7$

18. $s(0.7 + 0.5) = (0.5 + 0.7)17$

19. $(2 \cdot 5)x = (5 \cdot 2)8$

20. $(r \cdot 9)21 = (9 \cdot 5)21$

21. $(3x + 5) + 2 = (2 + 5 \cdot 3) + 5$

22. $6 + (5q + 1) = (11 \cdot 5 + 6) + 1$

23. $\frac{3}{3}(5a) = \frac{1}{2} \cdot 5$

24. $(10x)\frac{7}{7} = 23 \cdot 10$

25. $(\frac{8}{13})x = x(\frac{8}{13})$

26. $y(\frac{5}{17}) + 1 = 1 + (\frac{5}{17})y$

C Let * mean square the first number and then multiply by the second number. Thus, $3 * 2 = 18$ is true because $3^2 \cdot 2$ equals 18. Find the value of each of the following.

27. $2 * 3$ **28.** $3 * 5$ **29.** $5 * 3$

30. Is * a commutative operation?

Suppose a, b, c, and d represent any numbers of arithmetic. State the property that is used in each of the following.

31. $(ab + c) + d = (c + ab) + d$

32. $(c + ab) + d = (c + ba) + d$

33. $(c + ba) + d = d + (c + ba)$

34. $d + (c + ba) = (d + c) + ba$

3.6   Associative Property of Multiplication

You have just learned that the numbers of arithmetic have a Commutative Property of Multiplication. Now you are going to observe another property that these numbers have when they are multiplied.

Suppose you are to find a common name for the product $(3 \cdot 4) \cdot 5$. Remember that a symbol such as $(3 \cdot 4)$ is usually read "the quantity three times four." You can think of $(3 \cdot 4)$ as naming a single number, and you know it has the common name 12. Then you may find the common name for $12 \cdot 5$, that is, 60. Thus, $(3 \cdot 4) \cdot 5 = 60$ is true.

Compare this with finding a common name for the phrase $3 \cdot (4 \cdot 5)$. Again you can treat $(4 \cdot 5)$ as a single numeral, which has the common name 20. Then $3 \cdot 20$ is found to be 60, and you have shown that $3 \cdot (4 \cdot 5) = 60$ is true. These two examples have proved that the following sentence is true.

$$(3 \cdot 4) \cdot 5 = 3 \cdot (4 \cdot 5)$$

Now examine another example in which you find a common name for $(10 \cdot 5) \cdot 2$.

■ **P-1** What two numbers are to be multiplied first? What is their product?

■ **P-2** What two numbers are multiplied next?

■ **P-3** What is the common name for $(10 \cdot 5) \cdot 2$?

Now consider the phrase $10 \cdot (5 \cdot 2)$.

■ P-4 What two numbers will you multiply first? What is their product?

■ P-5 What will you multiply next?

■ P-6 What is the common name for $10 \cdot (5 \cdot 2)$?

The results of these two problems prove that the following sentence is true.

$$(10 \cdot 5) \cdot 2 = 10 \cdot (5 \cdot 2)$$

Of course, the examples indicate that, when you find the product of three numbers, it does not make any difference how you group the numbers, or pair them off. This property is called the **Associative Property of Multiplication** and can be stated as follows.

> If a, b, and c are any numbers of arithmetic, then it is true that
>
> $$(a \cdot b) \cdot c = a \cdot (b \cdot c).$$

Again, as in the statement of the Associative Property of Addition, notice that the order of the numbers is not changed — only the grouping is changed.

The sentence $(\frac{1}{5} \cdot \frac{1}{7}) \cdot \frac{1}{9} = \frac{1}{7} \cdot (\frac{1}{5} \cdot \frac{1}{9})$ is true, but it uses both the Commutative and Associative Properties of Multiplication.

You may use the Associative Property of Multiplication to find the product $(5 \cdot \frac{2}{3}) \cdot 3$ more easily.

■ P-7 What phrase do you get by applying the Associative Property of Multiplication to $(5 \cdot \frac{2}{3}) \cdot 3$?

■ P-8 What is a common name for $\frac{2}{3} \cdot 3$?

■ P-9 What is a common name for $5(\frac{2}{3} \cdot 3)$?

The Associative Property of Multiplication can be used to find a common name for products such as $4(3x)$ as follows.

$$4(3x) = (4 \cdot 3)x = 12x$$

■ P-10 What is a common name for $7(3a)$?

Tell whether each of the following sentences is an example of the *Commutative Property of Multiplication*, the *Associative Property of Multiplication*, or *Both*.

1. $5(8 \cdot 3) = 5(3 \cdot 8)$

2. $(7 \cdot 10) \cdot 2 = 7 \cdot (10 \cdot 2)$

3. $10 \cdot (20 \cdot 30) = (10 \cdot 20) \cdot 30$

4. $(17 \cdot 3) \cdot 8 = 8 \cdot (3 \cdot 17)$

5. $(\frac{4}{5} \cdot \frac{2}{3})\frac{1}{2} = \frac{1}{2}(\frac{4}{5} \cdot \frac{2}{3})$

6. $(2 \cdot 16) \cdot 30 = 2 \cdot (16 \cdot 30)$

7. $\frac{1}{3}(\frac{1}{2} \cdot 1) = (1 \cdot \frac{1}{2})\frac{1}{3}$

8. $20 \cdot (15 \cdot 5) = 5 \cdot (15 \cdot 20)$

Find a common name for each of the following phrases. Use the Associative Property of Multiplication to make the work easy.

9. $(7 \cdot 6) \cdot \frac{1}{3}$

10. $(23 \cdot 8)\frac{1}{4}$

11. $\frac{2}{3}(9 \cdot 5)$

12. $\frac{1}{3}(15 \cdot 12)$

13. $\frac{1}{8}(16 \cdot 12)$

14. $(12 \cdot 16)\frac{3}{4}$

Find the truth sets of the following, letting {numbers of arithmetic} be the domain.

15. $3(5x) = (3 \cdot 5)8$

16. $a(7 \cdot 8) = (3 \cdot 7)8$

17. $(\frac{1}{2} \cdot 7)\frac{2}{3} = \frac{1}{2}(7y)$

18. $(2t)\frac{1}{5} = 2(5 \cdot \frac{1}{5})$

19. $(3r)5 = 5(7 \cdot 3)$

20. $n(\frac{3}{4} \cdot 7) = 7(\frac{3}{4} \cdot \frac{1}{2})$

Identify the property of addition or multiplication that each of the following sentences illustrates.

21. $(7.2)(3.5) = (3.5)(7.2)$

22. $5 + (3\frac{1}{2} + 9) = (5 + 3\frac{1}{2}) + 9$

23. $5x + 8 = 8 + 5x$

24. $2(3x) = (2 \cdot 3)x$

25. $7 + 3y = 7 + y \cdot 3$

26. $5(a + 2) = (a + 2)5$

Use the Associative Property of Multiplication to find a common name for each of the following.

27. $10(5y)$

28. $\frac{1}{2}(12t)$

29. $\frac{2}{3}(15x)$

30. $5(\frac{3}{5}n)$

WRITTEN EXERCISES 3.6

A Copy each of the following sentences and show parentheses in the right-hand phrase to illustrate the Associative Property of Multiplication.

1. $22(7 \cdot 18) = 22 \cdot 7 \cdot 18$

2. $(33 \cdot 5) \cdot 9 = 33 \cdot 5 \cdot 9$

3. $(\frac{3}{8} \cdot \frac{5}{6})\frac{5}{12} = \frac{3}{8} \cdot \frac{5}{6} \cdot \frac{5}{12}$

4. $\frac{1}{2}(\frac{1}{3} \cdot \frac{1}{5}) = \frac{1}{2} \cdot \frac{1}{3} \cdot \frac{1}{5}$

5. $7(8x) = 7 \cdot 8 \cdot x$

6. $(15 \cdot 16)y = 15 \cdot 16 \cdot y$

Indicate whether each of the following is an example of the *Commutative Property of Multiplication*, the *Associative Property of Multiplication*, or *Both*.

7. $(8 \cdot 3)7 = 8(3 \cdot 7)$

8. $(17 \cdot 2)3 = (17 \cdot 3)2$

9. $13(11 \cdot 12) = (13 \cdot 12)11$

10. $1(9 \cdot 5) = (1 \cdot 9)5$

11. $(7 \cdot 13)9 = (13 \cdot 7)9$

12. $(11 \cdot 7) \cdot 19 = (19 \cdot 7) \cdot 11$

13. $q(xa) = a(xq)$

14. $(qx)a = a(xq)$

Find the truth sets of the following sentences. Let the domain be {numbers of arithmetic}.

15. $x(7 \cdot 8) = (8 \cdot 3)7$

16. $(13 \cdot 15)y = 10(15 \cdot 13)$

17. $a(9 + 13) = (13 + 9)10$

18. $5(2 + x) = (27 + 2)5$

19. $(0.4 + 0.6)0.7 = 0.7(y + 0.4)$

20. $(0.9 + 1.1)b = 2(1.1 + 0.9)$

21. $\frac{1}{3}(3x) = 10$

22. $\frac{1}{5}(5y) = 8$

Identify, by using the abbreviations shown, which property or properties are illustrated by each of the following.

   CA means the Commutative Property of Addition.
   CM means the Commutative Property of Multiplication.
   AA means the Associative Property of Addition.
   AM means the Associative Property of Multiplication.

23. $5 \cdot x = x \cdot 5$

24. $a(5 \cdot 3) = (a \cdot 5)3$

25. $7 + x = x + 7$

26. $2 + (a + 8) = (2 + a) + 8$

27. $15 + (17 + 12) = (17 + 15) + 12$

28. $(9 \cdot 15)8 = (8 \cdot 15)9$

29. $3(13 + 2) = (2 + 13)3$

30. $2 \cdot 17 + 5 = 5 + 17 \cdot 2$

31. $(3 \cdot 5 + 1) + 7 = 3 \cdot 5 + (1 + 7)$

32. $6 + (3 + 8 \cdot 7) = (3 + 8 \cdot 7) + 6$

Use the Associative Property to obtain common names for the following.

33. $5(7x)$

34. $6(4y)$

35. $\frac{2}{3}(6a)$

36. $\frac{1}{5}(10b)$

37. $0.3(5x)$

38. $0.5(9t)$

39. $0.7(8s)$

40. $10(0.5q)$

41. $\frac{15}{8}(24y)$

42. $\frac{19}{9}(36x)$

43. $1.2(\frac{13}{3}s)$

44. $2.4(\frac{19}{8}t)$

3.7 Distributive Property

Shown below are stars arranged in rows and columns. The horizontal lines are the rows, and the vertical lines are the columns. This can be called an **array** of stars.

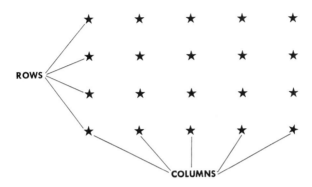

You can see that there are 4 rows and 5 columns in this array. The number of stars in the array can be found by multiplying the number of rows and the number of columns. In this array, there are 20 stars, that is, $4 \cdot 5 = 20$.

Now consider a larger array:

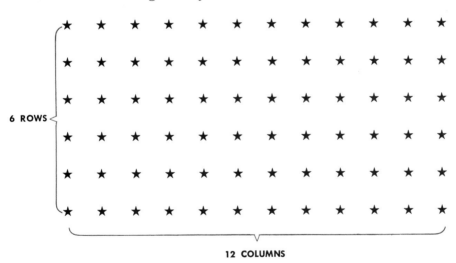

6 ROWS

12 COLUMNS

This array has 6 rows and 12 columns.

■ **P-1** How can you find the total number of stars in this array without counting them? How many are there?

Now suppose the array is separated into two smaller arrays like this:

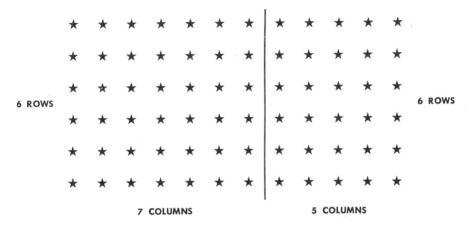

6 ROWS

6 ROWS

7 COLUMNS

5 COLUMNS

The number of stars in the array on the left is 6 · 7, or 42.

■ **P-2** What product represents the number of stars in the array at the right?

You can find the number of stars in the two arrays by adding. Therefore, 6 · 7 + 6 · 5 represents the total number of stars. However, you also saw that the total number could be found by the phrase 6 · 12. You have shown that the following sentence is true.

$$6 \cdot 12 = 6 \cdot 7 + 6 \cdot 5$$

This sentence is said to express a product as a sum, and it is an example of the **Distributive Property** of multiplication over addition.

Look at it this way. The sentence 6 · 12 = 6(7 + 5) is true since (7 + 5) is a name for 12, and

$$6(7 + 5) = 6 \cdot 7 + 6 \cdot 5,$$

as you have just shown. Multiplication by 6 is distributed over addition. The Distributive Property can be stated as follows.

If *a*, *b*, and *c* are any numbers of arithmetic, then it is true that

$$a(b + c) = ab + ac.$$

Observe that the Distributive Property involves both multiplication and addition.

■ **P-3** Is $a(b + c)$ a product or a sum?

■ **P-4** Is $ab + ac$ a product or a sum?

The Distributive Property has two important uses: $\boxed{1}$ to change products to sums, and $\boxed{2}$ to change sums to products.
Here are some examples:

Product		Sum
$2(5 + 8)$	$=$	$2 \cdot 5 + 2 \cdot 8$
$3(x + 3)$	$=$	$3 \cdot x + 3 \cdot 3$
$5(x + y)$	$=$	$5 \cdot x + 5 \cdot y$
$r(s + t)$	$=$	$r \cdot s + r \cdot t$

■ **P-5** Is the sentence $5(3 + x) = 5 \cdot 3 + x$ true for all numbers of arithmetic?

ORAL EXERCISES 3.7

Is each of the following phrases a product or a sum?

1. $2(10 + 3)$
2. $2 \cdot 10 + 2 \cdot 3$
3. $3(x + y)$
4. $5a + 5b$
5. $(5 + 3)10$
6. $5a + 3a$
7. $3x + 5$
8. $\frac{1}{2}(x + 2)$

Tell which of the following illustrate the Distributive Property.

9. $10(3 + 8) = 10 \cdot 3 + 10 \cdot 8$
10. $5(7 + 13) = 5 \cdot 7 + 1 \cdot 13$
11. $3(x + 2) = 3x + 3 \cdot 2$
12. $5(7x) = (5 \cdot 7)x$
13. $2 \cdot 7 + 2 \cdot 10 = 2(7 + 10)$
14. $3 + (5 + 2) = (3 + 5) + 2$
15. $3(x + y) = 3x + 3y$
16. $4(x + 3) = 4x + 12$
17. $3(x + y) = 3x + y$
18. $3(7 + 5) = (7 + 5)3$

Change the following products to sums; then give a common name for each sum.

19. $2(10 + 3)$
20. $3(5 + 2)$
21. $3(5 + \frac{1}{3})$
22. $4(12 + \frac{1}{2})$
23. $5(100 + 12)$
24. $2(x + 3)$
25. $3(y + 5)$
26. $5(3 + a)$

A Indicate whether each of the following is a *Product* or a *Sum*.

1. $2x + 5$

2. $3 + 7s$

3. $5(2 + 10)$

4. $3 \cdot 8 + 3 \cdot 9$

5. $7y + 7 \cdot 6$

6. $3(a + 10)$

7. $(x + 2)5$

8. $(3 + t)10$

Indicate whether each of the following sentences is *True* or *False* by finding a common name for the left-hand phrase and the right-hand phrase.

9. $6(5 + 2) = 6 \cdot 5 + 6 \cdot 2$

10. $7(3 + 10) = 7 \cdot 3 + 7 \cdot 10$

11. $5(8 + 3) = 5 \cdot 8 + 3$

12. $4(12 + 5) = 4 \cdot 12 + 5$

13. $(7 + 8)10 = 7 \cdot 10 + 8 \cdot 10$

14. $(5 + 9)3 = 5 \cdot 3 + 9 \cdot 3$

Use the Distributive Property to rename the following products as sums.

15. $25(13 + 17)$

16. $15(23 + 28)$

17. $\frac{2}{3}(5 + 8)$

18. $\frac{3}{4}(7 + 13)$

19. $3(x + 2)$

20. $5(y + 10)$

21. $s(b + d)$

22. $t(p + q)$

Find the truth sets of the following sentences. Let the domain be {numbers of arithmetic}.

23. $2(x + 5) = 2 \cdot 7 + 2 \cdot 5$

24. $3(y + 7) = 3 \cdot 8 + 3 \cdot 7$

25. $5(3 + x) = 15 + 5 \cdot 8$

26. $7(8 + a) = 56 + 7 \cdot 10$

27. $x(7 + 2) = 8 \cdot 7 + 8 \cdot 2$

28. $t(10 + 13) = 12 \cdot 10 + 12 \cdot 13$

Rename each of the following products as a sum. Then find a common name.

29. $3(5 + \frac{2}{3})$

30. $5(7 + \frac{3}{5})$

31. $7(10 + 3)$

32. $5(100 + 8)$

33. $6(x + 5)$

34. $7(3 + y)$

35. $3(2a + 3)$

36. $5(3b + 2)$

37. $\frac{1}{2}(4x + 2)$

38. $\frac{1}{3}(3x + 9)$

39. $4(\frac{1}{2}a + \frac{3}{4})$

40. $8(\frac{1}{4}y + \frac{3}{4})$

3.8 Changing Sums to Products

As you progress through algebra, you will find that the Distributive Property has many uses. You worked many problems using this property to change products to sums. Before you learn how to use it in changing sums to products, look at the Distributive Property again: If a, b, and c are any numbers of arithmetic, $a(b + c) = ab + ac$ is true.

■ **P-1** What phrase do you get by applying the Commutative Property of Multiplication to $a(b + c)$? to $a \cdot b$? to $a \cdot c$?

Because of the Commutative Property of Multiplication, you can see that the Distributive Property can also be stated in the following way.

> If a, b, and c are any numbers of arithmetic, then it is true that
> $$(b + c)a = ba + ca.$$

■ **P-2** How can you express $(3 + 5)8$ as a sum?

■ **P-3** Is the sentence $(2 + 3)9 = 2(9) + 3(9)$ true?

Since the phrase $(2 + 3)9$ and $2(9) + 3(9)$ are names for the same number, $2(9) + 3(9) = (2 + 3)9$ is also a true sentence. You see that the Distributive Property can also be stated as follows: If a, b, and c are any numbers of arithmetic, $ab + ac = a(b + c)$ is true and $ba + ca = (b + c)a$ is true.

Here, the phrase on the left is a sum, and the phrase on the right is a product. You will use it in this way to change sums to products. For example, $5(2) + 5(3) = 5(2 + 3)$ is true. Remember that $5(2 + 3)$ is read "five times the quantity two plus three."

■ **P-4** How can you express $4(10) + 4(13)$ as a product?

■ **P-5** How can you express $3(8) + 3(1)$ as a product?

■ **P-6** How can you express $3x + 3(5)$ as a product?

A very common sum to express as a product is one such as $3x + 3$. Using the Multiplication Property of One, you know that $3x + 3$ is equal to $3x + 3(1)$. So $3x + 3 \cdot 1$ is equal to $3(x + 1)$. A very common error here is to say that $3x + 3$ is equal to $3(x + 3)$. You know, however, $3(x + 3)$ is equal to $3x + 3(3)$, or $3x + 9$.

When you want to change a phrase such as $3 \cdot 5 + 7 \cdot 5$ to a product, you probably will write it as $(3 + 7)5$.

■ **P-7** How would you express $10(3) + 13(3)$ as a product?

■ **P-8** How would you express $5x + 3x$ as a product?

You can see that $5x + 3x$ is equal to $(5 + 3)x$, but $(5 + 3)$ has the common name 8. Therefore, $5x + 3x = 8x$ is true.

■ **P-9** What is a common name for $3y + 7y$?

In order to write a phrase such as $3x + x$ as a product, you must again use the Multiplication Property of One.

Using the Multiplication Property of One⟶$3x + x = 3x + 1 \cdot x$
Using the Distributive Property⟶ $= (3 + 1)x$
Because 4 is the common name for $(3 + 1)$⟶ $= 4x$

■ **P-10** What is the common name for $t + 6t$?

ORAL EXERCISES 3.8

Use the Distributive Property to express these products as sums.

1. $(8 + 2)3$ **2.** $(7 + 1)5$
3. $(5 + 13)\frac{1}{2}$ **4.** $(9 + 17)\frac{1}{3}$
5. $(x + 2)3$ **6.** $(y + 3)7$
7. $(2 + 7)x$ **8.** $(3 + 10)y$

Express the following sums as products.

9. $2(8) + 2(7)$ **10.** $3(12) + 3(18)$
11. $5(3) + 8(3)$ **12.** $4(10) + 5(10)$
13. $\frac{1}{2}(8) + \frac{1}{2}(5)$ **14.** $\frac{1}{3}(7) + \frac{1}{3}(8)$
15. $3(8) + 3$ **16.** $5(7) + 5$
17. $3x + 3(7)$ **18.** $4x + 4(5)$
19. $t(5) + 3(5)$ **20.** $n(12) + 5(12)$
21. $5y + 5$ **22.** $7 + 7a$

First express as products, then give a common name for each.

23. $3a + 2a$ **24.** $8x + 5x$
25. $10y + 20y$ **26.** $\frac{1}{2}a + 3a$
27. $t(3) + t(5)$ **28.** $2r + r$
29. $a + a$ **30.** $5y + y$

WRITTEN EXERCISES 3.8

A Use the Distributive Property to rename these products as sums.

1. $(13 + 19)7$ **2.** $(23 + 17)11$
3. $(5 + 8)\frac{1}{4}$ **4.** $(10 + 5)\frac{1}{3}$
5. $(7 + x)3$ **6.** $(8 + y)5$

7. $(9 + 8)n$
8. $(5 + 7)t$
9. $(d + p)r$
10. $(q + c)w$

Use the Distributive Property to rename these sums as products.

11. $13(5) + 13(7)$
12. $7(19) + 7(5)$
13. $8(4) + 7(4)$
14. $23(11) + 29(11)$
15. $\frac{3}{4}(5) + \frac{3}{4}(21)$
16. $\frac{2}{3}(7) + \frac{2}{3}(13)$
17. $5y + 5(12)$
18. $8t + 8(15)$
19. $8p + 8$
20. $10 + 10q$
21. $3(12) + n(12)$
22. $y(7) + 31(7)$
23. $35b + 17b$
24. $13w + 12w$

Use the Distributive Property to express the following as products; then find the common names.

25. $13n + 17n$
26. $19q + 11q$
27. $\frac{1}{2}x + 3x$
28. $5x + \frac{1}{4}x$
29. $s + 12s$
30. $15w + w$
31. $0.1y + 1.9y$
32. $3.4r + 0.6r$
33. $a(\frac{1}{2}) + a(7)$
34. $g(2) + g(\frac{1}{3})$
35. $5(ab) + 2(ab)$
36. $3(xy) + 4(xy)$
37. $3(5) + 3^2$
38. $8(5) + 5^2$
39. $3x + x^2$
40. $y^2 + 5y$

3.9 Other Uses of the Number Properties

You have already seen the use of the Associative Property in finding a simpler name for products such as $3(5x)$.

$$3(5x) = (3 \cdot 5)x$$
$$= 15x$$

Now consider an example for which you will need two properties. Suppose you want to find a common name for $(5y)8$.

By the Commutative Property of Multiplication⟶ $(5y)8 = 8(5y)$
By the Associative Property of Multiplication⟶ $= (8 \cdot 5)y$
Since 40 is the common name for $(8 \cdot 5)$⟶ $= 40y$

You will sometimes be given the instructions to simplify a phrase. To **simplify** means to find a common name. The common name is often called the **simplest form.**

Suppose you want to simplify $(10a)\frac{1}{2}$.

■ **P-1** What property tells you that $(10a)\frac{1}{2} = \frac{1}{2}(10a)$ is true?

■ **P-2** What property tells you that $\frac{1}{2}(10a) = (\frac{1}{2} \cdot 10)a$ is true?

■ **P-3** What is the common name for $(\frac{1}{2} \cdot 10)a$? for $(10a)\frac{1}{2}$?

You will recall that a product such as $2 \cdot 3 \cdot 4$ means $(2 \cdot 3) \cdot 4$. It is usually preferable to name such a product without using parentheses. By this agreement $(2x)y$ has the common name $2xy$.

There are many names for the product $(2a)(bc)$, namely, $(2ab)c$, $2(abc)$, $(2b)(ca)$, and so forth. You may consider its common name to be $2abc$, without parentheses. It is common to write the numeral for the number first followed by the variables. The order of the variables is not important.

Suppose you want to find the common name for $(2a)(3b)$. By using both the commutative and associative properties again, you see that $(2a)(3b)$ is equal to $(2 \cdot 3)(ab)$. Thus, a common name for $(2a)(3b)$ is $6ab$.

■ **P-4** What is a common name for $(5x)(6y)$?

■ **P-5** What is a common name for $(2a)(3b)(4c)$?

■ **P-6** What is a common name for $(5n)(4n)$?

Usually, $n \cdot n$ is written as n^2.

Now look at a problem that will require the use of three properties — expressing $2x(5 + 3y)$ as a sum in simplest form.

By the Distributive Property $\longrightarrow 2x(5 + 3y) = (2x)5 + (2x)3y$
By the Commutative and Associative
   Properties of Multiplication $\longrightarrow = (2 \cdot 5)x + (2 \cdot 3)(x \cdot y)$
Using common names $\longrightarrow = 10x + 6xy$

■ **P-7** How can you express $2(3x + a)$ as a sum in simplest form?

ORAL EXERCISES 3.9

Tell whether you think each of the following phrases is in the simplest form.

1. $(6x)5$ **2.** $(ry)9$

3. $a \cdot 5b$ **4.** $y(7)$

5. $3qar$

6. $5(wn)$

7. $\frac{1}{2}(3q)$

8. $(\frac{1}{2}x)y$

9. $(\frac{1}{3}x)(3y)$

10. $3x^2$

Find the common name for each of the following.

11. $x(12)$

12. $3 \cdot a \cdot a$

13. $(3t)7$

14. $9 \cdot r \cdot 3$

15. $m(5n)$

16. $y \cdot t \cdot 10$

17. $(5p)(2q)$

18. $(3xy)10$

19. $(\frac{1}{2}a)(4b)$

20. $m(\frac{1}{3})(n)(9)$

Use the Distributive Property to express the following products as sums. Give the results in simplest form.

21. $2(x + 3)$

22. $a(3 + b)$

23. $2(3a + 7)$

24. $2x(3 + x)$

25. $3y(2x + 5)$

26. $\frac{1}{2}x(2y + 4)$

WRITTEN EXERCISES 3.9

A Indicate what number property is illustrated by each of the following.

1. $(2x)12 = 2(x \cdot 12)$

2. $3(a \cdot 7) = (3a)7$

3. $(3y)9 = (y \cdot 3)9$

4. $2(3x + 1) = 2(1 + 3x)$

5. $2x(3 + y) = (2x)3 + (2x)y$

6. $2 \cdot b \cdot 3 = 2 \cdot 3 \cdot b$

7. $\frac{1}{2}(n \cdot 8) = (n \cdot 8)\frac{1}{2}$

8. $\frac{1}{2}(n \cdot 8) = \frac{1}{2}(8 \cdot n)$

Find a common name for each of the following.

9. $\frac{1}{3}(15y)$

10. $\frac{1}{4}(12r)$

11. $(7x)(9y)$

12. $(11a)(7b)$

13. $(4m)8$

14. $(5w)10$

15. $x \cdot 2 \cdot y \cdot 3 \cdot n$

16. $7 \cdot p \cdot q \cdot 3 \cdot t$

17. $(\frac{1}{2}x)(18x)$

18. $(\frac{1}{3}n)(27n)$

19. $(6a)(\frac{1}{2}ab)$

20. $(20q)(\frac{1}{5}qp)$

Rename the following products as sums in simplest form.

21. $\frac{1}{2}(8 + 6a)$

22. $\frac{1}{2}(10b + 12)$

23. $(3 + 7x)8$

24. $(9y + 2)6$

25. $a(3b + 2)$

26. $x(8 + 5y)$

27. $2p(\frac{1}{2} + q)$

28. $3r(s + \frac{1}{3})$

29. $4x(2 + 3y)$

30. $5n(3m + 7)$

31. $(1 + 5t)3t$

32. $(4x + 3)2s$

C Show that each of the following sentences is *not* true when the variable is replaced by 3.

Example:

$$2(3y) = (2 \cdot 3)(2y)$$

$$
\begin{array}{c|c}
2(3 \cdot 3) & 6(2 \cdot 3) \\
2 \cdot 9 & 6 \cdot 6 \\
18 & 36
\end{array}
$$

33. $5(x + 2) = 5x + 2$ **34.** $3x + 2x = 5x^2$

35. $5x + x = 5x$ **36.** $3x + 3 = 3(x + 3)$

3.10   The Product of Two Binomials

A phrase that indicates the sum of two numbers is sometimes called a **binomial.** Each of the two numerals that make up the indicated sum is called a **term** of the binomial. You may use the Distributive Property in renaming the product of two binomials as a sum. Consider $(10 + 3)(10 + 7)$ as an example. One way to apply the Distributive Property is as follows.

Since 13 is a common name
for $(10 + 3)$ ⟶ $(10 + 3)(10 + 7) = 13(10 + 7)$
Using the Distributive Property ⟶ $= 13 \cdot 10 + 13 \cdot 7$
$= 130 + 91$
$= 221$

Suppose, however, instead of using 13 when you apply the Distributive Property, you use $(10 + 3)$.

$$(10 + 3)(10 + 7) = (10 + 3)10 + (10 + 3)7$$
Again using the Distributive
Property ⟶ $= 10 \cdot 10 + 3 \cdot 10 + 10 \cdot 7 + 3 \cdot 7$
$= 100 + 30 + 70 + 21$
$= 221$

You have actually found the product $13 \cdot 17$ by using the Distributive Property!

Now consider the product $(x + 2)(x + 3)$. Think of $(x + 2)$ as naming a single number—call it A. The product is now $A(x + 3)$.

$$A(x + 3) = A \cdot x + A \cdot 3$$

or

$$(x + 2)(x + 3) = (x + 2)x + (x + 2)3$$
$$= x \cdot x + 2 \cdot x + x \cdot 3 + 2 \cdot 3$$
$$= x^2 + 2x + 3x + 6$$

■ **P-1** What did you learn is a common name for $(2x + 3x)$?

The phrase $x^2 + 2x + 3x + 6$ can be given the simpler name $x^2 + 5x + 6$. You have shown the following sentence to be true for all numbers of arithmetic.

$$(x + 2)(x + 3) = x^2 + 5x + 6$$

Try another example: $(a + 5)(a + 7)$.

■ **P-2** What will fill in the blanks correctly in the following?

$$(a + 5)(a + 7) = (a + 5) \cdot \underline{\;?\;} + (a + 5) \cdot \underline{\;?\;}$$

■ **P-3** How can you express $(a + 5)a$ as a sum in simplest form?

■ **P-4** How can you express $(a + 5)7$ as a sum in simplest form?

■ **P-5** What is a common name for $a^2 + 5a + 7a + 35$?

ORAL EXERCISES 3.10

1. What is meant by a binomial?
2. What are the two parts of a binomial called?

Tell whether each of the following phrases is a binomial.

3. $2y$
4. $x + y$
5. $2x + 3$
6. $2 \cdot 5 + 3x$
7. $5(x + y)$
8. $3 + a + 7$

Express each of the following products as the product of two binomials.

9. $(25)(17)$
10. $(38)(92)$
11. $(15)(17)$
12. $(112)(156)$

Give the first step in writing the following products as sums.

13. $(x + 1)(x + 2)$
14. $(a + 1)(a + 3)$
15. $(y + 5)(y + 2)$
16. $(b + 3)(b + 4)$
17. $(m + 7)(m + 2)$
18. $(n + 6)(n + 3)$

WRITTEN EXERCISES 3.10

A Find the following products by using a common name for the binomial on the left; then apply the Distributive Property.

Example: $(20 + 3)(30 + 5) = 23(30 + 5)$
$$= 23 \cdot 30 + 23 \cdot 5$$
$$= 690 + 115$$
$$= 805$$

1. $(10 + 8)(10 + 2)$
2. $(10 + 9)(10 + 5)$
3. $(20 + 7)(20 + 1)$
4. $(30 + 3)(10 + 7)$
5. $(10 + 9)(20 + 4)$
6. $(20 + 5)(20 + 5)$

Use the Distributive Property to find the following products without first simplifying either binomial.

7. $(10 + 8)(10 + 2)$ **8.** $(10 + 9)(10 + 5)$ **9.** $(20 + 7)(20 + 1)$
10. $(30 + 3)(10 + 7)$ **11.** $(10 + 9)(20 + 4)$ **12.** $(20 + 5)(20 + 5)$

Change the following products to sums and express them in simplest form.

13. $(x + 1)(x + 2)$ **14.** $(a + 1)(a + 3)$
15. $(y + 5)(y + 2)$ **16.** $(b + 3)(b + 4)$
17. $(m + 7)(m + 2)$ **18.** $(n + 6)(n + 3)$
19. $(t + 10)(t + 10)$ **20.** $(s + 8)(s + 8)$

B Show that each of the following sentences is false when x is replaced by 2.

21. $(x + 5)(x + 4) = x^2 + 20$ **22.** $(x + 7)(x + 7) = x^2 + 49$

CHAPTER SUMMARY

Important Terms

1. Zero is the **identity element in addition.**
2. One is the **identity element in multiplication.**
3. A **binary operation** is performed on two elements of a set.
4. A set has the **closure** property if an operation on any two of its elements gives a result that is an element of the set.
5. A **binomial** is a phrase that indicates the sum of two numbers.
6. The two numerals that make up a binomial are called **terms.**

Important Ideas

For all numbers of arithmetic, a, b, and c, the following sentences are true.

1. *Addition Property of Zero:* $a + 0 = a$.
2. *Multiplication Property of One:* $a \cdot 1 = a$.
3. The set of numbers of arithmetic is closed under both addition and multiplication.
4. *Commutative Property of Addition:* $a + b = b + a$.
5. *Associative Property of Addition:* $(a + b) + c = a + (b + c)$.
6. *Commutative Property of Multiplication:* $ab = ba$.
7. *Associative Property of Multiplication:* $(ab)c = a(bc)$.
8. *Distributive Property:* $a(b + c) = ab + ac$.

Which number property is illustrated by each of the following?

1. $\frac{3}{4} + 0 = \frac{3}{4}$ **2.** $15(1) = 15$

3. $5(8 + 3) = 5 \cdot 8 + 5 \cdot 3$ **4.** $\frac{1}{2}(\frac{1}{3} \cdot \frac{1}{5}) = (\frac{1}{2} \cdot \frac{1}{3})\frac{1}{5}$

5. $(6 + 3) + 7 = 6 + (3 + 7)$ **6.** $(10 + 3)5 = 10(5) + 3(5)$

Copy each of the following phrases, and place parentheses to indicate the meaning of the phrase when you consider that the operation in each is a binary operation.

7. $10 + 12 + 14$ **8.** $\frac{1}{2} \cdot \frac{1}{3} \cdot \frac{1}{4}$ **9.** $15 - 18 - 4$ **10.** $100 \div 4 \div 5$

Which of the following sets are closed under division?

11. {counting numbers}   **12.** {whole numbers}

13. {numbers of arithmetic}   **14.** {even whole numbers}

15. {even counting numbers}   **16.** {odd whole numbers}

Let the domain be {numbers of arithmetic}. If the truth set of each sentence is the entire domain, write *True;* otherwise, write *False.* If true, indicate the number property or properties that are illustrated.

17. $2x + 3 = 3 + 2x$ **18.** $2x + 3 = 3x + 2$

19. $7 + 3x = 7 + x(3)$ **20.** $(7 + 3)x = 7x + 3x$

21. $(x + 5) + 3x = x + (5 + 3x)$ **22.** $(7 \cdot 5)3x = 7(5 \cdot 3x)$

23. $x + (2 + 5 \cdot 7) = x + (5 \cdot 2 + 7)$ **24.** $8 + 5x \cdot 3x = 8 + 15x^2$

25. $3x + 5x = 8x$ **26.** $7x + x = 7x^2$

Use the Distributive Property to rename these products as sums.

27. $25(35 + 45)$ **28.** $(\frac{3}{4} + \frac{1}{2})\frac{2}{3}$ **29.** $17(a + 3)$ **30.** $(15 + x)a$

Use the Distributive Property to rename these sums as products.

31. $15x + 15 \cdot 16$ **32.** $9 \cdot 5 + t \cdot 5$ **33.** $19y + 19$ **34.** $29x + 2x$

Find a common name for each of the following.

35. $8(3r)$ **36.** $(17m)3$ **37.** $(8x)(\frac{3}{4}x)$ **38.** $(7y)(6x)$

Express each of the following as a sum in simplest form.

39. $\frac{1}{2}t(8t + 16s)$ **40.** $0.10x(0.20y + 0.08)$

Change the following products to sums and express in simplest form.

41. $(10 + 9)(10 + 3)$ **42.** $(x + 2)(x + 6)$

43. Which number properties involve the order in which operations are performed?

44. Which number properties are related to the grouping of numbers in pairs?

Describe the following sets by the roster method.
1. {whole numbers less than 5}
2. {counting numbers greater than 3 and less than 10}
3. {two largest cities in your state}
4. {fractions having 1 as numerator and a whole number between 2 and 7 as denominator}

Describe the following sets by the modified roster method.
5. {whole numbers greater than 10}
6. {counting numbers less than 100}
7. {counting numbers between 50 and 100}
8. {whole numbers that are multiples of 10}

Make a graph of each of the following sets.
9. $\{3, \frac{1}{2}, 1\frac{2}{3}, 0\}$ 10. $\{\frac{1}{2}, \frac{3}{2}, \frac{5}{2}, \frac{7}{2}\}$

Indicate whether the following pairs of sets are *Equal*, *Equivalent*, *Both equal* and *equivalent*, or *Neither*.
11. $\{\frac{1}{2}, \frac{2}{3}\}$ and {A, B}   12. $\{0.75, 1.2\}$ and $\{\frac{3}{4}, 1\frac{1}{5}\}$
13. $\{\triangle, \bigcirc, \square\}$ and $\{\square, \triangle, \bigcirc\}$ 14. { } and {0}

Indicate by *Yes* or *No* whether each of the following is a correct subset relation.
15. {whole numbers} is a subset of {counting numbers}.
16. {whole numbers} is a subset of {numbers of arithmetic}.

Tell whether each of the following is an indicated *Sum*, *Difference*, *Product*, or *Quotient*; then find a common name for each.
17. $2 \cdot 5 + 7$ 18. $(2 + 7)(8 + 5)$ 19. $17 - 20 \div 5$
20. $\dfrac{40 - 5}{6 + 2}$ 21. $19 + 17 - 8 \div 2$ 22. $(2 \cdot 5 + 3)8$

23. What is the set that has no elements called?
24. What is a set called if its elements can be counted and the counting comes to an end?
25. What is a symbol that is used as a name for a number called?
26. What is a number that is associated with a point on the number line called?
27. What is the set called from which the replacements for a variable are chosen?
28. What is a phrase called if it contains a variable?

Find the value of each open phrase if the variable is replaced by 5.

29. $7 + 2x$ **30.** $19 - 3y$ **31.** $3(x + 7)$ **32.** $(10 + a)9$

Express each of the following word phrases as an open phrase by using the variable that is suggested.

33. The product of r and 45.   **34.** Twice the sum of x and 7.

35. $8t$ increased by 11.   **36.** The cost of n pencils at 8¢ each.

Using $\{0, 1, 2, \cdots, 10\}$ as the domain, find the truth set for each of the following sentences.

37. $x \leq 6$ **38.** $2x + 1 > 15$ **39.** $2x - 5 \geq 25$

40. $a + 2 < 3$ **41.** $3x^2 = 48$ **42.** $a^2 + 1 = 26$

Draw the graph of the truth set of each of the following open sentences if the domain is {numbers of arithmetic}.

43. $a \geq 5$ **44.** $y < 6$

45. $x \leq 4$ and $x > 1$ **46.** $t < 3$ or $t \geq 5$

47. $n = 5$ and $n = 1$ **48.** $p = 5$ or $p = 1$

State an open sentence whose truth set is graphed in each of the following.

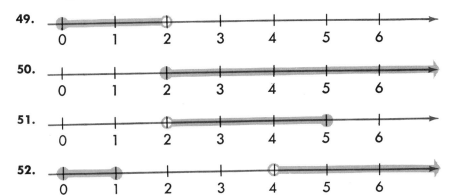

49.

50.

51.

52.

Complete each of the following sentences so that the property named will be illustrated.

53. $x + y = $?   Commutative Property of Addition

54. $2a + 2b = $?   Distributive Property

55. $(5 + 10) + x = $?   Associative Property of Addition

56. $t + 0 = $?   Addition Property of Zero

57. $\frac{5}{5}(n) = $?   Multiplication Property of One

58. $10(20 \cdot 30) = $?   Associative Property of Multiplication

59. $5(x + y) = $?   Commutative Property of Multiplication

60. $c(a + b) = $?   Distributive Property

Many of the facts about prime numbers that you will study in this chapter were discovered by the ancient Greek mathematicians. Their contribution to knowledge in mathematics is very great. There is evidence that they may have even tried to make a computer. The fragments shown here have been corroded by sea water, for this ancient Greek device was submerged for over 2000 years. It is believed that the mechanism was designed to compute mechanically the positions of stars.

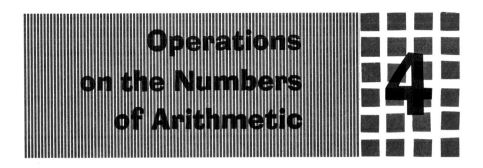

Operations on the Numbers of Arithmetic

4

4.1 Factors

In this chapter, unless stated otherwise, you will be using the set of counting numbers, $\{1, 2, 3, 4, 5, \cdots\}$. Consider the following problem in division in which 71 is divided by 13:

$$
\boxed{1} \quad 13\overline{)71} \\
\underline{65} \\
6 \quad \overset{5}{}
$$

Remember that 71 is the **dividend** and 13 is the **divisor.** The work here indicates that the **quotient** is 5 and the **remainder** is 6.

Now consider the problem of dividing 273 by 35 and continuing until a remainder of zero is obtained:

$$
\boxed{2} \quad 35\overline{)273.0} \quad \overset{7.8}{} \\
\underline{245} \\
280 \\
\underline{280} \\
0
$$

Now the quotient is 7.8 and the remainder is 0.

If you now divide 1924 by 52 and continue until a remainder of zero is obtained, the work looks like this:

$$
\boxed{3} \quad 52\overline{)1924} \quad \overset{37}{} \\
\underline{156} \\
364 \\
\underline{364} \\
0
$$

Example $\boxed{3}$ is a very special one for two reasons. Not only is the remainder zero but the quotient is a counting number. Because of this, you can say that 1924 is **divisible** by 52.

Example $\boxed{1}$ shows that 71 is *not* divisible by 13. Example $\boxed{2}$ shows that 273 is *not* divisible by 35.

> Any counting number *n* is said to be divisible by another counting number *d* if the quotient, *n* ÷ *d*, is also a counting number and the remainder is 0.

The idea can be expressed very simply by the open sentence

$$n = qd,$$

where n represents the dividend, q the quotient, and d the divisor. For example $\boxed{3}$, this becomes $1924 = 37 \cdot 52$.

■ **P-1** Is 17 divisible by 8? Why?

■ **P-2** Is 28 divisible by 7?

Notice that $28 = 4 \cdot 7$ expresses the idea that 28 is divisible by 7. Numbers that form a product, such as 4 and 7 in this example, are called **factors.** The number 7 is said to be a factor of 28.

■ **P-3** Is 28 divisible by 4?

■ **P-4** Is 4 a factor of 28?

You can show that the sentence $90 = 6 \cdot 3 \cdot 5$ is true.

The numbers 6, 3, and 5 are called factors of 90 because their product is 90. You can show that 90 is divisible by 5 as follows.

$$90 = 6 \cdot 3 \cdot 5$$

By the agreement that $a \cdot b \cdot c = (ab)c$ ⟶ $= (6 \cdot 3) \cdot 5$

Since 18 is a common name for $(6 \cdot 3)$ ⟶ $= 18 \cdot 5$

When 90 is divided by 5, the quotient is 18.

■ **P-5** Is 90 divisible by 6? What is the quotient?

■ **P-6** Is 90 divisible by 3? What is the quotient?

You can see that the following is true.

> Any counting number is always divisible by any one of its counting-number factors.

Each counting number may have several factors that are counting numbers. For example, 1, 2, 3, and 6 are all factors of 6. Often you will be interested in a particular set of factors called the **proper factors.**

> The **proper factors** of a counting number are all of its counting-number factors except 1 and the number itself.

The set of proper factors of 12 is {2, 3, 4, 6}. Caution! Although $12 = 3 \cdot 4$ is true, this sentence does not give all the proper factors of 12.

■ **P-7** What are the proper factors of 14? of 15? of 18?

■ **P-8** What can you say about the set of proper factors of 7?

ORAL EXERCISES 4.1

Make a true statement about each number pair, using the expression *is divisible by.*

1. 35; 7	**2.** 9; 45	**3.** 10; 10	**4.** 26; 13
5. 5; 30	**6.** 20; 100	**7.** 18; 1	**8.** 3; 21

Make a true statement about each number pair, using the expression *is a factor of.*

9. 2; 10	**10.** 15; 3	**11.** 35; 7	**12.** 5; 75
13. 19; 1	**14.** 23; 23	**15.** 17; 34	**16.** 39; 13

Tell whether each statement is *True* or *False.*

17. 18 is a factor of 6.	**18.** 18 is divisible by 6.
19. 10 is a proper factor of 60.	**20.** 17 is a factor of 17.
21. 17 is a proper factor of 17.	**22.** 23 is divisible by 7.
23. 1 is a factor of 93.	**24.** 9 is divisible by 27.

Express each of the following as a product of proper factors in two ways.

25. 24	**26.** 18	**27.** 36	**28.** 48	**29.** 50	**30.** 28

A Indicate by *Yes* or *No* whether the first number given is divisible by the second number. If your answer is *Yes*, write the relation as a product in the form $n = qd$.

1. 52; 13
2. 65; 13
3. 121; 17
4. 151; 19
5. 95; 19
6. 115; 23
7. 10; 100
8. 5; 35

Express each of the following numbers as a product of proper factors. If more than one way is possible, give at least two products.

9. 10
10. 14
11. 56
12. 74
13. 135
14. 123
15. 72
16. 96
17. 49
18. 121

Find the set of proper factors for each of the following numbers. Use the roster method for naming the sets.

19. 18
20. 24
21. 36
22. 48
23. 60
24. 90
25. 19
26. 23
27. 35
28. 21
29. 95
30. 91

Indicate whether each of the following sentences is *True* or *False*.

31. 258 is divisible by 13.
32. 19 is a factor of 57.
33. 11 is a proper factor of 99.
34. 29 is a factor of 29.
35. 12 is divisible by 24.
36. 28 is a factor of 7.

4.2 Tests of Divisibility

You just learned that division can be used to find out if one counting number is a factor of another. You have probably seen some of the short cuts for testing this. Before looking at these, consider a special set of numerals called the **digits**. This set is

$$\{0, 1, 2, 3, 4, 5, 6, 7, 8, 9\}.$$

It contains as elements the ten symbols that are used in naming the entire set of counting numbers. The numeral 1728, for example, is made up of four digits.

You will recall that the set of even whole numbers, that is, $\{0, 2, 4, 6, 8, 10, 12, \cdots\}$, can be formed by multiplying each of the whole numbers in succession by 2. It is then clear that each even whole number is divisible by 2.

> A whole number is divisible by 2 if the last digit in its common name names an even number.

■ **P-1**   Is 155,284 divisible by 2?

■ **P-2**   Is 1,270,867 divisible by 2?

> If the last digit of a numeral names an odd number, then the number named by the numeral is not divisible by 2.

Now look at some examples to see if there is a connection between divisibility of a number by 3 and the sum of the numbers named by the digits.

Number	Sum	Is 3 a Factor of This Sum?	Is 3 a Factor of Given Number?
84	$8 + 4 = 12$	Yes, $3 \cdot 4 = 12$	Yes, $3 \cdot 28 = 84$
567	$5 + 6 + 7 = 18$	Yes, $3 \cdot 6 = 18$	Yes, $3 \cdot 189 = 567$
51	$5 + 1 = 6$	Yes, $3 \cdot 2 = 6$	Yes, $3 \cdot 17 = 51$
92	$9 + 2 = 11$	No	No

■ **P-3**   What is the sum of the numbers named by the digits of 5274?

■ **P-4**   Is this sum divisible by 3?

■ **P-5**   Is 5274 divisible by 3?

These examples suggest the following result.

> If the sum of the numbers named by the digits is divisible by 3, then the number is divisible by 3.

■ **P-6**   What is the sum of the numbers named by the digits of 872? Is 3 a factor of this sum?

■ **P-7**   Is 872 divisible by 3?

> If the sum of the numbers named by the digits is not divisible by 3, then the number is not divisible by 3.

Again consider the subset of the counting numbers that are multiples of 5,

$$\{5, 10, 15, 20, \cdots\}.$$

This set can be obtained by multiplying each counting number in succession by 5. It is clear, then, that each number in this set is divisible by 5. Observe that each of the numerals ends in either 0 or 5.

> If the last digit in a numeral is 0 or 5, then the number named by the numeral is divisible by 5.

■ **P-8** Is 5 a factor of 1735?

■ **P-9** Is 283 divisible by 5?

> It is also true that 5 is not a factor of a number if the numeral for that number does not end in either 0 or 5.

Suppose you multiply each of the counting numbers by 4 to obtain the subset of counting numbers that are multiples of 4,

$$\{4, 8, 12, 16, 20, 24, \cdots\}.$$

Notice that all the numerals end in digits that name even numbers. If a number is divisible by 4, then it ends in a digit naming an even number.

■ **P-10** Is 18 divisible by 4? Is 4 a factor of 26?

Since there are numerals that end in digits naming even numbers for which the number is not divisible by 4, you cannot use this as a test for divisibility by 4.

There is, however, a simple test for divisibility by 4.

> If the number named by the last two digits is divisible by 4, then so is the given number.

The number 516 is divisible by 4 since 16 is divisible by 4.
The number 1812 is divisible by 4 since 12 is divisible by 4.

■ **P-11** Is 25,332 divisible by 4?

■ **P-12** Is 1826 divisible by 4?

> If the number named by the last two digits is not divisible by 4, then neither is the given number.

■ **P-13** How can you easily test whether or not a number is divisible by 10?

ORAL EXERCISES 4.2

1. What is the set of digits?

2. Which digits name even numbers? odd numbers?

Tell whether each of the following has 2 as a factor.

3. 958 **4.** 10,381 **5.** 706 **6.** 197

First give the sum of the numbers named by digits; then tell whether the given number is divisible by 3.

7. 85 **8.** 96 **9.** 127 **10.** 138

11. 276 **12.** 382 **13.** 8217 **14.** 4136

Which of the following numbers is divisible by 4?

15. 916 **16.** 504 **17.** 274

18. 1738 **19.** 5212 **20.** 3814

21. If a number is divisible by 10, is it also divisible by 5?

22. If a number is divisible by 5, is it also divisible by 10?

Which of the following is divisible by 5? by 10?

23. 835 **24.** 1840 **25.** 538

26. 1095 **27.** 3400 **28.** 547

WRITTEN EXERCISES 4.2

A Name the following subsets of the counting numbers by the modified roster method.

1. {multiples of 2} **2.** {multiples of 3}

3. {multiples of 4} **4.** {multiples of 5}

5. {multiples of 8} **6.** {multiples of 10}

Indicate by *Yes* or *No* whether each of the following is divisible by 2.

7. 546   **8.** 838   **9.** 513   **10.** 811

11. 1048   **12.** 2040   **13.** 10,876   **14.** 15,207

Indicate by *Yes* or *No* whether each of the following has 3 as a factor, using the test on the sum of the numbers named by the digits.

15. 813   **16.** 747   **17.** 82   **18.** 91

19. 3036   **20.** 5193   **21.** 10,521,175   **22.** 15,281,923

Determine whether 4 is a factor of each of the following numbers by the test for divisibility by 4.

23. 324   **24.** 416   **25.** 814   **26.** 938

27. 1028   **28.** 2540   **29.** 5332   **30.** 11,108

If each number is divisible by 5, express it as a product of 5 and another factor. Otherwise write *No*.

31. 45   **32.** 85   **33.** 56

34. 92   **35.** 120   **36.** 160

If each number has 10 as a factor, express it as a product of 10 and another factor. Otherwise write *No*.

37. 180   **38.** 230   **39.** 105

40. 255   **41.** 2300   **42.** 18,000

B   A test for divisibility by 6 is that the given number has both 2 and 3 as factors. Which of the following are divisible by 6?

43. 108   **44.** 738   **45.** 836   **46.** 915

4.3 Prime Numbers

In this section, you will be working with a special set of numbers called the prime numbers. A **prime number** is a counting number greater than 1 that has no proper factors. The set

$$\{2, 3, 5, 7, 11, 13, 17, 19, 23\}$$

is the set of prime numbers less than 25. Remember that the proper factors of a counting number are those counting-number factors besides 1 and the given number.

■ **P-1** Does 17 have any factor other than 1 and 17?

■ **P-2** Can you name the next greater prime after 23?

■ **P-3** Why is 9 not a prime?

The prime numbers are very necessary and useful in mathematics. It is important that you know at least the prime numbers less than 25.

Now look at a device called the prime-number sieve, which is used in finding the prime numbers less than a given number. The example will give the primes that are less than 50.

In order for you to understand this process, make an array of the counting numbers from 1 to 50 like the one shown. Follow the steps that are given.

1	2	3	4	5	6	7	8	9	10
11	12	13	14	15	16	17	18	19	20
21	22	23	24	25	26	27	28	29	30
31	32	33	34	35	36	37	38	39	40
41	42	43	44	45	46	47	48	49	50

The prime-number sieve will sort out the prime numbers from those that are not prime. Your job will be to cross out the numerals that do not name primes.

These are the steps:

1. Cross out 1 since, by definition, a prime must be greater than 1.

2. Cross out the names of the numbers that have 2 as a proper factor. These are 4, 6, 8, $\cdots$.

3. Cross out the names of the numbers that have 3 as a proper factor. These are 6, 9, 12, $\cdots$. (Notice that some of these have already been crossed out, for example, 6.)

4. Cross out the names of the numbers having 5 as a proper factor. These are 10, 15, 20, $\cdots$. (Some of these have already been crossed out, for example, 10 and 15. You choose 5 because it is the next number after 3 that still remains in the array.)

■ **P-4** What numbers having 5 as a proper factor have not yet had their names crossed out?

5. Next, cross out the names for those numbers that have 7 as a proper factor. Again, 7 is the next number left in the array after 5.

P-5 What number had its name crossed out in step 5?

P-6 Is there any number whose name has not been crossed out in the array that has 11 as a proper factor?

The numbers whose names in the array are unmarked are the prime numbers less than 50. Since 11 is not a proper factor of any number left in the array, it is not necessary to consider a larger one, for example, 13.

X̶	2	3	4̶	5	6̶	7	8̶	9̶	1̶0̶
11	1̶2̶	13	1̶4̶	1̶5̶	1̶6̶	17	1̶8̶	19	2̶0̶
2̶1̶	2̶2̶	23	2̶4̶	2̶5̶	2̶6̶	2̶7̶	2̶8̶	29	3̶0̶
31	3̶2̶	3̶3̶	3̶4̶	3̶5̶	3̶6̶	37	3̶8̶	3̶9̶	4̶0̶
41	4̶2̶	43	4̶4̶	4̶5̶	4̶6̶	47	4̶8̶	4̶9̶	5̶0̶

The set of prime numbers is actually an infinite set. Just like the rational numbers of arithmetic, however, you cannot list its elements by the modified roster method. There is no pattern that can be shown.

ORAL EXERCISES 4.3

1. What is a prime number?
2. What is the least prime number?
3. Can you name any even prime number?
4. What proper factor do all even numbers greater than 2 have?
5. Using the prime-number sieve, name all the primes less than 50.
6. Why is 49 not a prime?
7. Can you name the next greater prime after 47?

Express each of the following numbers as a product of two primes.

8. 10	**9.** 14	**10.** 15	**11.** 6
12. 21	**13.** 33	**14.** 35	**15.** 55

WRITTEN EXERCISES 4.3

A 1. Now make a sieve for the numbers from 1 to 150. Follow the same plan as was used in making a prime-number sieve for the numbers from 1 to 50. You can mark the name of each number to be removed with an X. Keep this sieve for future work.

2. List the set of prime numbers less than 150, using the roster method.

Express each of the following numbers as the product of two primes.

3. 26   **4.** 34   **5.** 51   **6.** 39

7. 65   **8.** 85   **9.** 91   **10.** 77

It is believed that each even number greater than 2 can be expressed as the sum of two primes. For example, $6 = 3 + 3$; $16 = 13 + 3$; $18 = 13 + 5$. Express each of the following numbers as the sum of two primes.

11. 8   **12.** 10   **13.** 12   **14.** 14   **15.** 20

16. 22   **17.** 28   **18.** 34   **19.** 48   **20.** 50

B   Primes such as 3 and 5 are called **twin primes** because their difference is 2.

     21. List all the twin primes less than 150. (Use the number sieve that you made in Exercise 1.)

4.4 Prime Factors of Counting Numbers

In the preceding section, you were asked to make a number sieve in order to find the primes less than 150. If your work was correct, you should have gotten the set

{2, 3, 5, 7, 11, 13, 17, 19, 23, 29, 31, 37, 41, 43, 47, 53, 59, 61, 67, 71, 73, 79, 83, 89, 97, 101, 103, 107, 109, 113, 127, 131, 137, 139, 149}.

As was stated before, you should be very familiar with the primes less than 25.

Your task in this section will be to express numbers that are not prime as the product of prime factors. Counting numbers that are not prime are called **composite** numbers. The number 36 is a composite number because it certainly has proper factors, for example, 2 and 9.

You can find the prime factors of 36 in the following way.

1. Check to see if the least prime, 2, is a factor of 36. It is. Divide 36 by 2 and get 18 as the quotient. The work is recorded at the right.   2 | 36 ⟶ 18

2. Now test 18 for divisibility by 2. You know that 2 is a factor of 18. Divide and get the quotient 9.   2 | 36 ⟶ 2 | 18

3. Test 9 for divisibility by 2. You know that 2 is not a factor of 9.   9

$\boxed{4}$ Go to the next greater prime, 3, and check to see if it is a factor of 9. It is, and 3 is the quotient. The task is finished because the last quotient is a prime. Thus,

$$36 = 2 \cdot 2 \cdot 3 \cdot 3.$$

$$\begin{array}{r|r} 2 & 36 \\ \hline 2 & 18 \\ \hline 3 & 9 \\ \hline & 3 \end{array}$$

You have expressed 36 as a product of prime factors.

Try another example. Find the prime factors of 165.

$\boxed{1}$ Start with the least prime, 2, to see if it is a factor of 165. It is not.

$\boxed{2}$ Then take the next greater prime, 3.

■ **P-1** Is 3 a factor of 165?

The work is shown at the right. The quotient is 55.

$$\begin{array}{r|r} 3 & 165 \\ \hline 5 & 55 \\ \hline & 11 \end{array}$$

$\boxed{3}$ Check again to see if 3 is a factor of 55. It is not.

$\boxed{4}$ Now try 5, which is the next greater prime. Of course, 5 is a factor of 55, and the quotient is 11. Since the last quotient, 11, is a prime, the task is over. Thus,

$$165 = 3 \cdot 5 \cdot 11.$$

Note these things about the method:

> You test each prime as a possible factor of the given number starting with the least prime, 2. Each prime may turn up as a factor more than once. The task is finished when the last quotient is a prime.

Consider the composite number 72.

■ **P-2** Is 72 divisible by 2? If so, what is the quotient?

■ **P-3** What prime do you try next as a factor of the quotient?

■ **P-4** How many times is 2 a factor of 72?

■ **P-5** Is 3 a factor of 72?

■ **P-6** How many times is 3 a factor?

Your work should look like this:

$$2 \mid \underline{72} \qquad 72 = 2 \cdot 2 \cdot 2 \cdot 3 \cdot 3$$
$$2 \mid \underline{36}$$
$$2 \mid \underline{18}$$
$$3 \mid \underline{9}$$
$$3$$

The phrase $2 \cdot 2 \cdot 2 \cdot 3 \cdot 3$ is called the **prime factorization** of 72. The number 72 has been factored into prime factors. In a prime factorization the primes can be written in any order, as you know by the Commutative and Associative Properties of Multiplication. Thus, $2 \cdot 3 \cdot 2 \cdot 2 \cdot 3$ is another correct way of expressing the prime factorization of 72.

> **There is only one selection of factors possible in any prime factorization.**

This is a very startling and important fact in mathematics.

ORAL EXERCISES 4.4

1. What do you call a counting number that is not prime?
2. In expressing a number as a product of primes, what prime do you test first as a possible factor?
3. Is the order in which the prime factors of a number are written important?
4. In how many ways can the prime factors of a number be chosen?

Give the common name for the composite numbers whose prime factorizations are shown.

5. $2 \cdot 2 \cdot 5$	**6.** $3 \cdot 2 \cdot 5$	**7.** $3 \cdot 3 \cdot 2$
8. $2 \cdot 5 \cdot 3$	**9.** $2 \cdot 7$	**10.** $3 \cdot 7$
11. $2 \cdot 5 \cdot 7$	**12.** $3 \cdot 11$	**13.** $2 \cdot 3 \cdot 11$
14. $2 \cdot 3 \cdot 3 \cdot 2$		

Find the prime factorizations of the following numbers.

15. 6 **16.** 8 **17.** 9 **18.** 12 **19.** 16 **20.** 20

21. Would it be correct to express the prime factorization of 12 as a set? Discuss.

WRITTEN EXERCISES 4.4

A Find the prime factorization of each of the following numbers.

1. 18	**2.** 24	**3.** 27	**4.** 32	**5.** 40
6. 42	**7.** 44	**8.** 48	**9.** 50	**10.** 52
11. 54	**12.** 56	**13.** 60	**14.** 81	**15.** 64
16. 70	**17.** 78	**18.** 84	**19.** 88	**20.** 96
21. 115	**22.** 125	**23.** 248	**24.** 378	**25.** 512
26. 729	**27.** 2431	**28.** 1547	**29.** 36,225	**30.** 56,840

B Here is a trick to show your friends. Choose any number named by a 3-digit numeral, such as 539. Make a 6-digit numeral by repeating the three digits: 539,539.

31. Divide your number named by the 6-digit numeral by 7.

32. Divide the quotient you got in Exercise 31 by 11.

33. Divide the quotient you got in Exercise 32 by 13.

34. What is your last quotient? (You should get the 3-digit numeral you started with.)

Here is how it works. Forming the 6-digit numeral is the same as multiplying by 1001, and the prime factorization of 1001 is $7 \cdot 11 \cdot 13$. Thus,

$$539{,}539 = (1001)(539).$$

Suppose you let n represent any number named by a 3-digit numeral. The steps look like this:

$$n$$

$$1001n$$

$$\frac{1001n}{7}$$

$$\frac{1001n}{7 \cdot 11}$$

$$\frac{1001n}{7 \cdot 11 \cdot 13}$$

$$\frac{(7 \cdot 11 \cdot 13)n}{7 \cdot 11 \cdot 13}$$

$$\frac{7 \cdot 11 \cdot 13}{7 \cdot 11 \cdot 13}\, n \;=\; 1 \cdot n \;=\; n$$

4.5 Using Exponents in Prime Factorization

You learned earlier that, in a phrase such as 5^2, the 2 is called an **exponent.** It indicates that 5 is used twice as a factor in the phrase. That is, $5^2 = 5 \cdot 5$.

Other numbers besides 2 can be used as exponents. However, for the time being, you will use only counting numbers as exponents.

The number 2^3 is equal to $2 \cdot 2 \cdot 2$, meaning that 2 is used as a factor three times.

The number 10^4 is equal to $10 \cdot 10 \cdot 10 \cdot 10$, meaning that 10 is used as a factor four times.

■ **P-1**   What is meant by 3^5?

> In a phrase such as 2^3, 2 is called the **base.** A counting number such as 3 used as an exponent shows how many times the base is to be used as a factor.

The common name for 2^3 is 8. Sometimes 8 is called the **third power** of 2. Of course, 2^3 and $2 \cdot 2 \cdot 2$ are also names for the third power of 2. A **power** is a number named by a phrase that involves a base and its exponent.

Consider the phrase 5^3.

■ **P-2**   What is the base here?

■ **P-3**   What is the exponent?

■ **P-4**   What is the common name for 5^3?

■ **P-5**   What do you call $5 \cdot 5 \cdot 5$?

■ **P-6**   In the open phrase x^6, what is the base? the exponent?

■ **P-7**   What does x^6 mean?

In the last section, you learned to find the prime factorizations of numbers. In many of these, a certain prime might appear more than once as a factor. For example, $72 = 2 \cdot 2 \cdot 2 \cdot 3 \cdot 3$. You can now use exponents to write such factorizations. The phrases 72 and $2^3 \cdot 3^2$ mean the same thing. The use of exponents makes it easier to write certain phrases.

■ **P-8** How can you write $3 \cdot 5 \cdot 3 \cdot 3 \cdot 5 \cdot 2 \cdot 2$, using exponents?

You will notice that an exponent is not used when a factor appears only once. Thus, $2^2 \cdot 3 \cdot 5 \cdot 7$ is usually not written $2^2 \cdot 3^1 \cdot 5^1 \cdot 7^1$.

You will recall that a phrase such as x^2 is usually read "x squared." You may read a phrase such as y^3 as "y cubed." The phrase a^4 is read "a to the fourth power," and b^5 is read "b to the fifth power," and so forth. It is also correct to read x^2 as "x to the second power" and y^3 as "y to the third power."

The phrase $2^2 \cdot 3 \cdot 5 \cdot 7^3$ is usually read "two squared times three times five times seven cubed."

■ **P-9** How would you read the phrases 10^3, 35^2, 5^4, 2^5, x^6, y^{10}?

■ **P-10** How would you read the factorization $2^4 \cdot 3^2 \cdot 5^3 \cdot 7^5$?

The prime factorizations of two counting numbers can be used to test the divisibility of one by the other.

The number 1080 is divisible by 180 since

$$6 \cdot 180 = 1080,$$
$$1080 = 2^3 \cdot 3^3 \cdot 5,$$
$$180 = 2^2 \cdot 3^2 \cdot 5.$$

Notice that each prime factor of 1080 appears at least as many times as it does in 180.

Here is another example:

$$4410 = 2 \cdot 3^2 \cdot 5 \cdot 7^2$$
$$105 = 3 \cdot 5 \cdot 7$$

Here each factor of 4410 appears at least as many times as it does in 105. The factor 2 appears once in 4410 and not at all in 105. The factors 3 and 7 each appear once more in 4410 than they do in 105. The factor 5 appears once in each. The number 4410 is divisible by 105. Actually, $4410 \div 105$ is equal to 42.

On the other hand, 1500 is not divisible by 42.

$$1500 = 2^2 \cdot 3 \cdot 5^3$$
$$42 = 2 \cdot 3 \cdot 7$$

Notice that each factor of 1500 does not appear at least as often as it does in 42. The number 7 is not a factor of 1500.

■ **P-11** Is $5^2 \cdot 7 \cdot 13^3$ divisible by $13 \cdot 5 \cdot 7$?

■ **P-12**   Is $2^3 \cdot 5 \cdot 19^2$ a factor of $2^3 \cdot 5 \cdot 19$?

> One counting number is divisible by a second if each factor in the prime factorization of the first appears at least as many times as it does in the prime factorization of the second counting number.

ORAL EXERCISES 4.5

Read the following phrases.
1. 8^2	**2.** 5^3	**3.** 7^4	**4.** 9^5
5. x^{11}	**6.** n^8	**7.** $2^3 \cdot 3^5$	**8.** $4^3 \cdot 10^2$
9. $3^5 \cdot 5^3 \cdot 7^4$	**10.** $2^3 \cdot x^5 \cdot y^4$		

Rename the following phrases by using exponents.
11. $2 \cdot 2 \cdot 3 \cdot 3 \cdot 5$ **12.** $2 \cdot 2 \cdot 2 \cdot 3 \cdot 7 \cdot 7$
13. $2 \cdot 3 \cdot 7 \cdot 2 \cdot 2 \cdot 3 \cdot 11$ **14.** $2 \cdot 5 \cdot 3 \cdot 5 \cdot 3 \cdot 3 \cdot 2 \cdot 2$
15. $7 \cdot 3 \cdot 5 \cdot 3 \cdot 2 \cdot 7$ **16.** $2^2 \cdot 3 \cdot 3 \cdot 2^3 \cdot 3 \cdot 5$
17. $13 \cdot 11 \cdot 23 \cdot 11 \cdot 2 \cdot 13$ **18.** $x \cdot x \cdot y \cdot y \cdot y$
19. $a \cdot b \cdot b \cdot c \cdot a \cdot b$ **20.** $r \cdot s \cdot r \cdot t \cdot t \cdot r$

Tell whether the first number is divisible by the second.
21. $3^2 \cdot 5^3;\ \ 3 \cdot 5^2$ **22.** $2^3 \cdot 7^2 \cdot 5;\ \ 2 \cdot 7^2$
23. $7 \cdot 11 \cdot 13;\ \ 2 \cdot 3 \cdot 5$ **24.** $2^4 \cdot 3^3 \cdot 5^2;\ \ 2 \cdot 3^3 \cdot 5$
25. $29 \cdot 31^2 \cdot 47;\ \ 29 \cdot 47$ **26.** $2 \cdot 3 \cdot 11^2 \cdot 13;\ \ 3 \cdot 11$
27. $4 \cdot 25;\ \ 8 \cdot 5$ **28.** $5 \cdot 7 \cdot 12;\ \ 7 \cdot 2^3 \cdot 3$

Rename each of the following by using a prime factorization and exponents.
29. $4 \cdot 25$	**30.** $8 \cdot 9$	**31.** $2 \cdot 6 \cdot 3^2$
32. $3 \cdot 15 \cdot 5^3$	**33.** $4 \cdot 5 \cdot 10$	**34.** $2 \cdot 14 \cdot 21$

WRITTEN EXERCISES 4.5

A   Express each of the following as a power of a prime number.
1. 4	**2.** 9	**3.** 8	**4.** 16
5. 27	**6.** 32	**7.** 25	**8.** 49
9. 64	**10.** 81	**11.** 125	**12.** 128
13. 625	**14.** 243		

Rename the following factorizations by using exponents.

15. $7 \cdot 7 \cdot 3 \cdot 3 \cdot 3$ **16.** $11 \cdot 11 \cdot 11 \cdot 23 \cdot 23$

17. $2 \cdot 3 \cdot 2 \cdot 2 \cdot 5 \cdot 7 \cdot 3 \cdot 5$ **18.** $5 \cdot 7 \cdot 3 \cdot 2 \cdot 7 \cdot 3 \cdot 3 \cdot 5$

19. $2 \cdot 3 \cdot 3 \cdot x \cdot x$ **20.** $5 \cdot 7 \cdot 5 \cdot a \cdot 3 \cdot a$

21. $2^2 \cdot 3 \cdot 2^3 \cdot 3^2$ **22.** $3 \cdot x^2 \cdot 3^3 \cdot x$

Use exponents to show the prime factorization of each of the numbers named below.

23. $4 \cdot 3 \cdot 5$ **24.** $9 \cdot 7 \cdot 11$

25. $2 \cdot 10 \cdot 5$ **26.** $3 \cdot 8 \cdot 3$

27. $14 \cdot 28$ **28.** $12 \cdot 15$

29. $24 \cdot 18$ **30.** $36 \cdot 30$

Indicate by *Yes* or *No* whether the first number is divisible by the second.

31. $2^3 \cdot 5^2 \cdot 13;\ \ 2 \cdot 5^2 \cdot 13$ **32.** $3^5 \cdot 7 \cdot 23^2;\ \ 3^2 \cdot 23$

33. $13 \cdot 17^2 \cdot 19;\ \ 17 \cdot 13 \cdot 17$ **34.** $23 \cdot 5 \cdot 7^3;\ \ 7 \cdot 5 \cdot 7$

35. $2^3 \cdot 3^4 \cdot 5^5;\ \ 2^2 \cdot 3^5 \cdot 5^4$ **36.** $19^3 \cdot 23^5 \cdot 5;\ \ 5 \cdot 23^3 \cdot 19^5$

37. $2^3 \cdot 5^2 \cdot 7;\ \ 4 \cdot 2 \cdot 5 \cdot 7$ **38.** $3^5 \cdot 11 \cdot 13^2;\ \ 9 \cdot 11 \cdot 13$

Write a common name for each of the following if x is replaced by 3.

39. $x^3 + 2$ **40.** $5 + x^4$ **41.** $2x^2 + 1$

42. $3 + 3x^2$ **43.** $2^x + 3^x$ **44.** $5^x + x^5$

4.6 Fractions as Names for Numbers

You remember that a **fraction** is a special numeral that is used to name a rational number. In the fraction $\frac{3}{5}$, the number 3 is called the **numerator** and the number 5, the **denominator.** Any counting number can be named by a fraction that shows a denominator of 1; for example, $15 = \frac{15}{1}$.

Also, you should recall the following.

> The product of two numbers named by fractions is the number named by a fraction whose numerator is the product of the numerators and whose denominator is the product of the denominators of the two fractions.

$$\frac{2}{3} \cdot \frac{5}{7} = \frac{2 \cdot 5}{3 \cdot 7} = \frac{10}{21}$$

Often in problems you need to change the name of a number from one form to another. You may use prime factorization and the Multiplication Property of One to get common names in fraction form for rational numbers. Consider the fraction $\frac{15}{18}$.

By prime factorization of numerator and denominator ⟶	$\frac{15}{18} = \frac{3 \cdot 5}{2 \cdot 3 \cdot 3}$
By the Commutative and Associative Properties of Multiplication ⟶	$= \frac{3 \cdot 5}{3(2 \cdot 3)}$
By the rule for multiplying fractions ⟶	$= \frac{3}{3} \cdot \frac{5}{(2 \cdot 3)}$
Using common names ⟶	$= 1 \cdot \frac{5}{6}$
By the Multiplication Property of One ⟶	$= \frac{5}{6}$

The fraction $\frac{5}{6}$ is called the common name of the fraction $\frac{15}{18}$. Sometimes it is said that $\frac{5}{6}$ is the **reduced form** of $\frac{15}{18}$.

Now look at the fraction $\frac{84}{360}$.

By prime factorization ⟶	$\frac{84}{360} = \frac{2 \cdot 2 \cdot 3 \cdot 7}{2 \cdot 2 \cdot 2 \cdot 3 \cdot 3 \cdot 5}$
By the Commutative and Associative Properties of Multiplication ⟶	$= \frac{(2 \cdot 3)(2 \cdot 7)}{(2 \cdot 3)(2 \cdot 2 \cdot 3 \cdot 5)}$
By the rule for multiplying fractions ⟶	$= \frac{(2 \cdot 3)}{(2 \cdot 3)} \cdot \frac{(2 \cdot 7)}{(2 \cdot 2 \cdot 3 \cdot 5)}$
Using common names ⟶	$= 1 \cdot \frac{14}{60}$
By the Multiplication Property of One ⟶	$= \frac{14}{60}$

However, $\frac{14}{60}$ is not the common name for $\frac{84}{360}$. Notice that the numerator and denominator still have a common factor 2. That is,

$$\frac{14}{60} = \frac{2 \cdot 7}{2 \cdot 2 \cdot 3 \cdot 5} = \frac{2}{2} \cdot \frac{7}{2 \cdot 3 \cdot 5} = 1 \cdot \frac{7}{30} = \frac{7}{30}.$$

The fraction $\frac{7}{30}$ is the common name for $\frac{84}{360}$.

The **common name** for a rational number that is not a whole number is the fraction whose numerator and denominator do not have a common prime factor.

Copy and complete the following sentences to find the common name for $\frac{12}{60}$.

$$\frac{12}{60} = \frac{2 \cdot 2 \cdot 3}{2 \cdot 2 \cdot 3 \cdot 5}$$

P-1
$$= \frac{?}{?} \cdot \frac{1}{5}$$

P-2
$$= \frac{?}{} \cdot \frac{1}{5}$$

P-3
$$= \frac{?}{}$$

P-4 Which of the fractions $\frac{14}{15}$, $\frac{15}{21}$, $\frac{35}{77}$, $\frac{33}{65}$ are common names?

Often, you have to rename a number with a fraction having a different denominator. The Multiplication Property of One is again useful.

By the Multiplication Property of One $\longrightarrow$ $\dfrac{2}{3} = \dfrac{2}{3} \cdot 1$

Using $\frac{4}{4}$ as a name for 1 $\longrightarrow$ $= \dfrac{2}{3} \cdot \dfrac{4}{4}$

Using the rule for the product of fractions $\longrightarrow$ $= \dfrac{2 \cdot 4}{3 \cdot 4}$

Using common names for counting numbers $\longrightarrow$ $= \dfrac{8}{12}$

This example shows how to find a fraction for $\frac{2}{3}$ that shows a denominator of 12.

What numbers could replace the question marks in the following to make the sentences true?

P-5
$$\frac{3}{4} = \frac{3}{4} \cdot 1 = \frac{3}{4} \cdot \frac{?}{?} = \frac{3 \cdot 5}{4 \cdot 5} = \frac{?}{?}$$

P-6
$$\frac{5}{8} = \frac{5}{8} \cdot 1 = \frac{5}{8} \cdot \frac{?}{?} = \frac{?}{24}$$

P-7
$$\frac{7}{12} = \frac{7}{12} \cdot \frac{?}{-} = \frac{7}{12} \cdot \frac{?}{?} = \frac{?}{60}$$

P-8 In naming $\frac{3}{5}$ by a fraction having 20 as a denominator, what name must you use for 1?

From these examples, you can see that the key step is in choosing the correct name for 1.

What name for 1 would you use in finding the common name for each of the following?

1. $\dfrac{2 \cdot 3}{2 \cdot 5}$

2. $\dfrac{3 \cdot 7}{3 \cdot 11}$

3. $\dfrac{2 \cdot 5 \cdot 3}{3 \cdot 2 \cdot 7}$

4. $\dfrac{2 \cdot 2 \cdot 2 \cdot 5}{2 \cdot 5 \cdot 2}$

5. $\dfrac{5 \cdot 3 \cdot 2 \cdot 3}{7 \cdot 3 \cdot 5}$

6. $\dfrac{2^4 \cdot 3^3}{2^2 \cdot 3}$

7. $\dfrac{5 \cdot 11 \cdot 29 \cdot 3}{7 \cdot 31 \cdot 5 \cdot 17}$

8. $\dfrac{5^2 \cdot 3^2 \cdot 2^3}{2^6 \cdot 3 \cdot 5}$

9. $\dfrac{19 \cdot 11 \cdot 3 \cdot 3 \cdot 5^2}{23 \cdot 5 \cdot 19 \cdot 3^5}$

10. $\dfrac{2 \cdot 2 \cdot 2 \cdot 2 \cdot 2 \cdot 2 \cdot 3}{2 \cdot 3 \cdot 3 \cdot 3 \cdot 3 \cdot 3}$

With what numbers could you replace the question marks in each of the following to find the common name? Simplify the fractions correctly.

11. $\dfrac{14}{16} = \dfrac{2 \cdot 7}{2^4} = \dfrac{?}{?} \cdot \dfrac{7}{2^3} = \dfrac{?}{?} \cdot \dfrac{7}{8} = \dfrac{?}{?}$

12. $\dfrac{6}{18} = \dfrac{2 \cdot 3}{2 \cdot 3 \cdot 3} = \dfrac{2 \cdot 3}{2 \cdot 3} \cdot \dfrac{?}{?} = 1 \cdot \dfrac{?}{?} = \dfrac{?}{?}$

13. $\dfrac{36}{48} = \dfrac{2 \cdot 2 \cdot 3 \cdot 3}{2^4 \cdot 3} = \dfrac{?}{?} \cdot \dfrac{3}{2 \cdot 2} = \dfrac{?}{?} \cdot \dfrac{3}{4} = \dfrac{?}{?}$

14. $\dfrac{54}{72} = \dfrac{2 \cdot 3 \cdot 3 \cdot 3}{2 \cdot 2 \cdot 2 \cdot 3 \cdot 3} = \dfrac{?}{?} \cdot \dfrac{3}{2 \cdot 2} = \dfrac{?}{?} \cdot \dfrac{3}{4} = \dfrac{?}{?}$

15. $\dfrac{630}{2700} = \dfrac{2 \cdot 3 \cdot 3 \cdot 5 \cdot 7}{2 \cdot 2 \cdot 3 \cdot 3 \cdot 3 \cdot 5 \cdot 5} = \dfrac{2 \cdot 3 \cdot 3 \cdot 5}{2 \cdot 3 \cdot 3 \cdot 5} \cdot \dfrac{?}{?} = 1 \cdot \dfrac{?}{?} = \dfrac{?}{?}$

Find the common name for each of the following.

16. $\frac{2}{12}$

17. $\frac{2}{16}$

18. $\frac{3}{12}$

19. $\frac{3}{15}$

20. $\frac{4}{10}$

21. $\frac{4}{30}$

22. $\frac{6}{15}$

23. $\frac{6}{14}$

With what numbers could you replace the question marks to make true sentences?

24. $\frac{2}{7} = \frac{2}{7} \cdot 1 = \frac{2}{7} \cdot \frac{?}{?} = \frac{?}{21}$

25. $\frac{7}{8} = \frac{7}{8} \cdot 1 = \frac{7}{8} \cdot \frac{?}{?} = \frac{?}{32}$

26. $\frac{3}{4} = \frac{3}{4} \cdot ? = \frac{3}{4} \cdot \frac{?}{?} = \frac{?}{36}$

27. $\frac{5}{2} = \frac{5}{2} \cdot ? = \frac{5}{2} \cdot \frac{?}{?} = \frac{?}{18}$

28. $\frac{11}{3} = \frac{11}{3} \cdot ? = \frac{11}{3} \cdot \frac{?}{?} = \frac{?}{15}$

A What name for 1 would you use in finding the common name for each of the following?

1. $\dfrac{3 \cdot 13}{3 \cdot 17}$

2. $\dfrac{5 \cdot 23}{5 \cdot 19}$

3. $\dfrac{7 \cdot 2 \cdot 5}{2 \cdot 7 \cdot 11}$

4. $\dfrac{3 \cdot 11 \cdot 19}{19 \cdot 11 \cdot 5}$

5. $\dfrac{2 \cdot 11 \cdot 5 \cdot 3 \cdot 2 \cdot 5}{11 \cdot 2 \cdot 5 \cdot 13}$

6. $\dfrac{2 \cdot 7 \cdot 3 \cdot 17}{3 \cdot 7 \cdot 3 \cdot 5 \cdot 7 \cdot 2 \cdot 3}$

7. $\dfrac{2 \cdot 3 \cdot 5}{2^3 \cdot 3^2 \cdot 5}$

8. $\dfrac{5 \cdot 7^2 \cdot 11}{5^3 \cdot 7 \cdot 11}$

9. $\dfrac{10}{12}$

10. $\dfrac{8}{18}$

11. $\dfrac{15}{21}$

12. $\dfrac{6}{33}$

Find a common name for each of the following, showing all steps as in the example.

Example: $\dfrac{12}{30} = \dfrac{2 \cdot 2 \cdot 3}{2 \cdot 3 \cdot 5} = \dfrac{2 \cdot 3}{2 \cdot 3} \cdot \dfrac{2}{5} = 1 \cdot \dfrac{2}{5} = \dfrac{2}{5}$

13. $\dfrac{10}{14}$

14. $\dfrac{14}{35}$

15. $\dfrac{15}{27}$

16. $\dfrac{8}{20}$

17. $\dfrac{9}{21}$

18. $\dfrac{25}{30}$

19. $\dfrac{16}{60}$

20. $\dfrac{27}{45}$

Copy the following and replace the question marks to make true sentences.

21. $\dfrac{3}{8} = \dfrac{3}{8} \cdot 1 = \dfrac{3}{8} \cdot \dfrac{?}{?} = \dfrac{?}{16}$

22. $\dfrac{5}{12} = \dfrac{5}{12} \cdot 1 = \dfrac{5}{12} \cdot \dfrac{?}{?} = \dfrac{?}{36}$

23. $\dfrac{7}{9} = \dfrac{7}{9} \cdot \dfrac{?}{?} = \dfrac{7}{9} \cdot \dfrac{?}{?} = \dfrac{?}{45}$

24. $\dfrac{9}{10} = \dfrac{9}{10} \cdot \dfrac{?}{?} = \dfrac{9}{10} \cdot \dfrac{?}{?} = \dfrac{?}{80}$

25. $\dfrac{5}{6} = \dfrac{5}{6} \cdot \dfrac{?}{?} = \dfrac{5}{6} \cdot \dfrac{?}{?} = \dfrac{55}{?}$

26. $\dfrac{6}{7} = \dfrac{6}{7} \cdot \dfrac{?}{?} = \dfrac{6}{7} \cdot \dfrac{?}{?} = \dfrac{48}{?}$

Supply the numerators that will make the sentences true.

27. $\dfrac{3}{8} = \dfrac{?}{24}$

28. $\dfrac{5}{12} = \dfrac{?}{48}$

29. $\dfrac{5}{16} = \dfrac{?}{64}$

30. $\dfrac{7}{15} = \dfrac{?}{45}$

31. $\dfrac{2 \cdot 3}{2 \cdot 2 \cdot 5} = \dfrac{?}{2 \cdot 2 \cdot 5 \cdot 3 \cdot 2}$

32. $\dfrac{2 \cdot 5}{3 \cdot 7} = \dfrac{?}{2 \cdot 3 \cdot 3 \cdot 7 \cdot 5}$

33. $\dfrac{3 \cdot 5}{2^2 \cdot 7^2} = \dfrac{?}{2^3 \cdot 3^2 \cdot 7^2}$

34. $\dfrac{7 \cdot 11}{2^2 \cdot 3 \cdot 13} = \dfrac{?}{2^2 \cdot 3^4 \cdot 5 \cdot 13}$

4.7 Multiplication of Numbers Named by Fractions

You used the rule for multiplying two numbers named by fractions in the last section. Now you need to gain some extra skill in using the rule.

■ **P-1** What is the fraction for the product $\frac{3}{4} \cdot \frac{5}{7}$?

■ **P-2** What fraction do you get when you apply the multiplication rule to $\frac{3}{5} \cdot \frac{2}{9}$?

Of course,

$$\frac{3}{5} \cdot \frac{2}{9} = \frac{3 \cdot 2}{5 \cdot 9} = \frac{6}{45}.$$

However, $\frac{6}{45}$ is not the common name for the product because

$$\frac{6}{45} = \frac{2 \cdot 3}{3 \cdot 3 \cdot 5} = \frac{3}{3} \cdot \frac{2}{3 \cdot 5} = 1 \cdot \frac{2}{15} = \frac{2}{15}.$$

The fraction $\frac{2}{15}$ is the common name, rather than $\frac{6}{45}$.

As you see here, you multiplied first and then found the common name for the result. This sometimes gives large numerators and denominators, making the work longer, as in the following problem.

$$\frac{16}{27} \cdot \frac{15}{32} = \frac{240}{864}$$

$$= \frac{2^4 \cdot 3 \cdot 5}{2^5 \cdot 3^3} = \frac{2^4 \cdot 3}{2^4 \cdot 3} \cdot \frac{5}{2 \cdot 3 \cdot 3} = \frac{5}{18}$$

Usually it is better to work such a problem as follows.

$$\frac{16}{27} \cdot \frac{15}{32} = \frac{2^4 \cdot 3 \cdot 5}{3^3 \cdot 2^5} = \frac{2^4 \cdot 3}{2^4 \cdot 3} \cdot \frac{5}{2 \cdot 3 \cdot 3} = \frac{5}{18}$$

Notice that this saves the step in which you got the fraction $\frac{240}{864}$.

Various short cuts are sometimes used on problems of this type. Just make sure that you understand the following basic steps.

1. Factor numerators and denominators.
2. Write the product as a single fraction.
3. Choose a name for 1, using factors that are common to numerator and denominator.
4. Apply the Multiplication Property of One to get the result.
5. Make sure the result is the common name.

When using a whole number to multiply a number expressed by a fraction, you will find that it is usually best to express the whole number in fraction form before you begin the multiplication. Thus, for example,

$$\frac{3}{4} \cdot 5 = \frac{3}{4} \cdot \frac{5}{1} = \frac{15}{4}.$$

■ **P-3** What fraction names the product $10 \cdot \frac{2}{3}$?

■ **P-4** What fraction names the product $\frac{1}{5} \cdot 7$? the product $\frac{1}{5} \cdot \frac{1}{7}$?

The problem of finding the product of three or more numbers named by fractions is much the same as that of finding the product of two numbers named by fractions. The Associative Property of Multiplication can be used to show the steps.

Since the phrase on the left is just a common name for the phrase on the right ⟶

$$\frac{2}{3} \cdot \frac{5}{7} \cdot \frac{11}{13} = \left(\frac{2}{3} \cdot \frac{5}{7}\right) \cdot \frac{11}{13}$$

$$= \frac{(2 \cdot 5)}{(3 \cdot 7)} \cdot \frac{11}{13}$$

$$= \frac{(2 \cdot 5) \cdot 11}{(3 \cdot 7) \cdot 13}$$

$$= \frac{2 \cdot 5 \cdot 11}{3 \cdot 7 \cdot 13}$$

The above example shows that the product of the three numbers is the product of the numerators over the product of the denominators. You may use this as the rule for multiplying two or more numbers named by fractions.

■ **P-5** What is the common name for $\frac{1}{2} \cdot \frac{1}{2} \cdot \frac{1}{2}$? for $\frac{1}{2} \cdot \frac{2}{3} \cdot \frac{3}{5}$?

ORAL EXERCISES 4.7

Find the common name for each of the following products.

1. $\frac{1}{2} \cdot \frac{1}{7}$	**2.** $\frac{1}{4} \cdot \frac{1}{5}$	**3.** $\frac{1}{3} \cdot \frac{1}{16}$	**4.** $\frac{1}{7} \cdot \frac{1}{8}$
5. $\frac{1}{10} \cdot \frac{1}{3}$	**6.** $\frac{1}{4} \cdot \frac{1}{12}$	**7.** $\frac{2}{3} \cdot 4$	**8.** $\frac{3}{5} \cdot 6$
9. $8 \cdot \frac{3}{7}$	**10.** $12 \cdot \frac{3}{25}$	**11.** $\frac{1}{5} \cdot 5$	**12.** $\frac{1}{9} \cdot 9$
13. $\frac{2}{3} \cdot 3$	**14.** $\frac{3}{4} \cdot 4$	**15.** $\frac{2}{5} \cdot \frac{3}{2}$	**16.** $\frac{3}{8} \cdot \frac{1}{3}$
17. $\frac{5}{12} \cdot \frac{3}{5}$	**18.** $\frac{2}{15} \cdot \frac{5}{2}$	**19.** $\frac{3}{5} \cdot \frac{5}{18}$	**20.** $\frac{7}{8} \cdot \frac{12}{7}$
21. $\frac{1}{3} \cdot \frac{1}{3} \cdot \frac{1}{3}$	**22.** $\frac{1}{4} \cdot \frac{1}{4} \cdot \frac{1}{4}$	**23.** $\frac{2}{5} \cdot \frac{5}{7} \cdot \frac{7}{9}$	**24.** $\frac{3}{11} \cdot \frac{12}{13} \cdot \frac{11}{12}$

Tell what numbers would make the following sentences true.

25. $\dfrac{4}{15} \cdot \dfrac{5}{24} = \dfrac{(2 \cdot 2)5}{(3 \cdot 5)(2 \cdot 2 \cdot 2 \cdot 3)} = \dfrac{?}{?} \cdot \dfrac{1}{2 \cdot 3 \cdot 3} = \dfrac{?}{\_}$

26. $\dfrac{6}{35} \cdot \dfrac{25}{27} = \dfrac{(2 \cdot 3) \cdot (5 \cdot 5)}{(5 \cdot 7) \cdot (3 \cdot 3 \cdot 3)} = \dfrac{3 \cdot 5}{3 \cdot 5} \cdot \dfrac{?}{?} = \dfrac{?}{\_}$

27. $\dfrac{8}{9} \cdot \dfrac{3}{10} = \dfrac{?}{?} = \dfrac{2 \cdot 3}{2 \cdot 3} \cdot \dfrac{?}{?} = \dfrac{?}{\_}$

28. $\dfrac{18}{25} \cdot \dfrac{10}{27} = \dfrac{(2 \cdot 3 \cdot 3) \cdot (?)}{(5 \cdot 5)(?)} = \dfrac{?}{?} \cdot \dfrac{2 \cdot 2}{3 \cdot 5} = \dfrac{?}{\_}$

WRITTEN EXERCISES 4.7

A Find the common name for each of the following products. (Give the answer without writing down any steps; write only the common name.)

1. $\dfrac{1}{12} \cdot \dfrac{1}{3}$ **2.** $\dfrac{1}{5} \cdot \dfrac{1}{11}$ **3.** $\dfrac{1}{8} \cdot \dfrac{1}{9}$ **4.** $\dfrac{1}{6} \cdot \dfrac{1}{9}$

5. $\dfrac{1}{2} \cdot 7$ **6.** $\dfrac{1}{4} \cdot 11$ **7.** $\dfrac{2}{3} \cdot 5$ **8.** $\dfrac{3}{4} \cdot 9$

9. $\dfrac{2}{3} \cdot \dfrac{5}{2}$ **10.** $\dfrac{3}{7} \cdot \dfrac{2}{3}$ **11.** $\dfrac{7}{8} \cdot \dfrac{8}{9}$ **12.** $\dfrac{4}{5} \cdot \dfrac{5}{11}$

13. $\dfrac{4}{5} \cdot \dfrac{5}{8}$ **14.** $\dfrac{6}{7} \cdot \dfrac{7}{12}$ **15.** $\dfrac{1}{2} \cdot \dfrac{2}{5} \cdot \dfrac{5}{7} \cdot \dfrac{7}{8}$ **16.** $\dfrac{2}{3} \cdot \dfrac{3}{7} \cdot \dfrac{7}{11} \cdot \dfrac{11}{12}$

Find the following products by factoring numerators and denominators and using the Multiplication Property of One. Show all steps.

Example: $\dfrac{6}{25} \cdot \dfrac{15}{28} = \dfrac{(2 \cdot 3)(3 \cdot 5)}{(5 \cdot 5)(2 \cdot 2 \cdot 7)} = \dfrac{2 \cdot 5}{2 \cdot 5} \cdot \dfrac{3 \cdot 3}{2 \cdot 5 \cdot 7} = \dfrac{9}{70}$

17. $\dfrac{12}{15} \cdot \dfrac{5}{8}$ **18.** $\dfrac{10}{27} \cdot \dfrac{9}{4}$

19. $\dfrac{5}{2} \cdot \dfrac{6}{35}$ **20.** $\dfrac{7}{3} \cdot \dfrac{6}{35}$

21. $\dfrac{7}{8} \cdot \dfrac{12}{35}$ **22.** $\dfrac{5}{27} \cdot \dfrac{18}{55}$

23. $\dfrac{18}{25} \cdot \dfrac{25}{18}$ **24.** $\dfrac{39}{85} \cdot \dfrac{85}{39}$

25. $\dfrac{2}{3} \cdot \dfrac{3 \cdot 7 \cdot 2 \cdot 2 \cdot 3}{2 \cdot 2 \cdot 3 \cdot 3 \cdot 7}$ **26.** $\dfrac{3^2 \cdot 5 \cdot 11^3}{3 \cdot 5 \cdot 11 \cdot 3 \cdot 11 \cdot 11} \cdot \dfrac{5}{8}$

27. $\dfrac{2}{3} \cdot \dfrac{6}{7} \cdot \dfrac{14}{15}$ **28.** $\dfrac{5}{6} \cdot \dfrac{8}{27} \cdot \dfrac{9}{10}$

4.8 Least Common Multiple

You remember that the set of counting numbers that are multiples of a number can be formed by multiplying the counting numbers in succession by the given number. This will be called the set of **counting-number multiples** of the given number.

The set of counting-number multiples of 3 is

$$\{3, 6, 9, 12, 15, \cdots\}.$$

The set of counting-number multiples of 7 is

$$\{7, 14, 21, 28, 35, \cdots\}.$$

■ **P-1**   What is the set of counting-number multiples of 4?

■ **P-2**   The set $\{12, 24, 36, 48, 60, \cdots\}$ is the set of counting-number multiples of what number?

You can see that each multiple of a given number has that given number as a factor.

The set of counting-number multiples of 2 is

$$\{2, 4, 6, 8, 10, 12, 14, 16, 18, 20, \cdots\}.$$

The set of counting-number multiples of 5 is

$$\{5, 10, 15, 20, 25, 30, \cdots\}.$$

You can form a set of multiples that are common to the above two sets. It is $\{10, 20, 30, \cdots\}$. This is the set of **common multiples** of 2 and 5. The number 10 is the **least common multiple** of 2 and 5 because it is the least element in this set.

Can you follow the steps in the following problem of adding two numbers named by fractions?

$$\begin{aligned} \tfrac{1}{2} + \tfrac{3}{5} &= \tfrac{1}{2}(1) + \tfrac{3}{5}(1) \\ &= \tfrac{1}{2}(\tfrac{5}{5}) + \tfrac{3}{5}(\tfrac{2}{2}) \\ &= \tfrac{5}{10} + \tfrac{6}{10} \\ &= \tfrac{11}{10} \end{aligned}$$

The key step in this problem is to know what to use as the denominator. It is 10, which is the least common multiple of the two denominators 2 and 5. This problem suggests the importance of the least common multiple.

Consider the numbers 12 and 18. The set of counting-number multiples of 12 is

$$\{12, 24, 36, 48, 60, 72, 84, 96, 108, \cdots\}.$$

The set of counting-number multiples of 18 is

$$\{18, 36, 54, 72, 90, 108, 126, 144, \cdots\}.$$

■ **P-3** What are three common multiples of 12 and 18?

■ **P-4** What is the least common multiple of 12 and 18?

> The **least common multiple** of two or more counting numbers is the least number in the set of their common counting-number multiples.

Suppose you want to find the least common multiple of 8, 30, and 45. The set of counting-number multiples of 8 is

$$\{8, 16, 24, 32, 40, 48, 56, 64, \cdots\}.$$

The set of counting-number multiples of 30 is

$$\{30, 60, 90, 120, 150, 180, \cdots\}.$$

The set of counting-number multiples of 45 is

$$\{45, 90, 135, 180, 225, 270, \cdots\}.$$

You have not named enough elements in the three sets to discover a common multiple. You could find one if you wanted to extend the lists of elements far enough.

Prime factorization gives you an easier way to find the least common multiple. Consider the prime factorizations of 8, 30, and 45:

$$8 = 2 \cdot 2 \cdot 2; \quad 30 = 2 \cdot 3 \cdot 5; \quad 45 = 3 \cdot 3 \cdot 5$$

Let m represent the least common multiple of these three numbers. Here is a way to build m in factored form:

1 For m to have 8 as a factor, m must contain at least the factors $2 \cdot 2 \cdot 2$.

2 For m to have 30 as a factor, m must have the factors $2 \cdot 3 \cdot 5$.

3 The number 2 has already been listed as a factor three times; so you need only to insert 3 and 5, that is, $2 \cdot 2 \cdot 2 \cdot (3 \cdot 5)$.

|4| For m to have 45 as a factor, m must have the factors $3 \cdot 3 \cdot 5$.

|5| One 3 and one 5 have been listed already; so you need to insert only one more 3.

|6| Thus, m is equal to $(2 \cdot 2 \cdot 2)(3 \cdot 5)(3)$, and the least common multiple of 8, 30, and 45 is $8 \cdot 15 \cdot 3 = 360$.

■ **P-5** What is the least common multiple of $2 \cdot 3$ and $2 \cdot 2 \cdot 5$?

■ **P-6** What is the least common multiple of $2(3)(5)$, $2^2(7)$, and $3(5^2)$?

You can see how to find the least common multiple by this method.

> To find the least common multiple, express each prime factor the greatest number of times it appears as a factor of any one of the given numbers.

Here is another example:

$$75 = 3 \cdot 5^2; \quad 24 = 2^3 \cdot 3; \quad 90 = 2 \cdot 3^2 \cdot 5$$

The least common multiple of 75, 24, and 90 is $2^3 \cdot 3^2 \cdot 5^2$, or 1800.

Of course, one or more of the given numbers may themselves be primes. For example,

$$12 = 2 \cdot 2 \cdot 3, \quad 13 = 13 \text{ (a prime)}, \quad 30 = 2 \cdot 3 \cdot 5.$$

The least common multiple of 12, 13, and 30 is $2 \cdot 2 \cdot 3 \cdot 13 \cdot 5$, or 780.

ORAL EXERCISES 4.8

1. Is 48 a multiple of 3?
2. Is 48 a multiple of 8?
3. Is 48 a common multiple of 3 and 8?
4. Name the first ten counting-number multiples of 3.
5. Name the first four counting-number multiples of 8.
6. Is 48 the least common multiple of 3 and 8?

What is the least common multiple of each of the following pairs?

7. 2 and 3	**8.** 3 and 5	**9.** 2 and 7
10. 2 and 5	**11.** 3 and 7	**12.** 5 and 7
13. 3 and 11	**14.** 5 and 11	

15. What can you say about the least common multiple of two primes?

Express the least common multiple of each of the following in factored form.

16. $2 \cdot 3$; $2^2 \cdot 5$

17. $3^2 \cdot 5 \cdot 7$; $5^2 \cdot 2$

18. 17; $11 \cdot 13$

19. $2 \cdot 3 \cdot 2 \cdot 5$; $3 \cdot 3 \cdot 5 \cdot 2$

20. $2 \cdot 3^2 \cdot 5$; $2^3 \cdot 3 \cdot 5^3$

21. $2 \cdot 3$; $3 \cdot 5$; $5^2 \cdot 3^2$

22. $3 \cdot 5^2 \cdot 7$; $2 \cdot 3 \cdot 7$; $3^2 \cdot 13$

23. 13; 17; 23

24. $2 \cdot 3$; $3 \cdot 5$; $2^2 \cdot 3 \cdot 5$

WRITTEN EXERCISES 4.8

A Use the modified roster method to show the first four elements of the set of common multiples of the two given sets.

1. $\{2, 4, 6, 8, \cdots\}$ and $\{4, 8, 12, 16, \cdots\}$

2. $\{3, 6, 9, 12, \cdots\}$ and $\{6, 12, 18, 24, \cdots\}$

3. $\{5, 10, 15, 20, \cdots\}$ and $\{4, 8, 12, 16, \cdots\}$

4. $\{6, 12, 18, 24, \cdots\}$ and $\{5, 10, 15, 20, \cdots\}$

5. $\{3, 6, 9, 12, \cdots\}$ and $\{4, 8, 12, 16, \cdots\}$

6. $\{5, 10, 15, 20, \cdots\}$ and $\{7, 14, 21, 28, \cdots\}$

Express the least common multiple of each of the following in factored form.

7. $2 \cdot 3$; $2^2 \cdot 7$

8. $3 \cdot 5$; $2 \cdot 5^2$

9. $2^3 \cdot 3 \cdot 5$; $2 \cdot 3 \cdot 5$

10. $3 \cdot 5^2$; $2 \cdot 3^2 \cdot 5$

11. $7 \cdot 3^2 \cdot 13$; $2 \cdot 3 \cdot 7^2$

12. $5 \cdot 11^2 \cdot 3$; $2 \cdot 5^2 \cdot 3$

13. 13; $2^3 \cdot 11$

14. $5^2 \cdot 17$; 19

15. $2 \cdot 5$; $3 \cdot 2^2$; $5 \cdot 3$

16. $2 \cdot 3^2$; $3 \cdot 5$; $7 \cdot 2^2$

17. 7; 11; 29

18. 23; 5; 13

19. $5 \cdot 2 \cdot 3 \cdot 2 \cdot 3 \cdot 3 \cdot 5$; $11 \cdot 2 \cdot 3 \cdot 5 \cdot 7 \cdot 2$

20. $2 \cdot 2 \cdot 5 \cdot 2 \cdot 3 \cdot 3 \cdot 7$; $3 \cdot 5 \cdot 2 \cdot 5$

Use the prime factorization method to find the least common multiple in each of the following. Give a common name for the result.

21. 6; 12

22. 8; 24

23. 10; 28

24. 12; 20

25. 45; 54

26. 36; 80

27. 8; 12; 15

28. 9; 15; 16

29. 24; 30; 42

30. 27; 35; 63

4.9 Addition of Numbers Named by Fractions

You probably remember the method for finding the sum of two numbers expressed in fraction form. The sum of two numbers named by fractions with like denominators is represented by a fraction whose numerator is the sum of the numerators and whose denominator is the common denominator of the given fractions.

The rule is illustrated by these examples:

$$\frac{2}{15} + \frac{11}{15} = \frac{2+11}{15} = \frac{13}{15}$$

$$\frac{1}{8} + \frac{5}{8} = \frac{1+5}{8} = \frac{6}{8} = \frac{3}{4}$$

■ **P-1** What fraction represents the sum $\frac{5}{24} + \frac{2}{24}$?

■ **P-2** What is the common name for the sum $\frac{5}{2} + \frac{1}{2}$?

Often, the fractions for the addends do not have the same denominator. In this case, the addends must be renamed so that their fractions have the same denominator.

Consider again the example that you used in the previous section:

Using the Multiplication Property of One $\longrightarrow$ $\dfrac{1}{2} + \dfrac{3}{5} = \dfrac{1}{2}(1) + \dfrac{3}{5}(1)$

Since $\dfrac{5}{5}$ and $\dfrac{2}{2}$ are names for 1 $\longrightarrow$ $= \dfrac{1}{2}\left(\dfrac{5}{5}\right) + \dfrac{3}{5}\left(\dfrac{2}{2}\right)$

Using the rule for the product of fractions $\longrightarrow$ $= \dfrac{5}{10} + \dfrac{6}{10}$

Using the rule for the sum of fractions with like denominators $\longrightarrow$ $= \dfrac{5+6}{10}$

Using the common name for $5 + 6$ $\longrightarrow$ $= \dfrac{11}{10}$

Recall that the common denominator 10 is the least common multiple of the denominators 2 and 5. You choose names for 1 in the problem in order to obtain the fractions with this least common multiple as their common denominator.

Here is another example, $\frac{3}{8} + \frac{5}{12}$.

First find the least common multiple of 8 and 12. Since $8 = 2 \cdot 2 \cdot 2$ and $12 = 2 \cdot 2 \cdot 3$, the least common multiple is $2 \cdot 2 \cdot 2 \cdot 3$, or 24. Use the Multiplication Property of One to rename $\frac{3}{8}$ and $\frac{5}{12}$ with a common denominator of 24.

$$\tfrac{3}{8} + \tfrac{5}{12} = \tfrac{3}{8} \cdot 1 + \tfrac{5}{12} \cdot 1$$
$$= \tfrac{3}{8} \cdot \tfrac{3}{3} + \tfrac{5}{12} \cdot \tfrac{2}{2}$$
$$= \tfrac{9}{24} + \tfrac{10}{24}$$
$$= \tfrac{19}{24}$$

■ **P-3** Why were $\tfrac{3}{3}$ and $\tfrac{2}{2}$ chosen as names for 1 in the problem?

Consider the sum $\tfrac{5}{12} + \tfrac{11}{42}$.

■ **P-4** What are the prime factors of 12?

■ **P-5** What are the prime factors of 42?

■ **P-6** What is the least common multiple of 12 and 42?

■ **P-7** What name for 1 is used to multiply $\tfrac{5}{12}$?

■ **P-8** What name for 1 is used to multiply $\tfrac{11}{42}$?

Here are the steps:

$$\tfrac{5}{12} + \tfrac{11}{42} = \tfrac{5}{12} \cdot \tfrac{7}{7} + \tfrac{11}{42} \cdot \tfrac{2}{2}$$
$$= \tfrac{35}{84} + \tfrac{22}{84}$$
$$= \tfrac{57}{84}$$

Later, you will work with fractions in which both the numerator and the denominator are represented with variables. The following example has fractions with only the numerator named with a variable.

$$\frac{x}{5} + \frac{3x}{5} = \frac{x + 3x}{5}$$
$$= \frac{4x}{5}$$

(Remember that $4x$ is a common name for $x + 3x$.)

ORAL EXERCISES 4.9

Find common names for the following.

1. $\tfrac{1}{5} + \tfrac{2}{5}$
2. $\tfrac{3}{8} + \tfrac{1}{8}$
3. $\tfrac{5}{12} + \tfrac{7}{12}$
4. $\tfrac{3}{16} + \tfrac{13}{16}$
5. $\tfrac{5}{13} + \tfrac{7}{13}$
6. $\tfrac{2}{11} + \tfrac{5}{11}$
7. $\tfrac{5}{2} + \tfrac{7}{2}$
8. $\tfrac{4}{3} + \tfrac{5}{3}$
9. $\tfrac{3}{25} + \tfrac{8}{25}$
10. $\tfrac{5}{16} + \tfrac{9}{16}$
11. $\tfrac{3}{4} + 3$
12. $\tfrac{5}{6} + 5$

What is the least common multiple of the denominators in each of the following problems?

13. $\tfrac{1}{4} + \tfrac{3}{8}$
14. $\tfrac{5}{12} + \tfrac{7}{24}$
15. $\tfrac{7}{15} + \tfrac{17}{30}$

16. $\frac{1}{5} + \frac{3}{25}$

17. $\frac{1}{3} + \frac{1}{5}$

18. $\frac{2}{7} + \frac{5}{11}$

19. $\frac{1}{2} + \frac{2}{13}$

20. $\frac{1}{6} + \frac{3}{10}$

21. $\frac{3}{4} + \frac{5}{6}$

22. $\frac{3}{8} + \frac{7}{12}$

23. $\frac{5}{9} + \frac{9}{10}$

24. $\frac{1}{2} + \frac{1}{4} + \frac{1}{8}$

25. $\frac{1}{3} + \frac{1}{6} + \frac{1}{18}$

Find common names for the following sums.

26. $\frac{a}{3} + \frac{4a}{3}$

27. $\frac{2x}{5} + \frac{x}{5}$

28. $\frac{3y}{7} + \frac{2y}{7}$

29. $\frac{5n}{13} + \frac{3n}{13}$

WRITTEN EXERCISES 4.9

A Find the common names for the following.

1. $\frac{2}{7} + \frac{3}{7}$

2. $\frac{6}{11} + \frac{2}{11}$

3. $\frac{5}{13} + \frac{8}{13}$

4. $\frac{7}{15} + \frac{8}{15}$

5. $\frac{7}{2} + \frac{9}{2}$

6. $\frac{5}{3} + \frac{7}{3}$

7. $\frac{5}{8} + \frac{1}{8}$

8. $\frac{3}{10} + \frac{1}{10}$

9. $\frac{5}{4} + \frac{1}{4}$

10. $\frac{7}{4} + \frac{3}{4}$

11. $\frac{5}{12} + \frac{5}{12}$

12. $\frac{3}{14} + \frac{3}{14}$

13. $\frac{1}{4} + \frac{3}{4} + \frac{5}{4}$

14. $\frac{1}{8} + \frac{3}{8} + \frac{5}{8}$

Copy the following problems, and replace the question marks with numbers that will make the sentence true.

15. $\frac{2}{3} + \frac{4}{5} = \frac{2}{3} \cdot \frac{?}{?} + \frac{4}{5} \cdot \frac{?}{?}$
$\qquad = \frac{?}{15} + \frac{?}{15}$
$\qquad = \frac{?}{?}$

16. $\frac{4}{7} + \frac{1}{3} = \frac{4}{7} \cdot \frac{?}{?} + \frac{1}{3} \cdot \frac{?}{?}$
$\qquad = \frac{?}{21} + \frac{?}{21}$
$\qquad = \frac{?}{?}$

17. $\frac{1}{2} + \frac{1}{3} + \frac{1}{4} = \frac{1}{2} \cdot \frac{?}{?} + \frac{1}{3} \cdot \frac{4}{4} + \frac{1}{4} \cdot \frac{?}{?}$
$\qquad = \frac{?}{?} + \frac{?}{?} + \frac{?}{?}$
$\qquad = \frac{?}{?}$

18. $\frac{1}{3} + \frac{1}{5} + \frac{1}{9} = \frac{1}{3} \cdot \frac{?}{?} + \frac{1}{5} \cdot \frac{?}{?} + \frac{1}{9} \cdot \frac{5}{5}$
$\qquad = \frac{?}{?} + \frac{?}{?} + \frac{?}{?}$
$\qquad = \frac{?}{?}$

Find common names for the following sums. Show steps as in Exercises 15–18.

19. $\frac{7}{8} + 5$

20. $3 + \frac{5}{16}$

21. $\frac{5}{6} + \frac{5}{9}$

22. $\frac{5}{8} + \frac{5}{6}$

23. $\frac{7}{18} + \frac{13}{60}$

24. $\frac{5}{24} + \frac{19}{36}$

25. $\frac{5}{12} + \frac{3}{20} + \frac{7}{45}$

26. $\frac{3}{8} + \frac{7}{12} + \frac{13}{40}$

B Find common names.

27. $\frac{x}{11} + \frac{5x}{11}$

28. $\frac{3a}{13} + \frac{7a}{13}$

29. $\frac{3x}{8} + \frac{x}{12}$

30. $\frac{2y}{15} + \frac{5y}{6}$

CHAPTER SUMMARY

Important Terms

1. A **proper factor** is any counting-number factor of a number except 1 and the number itself.

2. If a, b, and c represent counting numbers and $c = a \cdot b$, then c is said to be **divisible** by a and b; c is also a **multiple** of a and b; and a and b are factors of c.

3. A **prime number** is a counting number greater than 1 that does not have any proper factors.

4. A **composite number** is a counting number that is not prime.

5. In the phrase 10^3, the **base** is 10.

6. A counting number that shows the number of times the base is a factor is called an **exponent**. The number 3 is the exponent in 10^3.

7. The number 10^3 is called the third **power** of 10.

8. The **numerator** of a fraction is the number shown above the fraction bar.

9. The **denominator** of a fraction is the number shown below the fraction bar.

10. The set of **counting-number multiples** of a number is the set obtained by the multiplication of each counting number by the given number.

11. The **least common multiple** of two or more counting numbers is the least number in the set of their common counting-number multiples.

Important Ideas

1. Every even number is divisible by 2.

2. If the sum of the numbers named by the digits of a number is divisible by 3, then the given number is divisible by 3.

3. If the number named by the last two digits of a number is divisible by 4, then the given number is divisible by 4.

4. Any number whose numeral ends in 0 or 5 is divisible by 5.

5. Any number whose numeral ends in 0 is divisible by 10.

6. There is only one selection of factors in the prime factorization of a number.

7. One number is divisible by a second number if each number in the prime factorization of the first appears at least as many times (it may appear more times) as it does in the prime factorization of the second.

8. The common name of a rational-number fraction is that fraction for which the numerator and denominator do not have a common factor.

9. The product of two or more numbers in fraction form is named by the fraction whose numerator is the product of the numerators and whose denominator is the product of the denominators of the given fractions.

10. It is not necessary to find the least common multiple of the denominators when multiplying numbers named by fractions.

11. The sum of two or more numbers expressed as fractions with like denominators is named by the fraction whose numerator is the sum of the numerators and whose denominator is the common denominator of the given fraction.

12. The least common denominator of two fractions is the least common multiple of their denominators. If the denominators of fractions do not have any common factors, then their least common multiple is the product of all the denominators.

CHAPTER REVIEW

Use the roster method to list the proper factors of these numbers.

1. 10   **2.** 12   **3.** 15   **4.** 20

Indicate whether each of the following is *Prime* or *Composite*. If the number is *Composite*, show its prime factorization.

5. 39   **6.** 31   **7.** 57   **8.** 217

Use exponents to give the prime factorization of each of the following.

9. 288   **10.** 324   **11.** 216   **12.** 5400

Indicate whether each of the following statements is *True* or *False*.

13. 56 is divisible by 8.

14. 10 is a factor of 5.

15. 3 is a prime factor of 18.

16. $2 \cdot 3^2 \cdot 5$ is a multiple of $3 \cdot 5$.

17. $2^3 \cdot 3 \cdot 5$ is a multiple of $2 \cdot 3 \cdot 7$.

18. 18 is a common multiple of 3 and 2.

19. 5 is a multiple of 35.

20. 4 is a factor of 24.

21. 36 is a power of 6.

22. In the phrase 2^5, the number 5 is called the power.

23. The least common multiple of 3 and 6 is 3.

24. The sum of $\frac{1}{5}$ and $\frac{3}{8}$ is $\frac{4}{13}$.

Find the quotients.

25. $(2^3 \cdot 3) \div (2 \cdot 3)$

26. $(2 \cdot 3^2 \cdot 5) \div (3 \cdot 5)$

27. $(2 \cdot 3 \cdot 5^2 \cdot 7) \div (2 \cdot 3 \cdot 5 \cdot 7)$

28. $(11 \cdot 13 \cdot 17 \cdot 19) \div (13 \cdot 17)$

Find the common name for each of the following.

29. $\dfrac{2 \cdot 2 \cdot 3 \cdot 5}{2 \cdot 2 \cdot 3 \cdot 3 \cdot 7}$

30. $\dfrac{2 \cdot 3^2 \cdot 5}{2^3 \cdot 3 \cdot 11}$

31. $\dfrac{8}{18}$

32. $\dfrac{12}{27}$

33. $\dfrac{124}{356}$

34. $\dfrac{156}{412}$

Find the numbers that will make each of the following sentences true.

35. $\dfrac{5}{8} = \dfrac{?}{72}$

36. $\dfrac{7}{12} \cdot \dfrac{?}{?} = \dfrac{?}{96}$

37. $\dfrac{5}{2 \cdot 3 \cdot 7} = \dfrac{?}{2 \cdot 3^2 \cdot 7}$

38. $\dfrac{2 \cdot 3 \cdot 5}{7 \cdot 11} = \dfrac{?}{?} = \dfrac{?}{7 \cdot 2 \cdot 3 \cdot 2 \cdot 11 \cdot 2}$

Find the common name for each of the following products.

39. $\frac{2}{7} \cdot \frac{3}{5}$

40. $\frac{5}{8} \cdot \frac{9}{4}$

41. $\frac{5}{8} \cdot 9$

42. $\frac{5}{8} \cdot \frac{1}{9}$

43. $\frac{3}{16} \cdot \frac{4}{9}$

44. $\frac{3}{5} \cdot \frac{3}{10} \cdot \frac{5}{9}$

Find the least common multiple of each of the following sets of numbers.

45. $\{2, 4, 6\}$

46. $\{3, 9, 12\}$

47. $\{15, 18, 24\}$

48. $\{27, 36, 60\}$

Find the common name for each of the following sums.

49. $\frac{5}{19} + \frac{6}{19}$

50. $\frac{5}{24} + \frac{7}{24}$

51. $\frac{13}{10} + \frac{19}{10}$

52. $\frac{3}{4} + 3$

53. $7 + \frac{5}{8}$

54. $\frac{5}{6} + \frac{11}{18}$

55. $\frac{5}{12} + \frac{7}{27}$

56. $\frac{2}{3} + \frac{7}{15} + \frac{3}{40}$

Give common names for the following.

57. $\dfrac{3r}{13} + \dfrac{5r}{13}$

58. $\dfrac{t}{5} + \dfrac{3t}{7}$

To find the age of an ancient form of life, paleontologists may use a method called potassium-argon dating. This method measures the relative amounts of the two elements argon and potassium that are present in the igneous rock overlying the sedimentary strata from which the fossil remains were uncovered. The ratio of the amount of argon to the amount of potassium indicates the age of the rock; hence, the age of the fossil can be estimated. Potassium-argon dating is one of the many uses of ratio. In this chapter, you will study ratio and its importance in mathematical applications.

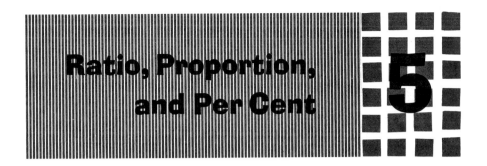

5.1 Property of Reciprocals

To begin this chapter, you will consider an important property of certain pairs of numbers.

■ **P-1** What is the common name for the product $5(\frac{1}{5})$?

■ **P-2** What is the common name for the product $\frac{3}{5}(\frac{5}{3})$?

You can probably think of many other pairs of numbers whose products are 1.

> Two numbers of arithmetic whose product is 1 are said to be **reciprocals** of each other.

■ **P-3** What is the reciprocal of $\frac{4}{7}$? of $\frac{7}{4}$?

■ **P-4** What is the reciprocal of 3? of $\frac{1}{3}$?

■ **P-5** How can you find a numeral that is the name for the reciprocal of a given number?

Your knowledge of multiplication of numbers named by fractions helps you see how to form reciprocals. If a given number is expressed as a fraction, then its reciprocal can be expressed as the fraction that is formed by interchanging the numerator and denominator of the given fraction. Therefore, the reciprocal of 10 is $\frac{1}{10}$, since

$$10 = \frac{10}{1} \quad \text{and} \quad \frac{10}{1}\left(\frac{1}{10}\right) = \frac{10}{10} = 1.$$

In relation to reciprocals, it is important that you recall another property.

■ **P-6**   What is the common name of each of the following products?

$$(5)(0); \quad (\tfrac{1}{2})(0); \quad (0)(0.17); \quad (0)(0); \quad (\pi)(0)$$

You are already familiar with this property from your study of arithmetic. It is called the **Multiplication Property of Zero** and can be stated as follows.

> If a is any number of arithmetic, then
>
> $$(a)(0) = 0.$$

Of course, the Commutative Property of Multiplication will then suggest that $(0)(a) = 0$.

■ **P-7**   What is the truth set of the sentence $0 \cdot x = 1$?

■ **P-8**   What can you say about the reciprocal of zero?

Since the truth set of the sentence $0 \cdot x = 1$ is empty, you can see that 0 has no reciprocal.

> Every number of arithmetic except zero has a reciprocal.

You remember that $\frac{0}{1}, \frac{0}{2}, \frac{0}{3}, \frac{0}{11}, \frac{0}{100}$, and so forth are all names for 0. The fractions $\frac{1}{0}, \frac{2}{0}, \frac{3}{0}$, and so forth are not names for numbers. The fraction $\dfrac{a}{0}$ does not define a number for any replacement of a!

■ **P-9**   What is the reciprocal of 7?

■ **P-10**   Can you find another number that is the reciprocal of 7?

> If a number of arithmetic has a reciprocal, then it has only one reciprocal.

Although a number can have only one reciprocal, you can give many different names to the same reciprocal. For example, the fractions $\frac{1}{7}$ and $\frac{2}{14}$ are different names for the reciprocal of 7.

Numbers of arithmetic may appear in various forms. For example, $\frac{6}{5}$, $1\frac{1}{5}$, and 1.2 are all names for the same number. You can always find a reciprocal easily by first expressing the number as a fraction. Thus, 0.18 is equal to $\frac{18}{100}$, and one name for its reciprocal is $\frac{100}{18}$.

■ **P-11** What is the reciprocal of $1\frac{3}{4}$? of 2.8?

■ **P-12** What is the reciprocal of 1?

The number 1 is the only number of arithmetic that is its own reciprocal.

ORAL EXERCISES 5.1

1. What is meant by the reciprocal of a number?
2. Do all numbers of arithmetic have reciprocals? Explain.
3. Can $\frac{1}{0}$ be a name for the reciprocal of a number?
4. How many reciprocals does 2 have?
5. What number is its own reciprocal?

Find the reciprocal of each of the following numbers.

6. $\frac{1}{3}$	7. 1	8. $\frac{1}{100}$	9. 12
10. $\frac{7}{8}$	11. $\frac{7}{3}$	12. $\frac{5}{12}$	13. $\frac{11}{5}$
14. 0.3	15. $1\frac{1}{3}$	16. 0.05	17. $2\frac{2}{5}$

By what number can you multiply each of the following to get a product of 1?

18. $\frac{1}{8}$	19. 13	20. $\frac{15}{16}$	21. 0.9

22. What is the truth set of the sentence $n \cdot 0 = 1$?

WRITTEN EXERCISES 5.1

A Give two names for the reciprocal of each of the following numbers.

1. $\frac{1}{4}$	2. $\frac{1}{8}$	3. 18	4. 20
5. $\frac{4}{5}$	6. $\frac{5}{7}$	7. $\frac{5}{2}$	8. $\frac{8}{3}$
9. 0.4	10. 0.6	11. $3\frac{5}{8}$	12. $4\frac{3}{4}$

Find the truth set of each of the following sentences, using {numbers of arithmetic} as the domain.

13. $\frac{1}{5}x = 1$	14. $\frac{1}{3}n = 1$	15. $\frac{2}{7}y = 1$
16. $\frac{3}{8}r = 1$	17. $s(\frac{10}{7}) = 1$	18. $t(\frac{13}{5}) = 1$
19. $0 \cdot p = 1$	20. $m \cdot 0 = 1$	21. $\frac{8}{8} \cdot x = 1$
22. $y(\frac{15}{15}) = 1$		

5.2 Truth Sets of Sentences Involving Multiplication

You may make use of your knowledge of reciprocals to find truth sets of sentences such as $2x = 12$. Replace x by the phrase $\frac{1}{2} \cdot 12$ and see if the sentence is true.

$$2 \cdot x = 12$$

By the Associative Property of Multiplication $\longrightarrow 2(\frac{1}{2} \cdot 12) = (2 \cdot \frac{1}{2})12$

Since 1 is a common name for $2 \cdot \frac{1}{2}$ $\longrightarrow$ $\qquad = 1 \cdot 12$

By the Multiplication Property of One $\longrightarrow$ $\qquad = 12$

You can see that $\frac{1}{2} \cdot 12$, or 6, is a truth number for $2x = 12$.

■ **P-1** What indicated product can you put in place of x to make the sentence $3x = 15$ true?

$$3(\tfrac{1}{3} \cdot 15) = (3 \cdot \tfrac{1}{3})15$$
$$= 15$$

You can see that $\frac{1}{3} \cdot 15$, or 5, is a truth number for this sentence. Of course, there is no other number by which you can multiply 3 to get 15 as the product. Therefore, $\{5\}$ is the truth set of $3x = 15$.

For the sentence $\frac{1}{3}x = 10$, the phrase $3(10)$ is a name for its truth number.

■ **P-2** How are the two factors 3 and 10 obtained from the given sentence $\frac{1}{3}x = 10$?

■ **P-3** What is the truth set of $\frac{1}{3}x = 10$?

Consider the sentence $ax = b$, where a and b are numbers of arithmetic.

■ **P-4** How can you name the truth number of this sentence?

■ **P-5** What number of arithmetic can a not represent?

> The truth number of an open sentence of the form $ax = b$, where a and b are numbers of arithmetic but $a \neq 0$, is b multiplied by the reciprocal of a.

■ **P-6** What is the truth number of $\frac{2}{3}x = 10$?

■ **P-7** What is the truth number of $0.1x = 5$?

■ **P-8** What is the truth number of $5x = \frac{1}{3}$?

ORAL EXERCISES 5.2

For each of the following examples, tell what number can replace the question mark to make the sentence true.

1. $5x = 20$
$5(\underline{?} \cdot 20) = 20$

2. $8x = 56$
$8(\frac{1}{8} \cdot \underline{?}) = 56$

3. $4x = 13$
$4(\underline{?} \cdot 13) = 13$

4. $3x = 8$
$3(\underline{?} \cdot \underline{?}) = 8$

5. $\frac{1}{5}x = 8$
$\frac{1}{5}(\underline{?} \cdot 8) = 8$

6. $\frac{1}{10}x = 5$
$\frac{1}{10}(\underline{?} \cdot \underline{?}) = 5$

7. $\frac{3}{5}x = 12$
$\frac{3}{5}(\underline{?} \cdot 12) = 12$

8. $\frac{5}{6}x = 20$
$\frac{5}{6}(\underline{?} \cdot \underline{?}) = 20$

9. $0.2x = 6$
$0.2(\underline{?} \cdot 6) = 6$

10. $1\frac{1}{2}x = 5$
$1\frac{1}{2}(\underline{?} \cdot 5) = 5$

For each of the following, express the truth number as a product first, and then give the common name.

11. $2x = 26$ **12.** $3x = 33$ **13.** $\frac{1}{12}x = 3$ **14.** $\frac{1}{9}x = 5$

15. $\frac{2}{5}x = 4$ **16.** $\frac{3}{4}x = 9$ **17.** $\frac{7}{3}x = 14$ **18.** $\frac{5}{2}x = 20$

19. $3x = 9$ **20.** $0.01x = 2$

WRITTEN EXERCISES 5.2

A   Name the truth set of each of the following in two ways. First express the truth number as a product, and then give its common name.

Example: $9x = 45$ *Answer:* $\{\frac{1}{9} \cdot 45\} = \{5\}$

1. $2x = 22$ **2.** $3x = 36$ **3.** $6x = 14$

4. $4x = 18$ **5.** $5x = 12$ **6.** $7x = 13$

7. $\frac{1}{8}x = 6$ **8.** $\frac{1}{6}x = 7$ **9.** $\frac{2}{5}x = 16$

10. $\frac{3}{7}x = 15$ **11.** $\frac{3}{4}x = 10$ **12.** $\frac{3}{5}x = 8$

13. $0.7x = 28$ **14.** $0.9x = 27$ **15.** $0.03x = 15$

16. $0.05x = 30$ **17.** $\frac{1}{2}x = \frac{2}{3}$ **18.** $\frac{1}{3}x = \frac{3}{5}$

19. $\frac{2}{3}x = \frac{3}{4}$ **20.** $\frac{3}{5}x = \frac{3}{8}$

Write an open sentence whose truth number is the product that is given.

21. $\frac{1}{2} \cdot 5$ **22.** $\frac{1}{3} \cdot 7$ **23.** $5 \cdot 8$ **24.** $3 \cdot 10$

25. $\frac{2}{3} \cdot 10$ **26.** $\frac{3}{4} \cdot 9$ **27.** $\frac{4}{3} \cdot 11$ **28.** $\frac{8}{5} \cdot 14$

5.3 Ratio

You have learned that a rational number of arithmetic is a number that can be represented as the quotient of two whole numbers when the divisor is not zero.

For example, 10 can be expressed as $\frac{40}{4}$. The number 10 gives us one method of comparing the numbers 40 and 4. When used in this way, the quotient is sometimes referred to as a **ratio.**

> A quotient of two numbers of arithmetic is called a **ratio** if it is considered to be a comparison of the two numbers.

Since $\frac{2}{5}$ and $\frac{5}{2}$ represent two different rational numbers, they are also different ratios. The order in which two numbers are compared affects their ratio.

To read $\frac{2}{5}$ as a ratio, say "the ratio of 2 to 5."
To read $\frac{5}{2}$ as a ratio, say "the ratio of 5 to 2."

■ **P-1**   How would you read $\frac{3}{10}$ as a ratio?

■ **P-2**   How would you read $\frac{a}{b}$ as a ratio?

The ratio of 2 to 5 can also be shown as 2 : 5.

> The ratio $\frac{a}{b}$ can also be shown as $a : b$.

■ **P-3**   How would you read the ratio 5 : 2?

The two numbers that are compared in a ratio are called its **terms.** In the ratio $a : b$, a is the first term and b is the second. The second term of a ratio can never be 0. Remember that $\frac{a}{0}$ cannot define a number no matter what replacement is made for a. Since a ratio is a quotient, its terms can be represented as the numerator and denominator of a fraction. Therefore, you can speak of finding the common name for a ratio as you speak of finding the common name for a fraction.

■ **P-4** What is the common name for the ratio 8 : 12?

■ **P-5** What is the common name for the ratio $\frac{6}{10}$?

Ratios are often used to compare lengths, weights, areas, volumes, values, and so forth. If a ratio is to have any meaning in these uses, then the terms of the ratio must be expressed in the same unit.

Suppose John is 4 feet tall and Bob is 50 inches tall. The ratio 4 : 50 will not tell how their heights compare unless you know that John's height is in feet and Bob's height is in inches. You can say, however, that the ratio of John's height to Bob's is 48 : 50.

■ **P-6** What is a common name for the ratio 48 : 50?

Also, a ratio does not have a label. You should not say that the ratio of John's height to Bob's height is 48 inches : 50 inches.

■ **P-7** What is the ratio of the value of 6 nickels to the value of 5 dimes?

■ **P-8** What is the ratio of 2 weeks to 3 days?

ORAL EXERCISES 5.3

Read the following as ratios.

1. $\frac{3}{5}$ **2.** $\frac{7}{10}$ **3.** $\frac{25}{3}$ **4.** $\frac{13}{17}$

5. 2 : 9   **6.** 10 : 3   **7.** 100 : 1   **8.** 1 : 10

Give a common name for each of the following ratios.

9. 8 : 12   **10.** 7 : 14   **11.** 22 : 11

12. 27 : 9   **13.** $\frac{10}{100}$ **14.** $\frac{300}{100}$

The following table shows the results of a survey taken in a class.

	Black Hair	Brown Hair	Red Hair	Blonde Hair	Total
Boys	11	8	1	3	23
Girls	4	6	2	5	17

What is the ratio of the number of
15. boys with black hair to girls with blonde hair?
16. girls with red hair to boys with red hair?
17. boys to girls?
18. girls with brown hair to girls with blonde hair?
19. boys with black hair to girls with black hair?

Give a common name for each of the following ratios.

20. 5 inches to 1 foot
21. 4 feet to 2 yards
22. 1 yard to 5 feet
23. 10 days to 2 weeks
24. value of 6 pennies to the value of 3 nickels
25. value of 4 dimes to the value of 2 quarters

WRITTEN EXERCISES 5.3

A Express each of the following ratios in two other ways. Use the common name for the ratio in each case.

1. 5 to 9
2. 13 to 27
3. 12 to 27
4. 15 to 33
5. 10 to 1000
6. 1000 to 100
7. 10 inches to 3 feet
8. 14 inches to 4 feet
9. 2 yards to 5 feet
10. 3 yards to 12 feet
11. 12 miles to 15 miles
12. 35 yards to 20 yards
13. 8 days to 2 weeks
14. 3 weeks to 9 days
15. x to 5
16. y to 13
17. b to a
18. y to x

The following table shows the number of different kinds of base hits that two teams got in a baseball game.

	Singles	Doubles	Triples	Home Runs	Total
Cougars	10	3	1	5	19
Panthers	5	1	2	1	9

What is the ratio of the number of
19. home runs by the Cougars to home runs by the Panthers?
20. singles by the Panthers to singles by the Cougars?
21. singles by the Cougars to singles by the Panthers?
22. doubles by the Cougars to doubles by the Panthers?
23. total hits by the Cougars to total hits by the Panthers?
24. total hits by the Panthers to total hits by the Cougars?

25. The population of Los Angeles is about 5 times the population of Phoenix. What is the ratio of the population of Phoenix to the population of Los Angeles?

26. The Packers scored $\frac{1}{3}$ as many points as the Bears. What is the ratio of the number of points scored by the Bears to the number scored by the Packers?

5.4 Proportion

A true statement of equality of two ratios is called a **proportion.**
The following are proportions.

$$\frac{2}{3} = \frac{4}{6}; \qquad \frac{5}{2} = \frac{10}{4}; \qquad \frac{7}{10} = \frac{21}{30}$$

■ **P-1** Is the sentence $\frac{5}{12} = \frac{10}{24}$ a proportion?

■ **P-2** Is the sentence $\frac{7}{8} = \frac{28}{31}$ a proportion?

> When you refer to $\frac{a}{b} = \frac{c}{d}$ as a proportion, a, b, c, and d
> are to be replaced by numbers of arithmetic that will
> make the sentence true. Of course, $b \neq 0$ and $d \neq 0$.

The four numbers that make up the two ratios are called **terms**
of the proportion. In the proportion $\frac{a}{b} = \frac{c}{d}$, the terms can be numbered as follows.

$$\boxed{1} \longrightarrow \frac{a}{b} = \frac{c}{d} \longleftarrow \boxed{3}$$
$$\boxed{2} \longrightarrow b \quad d \longleftarrow \boxed{4}$$

■ **P-3** In the proportion $\frac{3}{5} = \frac{9}{15}$, what is the product of the first
and fourth terms?

■ **P-4** What is the product of the second and third terms?

In the proportion $\frac{3}{5} = \frac{9}{15}$, you can see that $3 \cdot 15 = 5 \cdot 9$ is true.
In the proportion $\frac{2}{3} = \frac{4}{6}$, you can see that $2 \cdot 6 = 3 \cdot 4$ is true.
In the proportion $\frac{5}{2} = \frac{10}{4}$, you can see that $5 \cdot 4 = 2 \cdot 10$ is true.

> If the variables in $\frac{a}{b} = \frac{c}{d}$ are replaced by numbers that
> make it a proportion, then it is true that
> $$a \cdot d = b \cdot c.$$

The first and fourth terms of a proportion are called the **extremes,**
and the second and third are called the **means.** In a proportion the
product of the extremes equals the product of the means. This is
sometimes called the **cross-products property.**

■ **P-5** How can you use the cross-products property to tell whether or not the sentence $\frac{12}{13} = \frac{5}{6}$ is a proportion?

■ **P-6** Is the sentence $\frac{3}{8} = \frac{5}{15}$ a proportion?

When a proportion is given, it is easy to form other proportions from it using the same four numbers. The sentences $\frac{2}{3} = \frac{6}{9}$, $\frac{2}{6} = \frac{3}{9}$, $\frac{3}{2} = \frac{9}{6}$, and $\frac{6}{2} = \frac{9}{3}$ are all proportions using the same four numbers 2, 3, 6, and 9.

Look at the proportion $\frac{a}{b} = \frac{c}{d}$ to see how to form other proportions from it. You can probably see how to get the proportion

$$\frac{a}{c} = \frac{b}{d}.$$

This is sometimes called the property of **alternation** because terms of the original proportion are now in the order 1, 3, 2, 4.

■ **P-7** How can you change the proportion $\frac{3}{4} = \frac{9}{12}$ by alternation?

Again, given the proportion $\frac{a}{b} = \frac{c}{d}$, you can form the proportion

$$\frac{b}{a} = \frac{d}{c}.$$

Here, you can see that each ratio has just been reversed, or inverted. This is called the property of **inversion.**

■ **P-8** How can you change the proportion $\frac{5}{8} = \frac{10}{16}$ by inversion?

Consider the proportion $\frac{1}{4} = \frac{3}{12}$.

■ **P-9** What proportion do you get by alternation?

■ **P-10** What proportion do you get when you use inversion on $\frac{1}{3} = \frac{4}{12}$?

Given the proportion $\frac{a}{b} = \frac{c}{d}$, you can form $\frac{c}{a} = \frac{d}{b}$ as follows.

[1] First use alternation to get $\frac{a}{c} = \frac{b}{d}$.

[2] Then use inversion on $\frac{a}{c} = \frac{b}{d}$ to get $\frac{c}{a} = \frac{d}{b}$.

ORAL EXERCISES 5.4

Tell whether each of the following is a proportion or not.

1. $\frac{3}{5} = \frac{9}{15}$ **2.** $\frac{1}{2} = \frac{4}{10}$ **3.** $\frac{1}{3} = \frac{12}{36}$ **4.** $\frac{5}{4} = \frac{20}{15}$

5. $\frac{5}{6} = \frac{10}{12}$ **6.** $\frac{3}{2} = \frac{9}{6}$ **7.** $\frac{4}{3} = \frac{8}{5}$ **8.** $\frac{3}{100} = \frac{2}{75}$

Use the property of alternation to form new proportions from the following.

9. $\frac{3}{4} = \frac{9}{12}$ **10.** $\frac{5}{6} = \frac{15}{18}$ **11.** $\frac{3}{2} = \frac{12}{8}$ **12.** $\frac{1}{10} = \frac{3}{30}$

Use the property of inversion to form new proportions from the following.

13. $\frac{1}{4} = \frac{5}{20}$ **14.** $\frac{3}{5} = \frac{18}{30}$ **15.** $\frac{9}{10} = \frac{27}{30}$ **16.** $\frac{9}{16} = \frac{18}{32}$

Use the property of alternation followed by inversion to form new proportions from the following.

17. $\frac{5}{8} = \frac{15}{24}$ **18.** $\frac{3}{7} = \frac{9}{21}$ **19.** $\frac{2}{5} = \frac{20}{50}$ **20.** $\frac{x}{y} = \frac{r}{s}$

WRITTEN EXERCISES 5.4

A Use the cross-products property to answer by *Yes* or *No* whether each of the following is a proportion.

1. $\frac{2}{3} = \frac{16}{24}$ **2.** $\frac{3}{4} = \frac{18}{24}$ **3.** $\frac{5}{6} = \frac{21}{25}$

4. $\frac{4}{7} = \frac{23}{41}$ **5.** $\frac{23}{57} = \frac{19}{48}$ **6.** $\frac{17}{29} = \frac{33}{42}$

Use the alternation property to change the form of each of the following.

7. $\frac{3}{8} = \frac{15}{40}$ **8.** $\frac{5}{16} = \frac{10}{32}$ **9.** $\frac{6}{5} = \frac{24}{20}$ **10.** $\frac{8}{7} = \frac{24}{21}$

Use the inversion property to change the form of each of the following.

11. $\frac{13}{15} = \frac{26}{30}$ **12.** $\frac{15}{16} = \frac{30}{32}$ **13.** $\frac{12}{5} = \frac{48}{20}$ **14.** $\frac{25}{12} = \frac{75}{36}$

Use the alternation property followed by inversion to form new proportions from the following.

15. $\frac{3}{8} = \frac{9}{24}$ **16.** $\frac{5}{6} = \frac{25}{30}$ **17.** $\frac{5}{9} = \frac{25}{45}$ **18.** $\frac{7}{8} = \frac{35}{40}$

If the sentence $\frac{a}{b} = \frac{c}{d}$ is a proportion, indicate by *Yes* or *No* whether each of the following is always a proportion.

19. $\frac{a}{c} = \frac{b}{d}$ **20.** $\frac{c}{a} = \frac{d}{b}$ **21.** $\frac{a}{d} = \frac{b}{c}$ **22.** $\frac{d}{a} = \frac{c}{b}$

23. $\frac{b}{a} = \frac{d}{c}$ **24.** $\frac{d}{c} = \frac{b}{a}$ **25.** $ad = bc$ **26.** $cb = da$

Form a proportion from each of the following equalities of products.

27. $5 \cdot 6 = 15 \cdot 2$ **28.** $6 \cdot 6 = 4 \cdot 9$ **29.** $2 \cdot 12 = 3 \cdot 8$

30. $2 \cdot 24 = 6 \cdot 8$ **31.** $x \cdot y = r \cdot s$ **32.** $a \cdot b = c \cdot d$

B   What is the truth set of each open sentence?

33. $\dfrac{x}{2} = \dfrac{2}{4}$ **34.** $\dfrac{x}{3} = \dfrac{3}{9}$ **35.** $\dfrac{1}{x} = \dfrac{4}{20}$

36. $\dfrac{1}{x} = \dfrac{5}{50}$ **37.** $\dfrac{2}{3} = \dfrac{x}{9}$ **38.** $\dfrac{3}{4} = \dfrac{x}{16}$

5.5   Proportions as Open Sentences

Often open sentences are expressed in proportion form. The truth number of such a sentence makes the sentence a proportion when it replaces the variable.

The sentence $\dfrac{x}{4} = \dfrac{9}{12}$ becomes a proportion when x is replaced by 3. The truth set of this sentence is $\{3\}$. The cross-products property of proportions can be used to find such truth sets.

From $\dfrac{x}{4} = \dfrac{9}{12}$, you can form the sentence $12x = 4 \cdot 9$, using the cross-products property. Remember that the sentence $12x = 36$ has a truth number that can be expressed as a product, $\frac{1}{12} \cdot 36$, or 3.

■ **P-1**   What sentence can you form from $\dfrac{12}{x} = \dfrac{3}{2}$, using the cross-products property?

■ **P-2**   What product represents the truth number of $3x = 24$?

■ **P-3**   What is the truth set of $\dfrac{12}{x} = \dfrac{3}{2}$?

Suppose you want to find the truth set of the sentence

$$\frac{2}{24} = \frac{x}{6}.$$

By the cross-products property,

$$2 \cdot 6 = 24x,$$
$$\text{or} \quad 12 = 24x,$$
$$12 = 24(\tfrac{1}{24} \cdot 12).$$

Therefore, the truth number for the sentence $\frac{2}{24} = \frac{x}{6}$ is $\frac{1}{24} \cdot 12$, or $\frac{1}{2}$, and the truth set is $\{\frac{1}{2}\}$.

The height of an object such as a flagpole can be found by the use of proportion. A stake whose length is known is held vertically near the flagpole. The shadows of both the stake and the flagpole are measured. It is known that the heights of the stake and flagpole are proportional to the lengths of their shadows. That is, the ratio of the height of the flagpole to the height of the stake is equal to the ratio of the length of the flagpole's shadow to the length of the stake's shadow.

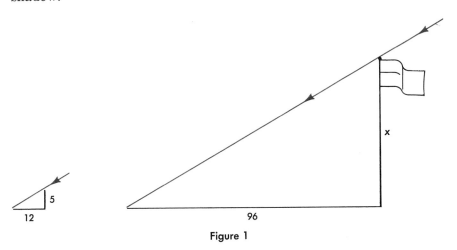

Figure 1

Suppose the length of the stake and the lengths of the shadows are as shown in Figure 1. You may represent the height of the flagpole by the variable x. The following open sentence describes the relationship among the four lengths.

$$\frac{x}{5} = \frac{96}{12}$$
$$12x = 5 \cdot 96$$
$$12x = 480$$
$$12(\tfrac{1}{12} \cdot 480) = 480$$

The truth number is $\frac{1}{12} \cdot 480$, or 40. The height of the flagpole is 40 units.

■ **P-4** Can you state another proportion that could be used to find the height of the flagpole in Figure 1?

There are many other types of problems that can be solved by the use of proportions. Often you may use proportions to predict results. Here are some examples:

Example 1: If a batter hits 20 home runs in the first 81 games, about how many can he expect to hit in the entire season of 162 games?

Here you assume that the number of home runs and the number of games are proportional. Let x represent the number of home runs for the season.

$$\frac{x}{20} = \frac{162}{81}$$
$$81x = 20 \cdot 162$$
$$81x = 3240$$
$$81(\tfrac{1}{81} \cdot 3240) = 3240$$
$$x = 40$$

On the basis of the work with proportions, such a prediction seems reasonable.

Example 2: If it takes 10 hours to drive 500 miles of a 2000-mile trip, about how many hours will it take to complete the trip?

There are 1500 miles left in the trip. Let x represent the number of hours to complete the trip.

$$\frac{500}{1500} = \frac{10}{x}$$
$$500x = 10 \cdot 1500$$
$$500x = 15,000$$
$$500(\tfrac{1}{500} \cdot 15,000) = 15,000$$

The truth number is $\frac{1}{500} \cdot 15,000$, or 30. It will take about 30 hours to complete the trip if it is made at the same rate.

ORAL EXERCISES 5.5

For each of the following proportions, first use the cross-products property. Then give the truth number of the resulting open sentence.

1. $\dfrac{1}{2} = \dfrac{x}{6}$

2. $\dfrac{2}{x} = \dfrac{1}{3}$

3. $\dfrac{a}{5} = \dfrac{1}{5}$

4. $\dfrac{2}{7} = \dfrac{b}{7}$

5. $\dfrac{t}{8} = \dfrac{3}{24}$

6. $\dfrac{w}{3} = \dfrac{4}{6}$

7. $\dfrac{1}{10} = \dfrac{2}{r}$

8. $\dfrac{2}{3} = \dfrac{p}{9}$

9. $\dfrac{x}{1} = \dfrac{9}{x}$

10. $\dfrac{2}{y} = \dfrac{y}{8}$

For each of the following, state an open sentence that relates the given quantities if they are proportional.

11. 100 miles in 3 hours; 500 miles in x hours.

12. y miles in 8 hours; 300 miles in 6 hours.

13. 12 ounces costing 35¢; 16 ounces costing x¢.

14. $150 earned in 40 hours; x dollars earned in 60 hours.

15. $200 earned in 1 week; w weeks and $3600.

16. 2 touchdowns in 1 game; x games and 18 touchdowns.

17. 2 chapters contain 60 pages; x pages in 24 chapters.

18. 125 points in 5 games; x points in 30 games.

WRITTEN EXERCISES 5.5

A Use the cross-products property to find the truth set of each of the following.

1. $\dfrac{1}{3} = \dfrac{x}{15}$

2. $\dfrac{1}{4} = \dfrac{n}{28}$

3. $\dfrac{x}{30} = \dfrac{3}{5}$

4. $\dfrac{y}{24} = \dfrac{5}{6}$

5. $\dfrac{5}{2} = \dfrac{45}{t}$

6. $\dfrac{4}{3} = \dfrac{32}{r}$

7. $\dfrac{7}{8} = \dfrac{x}{4}$

8. $\dfrac{9}{16} = \dfrac{x}{8}$

9. $\dfrac{s}{24} = \dfrac{13}{16}$

10. $\dfrac{3}{n} = \dfrac{27}{15}$

11. $\dfrac{y}{8} = \dfrac{180}{72}$

12. $\dfrac{t}{12} = \dfrac{54}{36}$

If the quantities in each of the following problems are proportional, state an open sentence in proportion form showing their relation.

13. 3 yards mowed in 1 day; x yards mowed in 5 days.

14. 8 cars washed in 10 hours; 40 cars washed in x hours.

15. 15 hits in 8 games; x hits in 25 games.

16. 25 free throws in 3 games; x free throws in 10 games.

17. 16 dollars earned in 8 hours; x hours to earn 40 dollars.

18. 3 hamburgers cost 55¢; x¢ for 10 hamburgers.

Solve the following problems by using properties of proportions.

19. The ratio of the number of boys to the number of girls in a school is 3 : 2. How many girls are there if there are 1200 boys?

20. The ratio of the number of teachers to the number of students in a school is 2 : 59. How many teachers are there if there are 649 students?

5.6 Meaning of Per Cent

A ratio in which the second term is 100 is often expressed as a per cent. "Per cent" means "per hundred." Thus, $\frac{23}{100}$ can be called 23 per cent, or 23%. Since per cent is such a commonly used term in our language, it is important that you clearly understand its meaning.

■ **P-1** How can you express each of the following ratios as a per cent?

$$\frac{5}{100}; \quad \frac{75}{100}; \quad \frac{125}{100}; \quad \frac{2}{50}$$

You can express any ratio whose second term is not 100 as a per cent by renaming the ratio. For example,

$$\frac{2}{5} = \frac{2}{5} \cdot \frac{20}{20}$$
$$= \frac{40}{100}$$
$$= 40\%.$$

Here again the Multiplication Property of One was used in order to get 100 as the second term of the ratio.

■ **P-2** How would you express each of the following as a per cent?

$$\frac{1}{4}; \quad \frac{3}{5}; \quad \frac{2}{25}; \quad \frac{3}{10}$$

■ **P-3** How would you express $\dfrac{x}{100}$ as a per cent?

When you try to express a ratio such as $\frac{1}{3}$ as a per cent, you have some trouble. It is difficult to find a name for 1 by which to multiply $\frac{1}{3}$. Now you can use your work with proportions. You need to find the truth number for the following sentence.

$$\frac{1}{3} = \frac{x}{100}$$
$$3x = 100$$
$$3(\tfrac{1}{3} \cdot 100) = 100$$

You see that its truth number is $\frac{1}{3} \cdot 100$, or $33\frac{1}{3}$. Therefore, $\dfrac{1}{3} = \dfrac{33\frac{1}{3}}{100}$ is a true sentence, and $\frac{1}{3}$ is equal to $33\frac{1}{3}\%$.

■ **P-4** What proportion can you use to express $\frac{1}{6}$ as a per cent?

Often you will see numbers expressed as decimals. You remember that decimals are just other names for numbers named by fractions whose denominators are powers of 10 like 10, 100, 1000, and so forth. Here are some true sentences showing the relationship of decimals to fractions:

$$0.3 = \tfrac{3}{10}; \quad 0.04 = \tfrac{4}{100}; \quad 0.007 = \tfrac{7}{1000}; \quad 5.4 = 5\tfrac{4}{10};$$
$$12.18 = 12\tfrac{18}{100}; \quad 0.0009 = \tfrac{9}{10,000}$$

You can always find a per cent that names the same number as a decimal. First find the fraction that names the same number as the decimal. Then change the form of the fraction so that it shows a denominator of 100. Use the numerator of this fraction to write the per cent.

$$0.8 = \frac{8}{10}$$
$$= \frac{8}{10} \cdot \frac{10}{10}$$
$$= \frac{80}{100}$$
$$= 80\%$$

$$0.142 = \frac{142}{1000}$$
$$= \frac{142}{1000} \cdot \frac{\tfrac{1}{10}}{\tfrac{1}{10}}$$
$$= \frac{14.2}{100}$$
$$= 14.2\%$$

$$8.005 = 8\frac{5}{1000}$$
$$= \frac{8000}{1000} + \frac{5}{1000}$$
$$= \frac{8005}{1000}$$
$$= \frac{8005}{1000} \cdot \frac{\tfrac{1}{10}}{\tfrac{1}{10}}$$
$$= 800.5\%$$

■ **P-5** How can you express the numbers named below as per cents?

$$0.5; \quad 2.4; \quad 0.25; \quad 0.002$$

Here are listed the preceding examples in table form:

Decimal	Per Cent
0.8	80%
0.142	14.2%
8.005	800.5%
0.5	50%
2.4	240%
0.25	25%
0.002	0.2%

■ **P-6** Can you make up an easy rule to use in changing from decimal form to per cent?

Such rules may be helpful in working many problems. However, you should be able to apply the method shown in the examples. This depends on the meaning of per cent and the Multiplication Property of One.

ORAL EXERCISES 5.6

Rename each of the following as a per cent.

1. $\frac{8}{100}$ 2. $\frac{17}{100}$ 3. $\frac{56}{100}$ 4. $\frac{78}{100}$ 5. $\frac{137}{100}$ 6. $\frac{251}{100}$

7. $\frac{37\frac{1}{2}}{100}$ 8. $\frac{66\frac{2}{3}}{100}$ 9. $\frac{1.8}{100}$ 10. $\frac{0.37}{100}$ 11. 0.37   12. 0.83

13. 0.05   14. 0.01   15. $\frac{3}{4}$ 16. $\frac{1}{2}$ 17. $\frac{4}{5}$ 18. $\frac{3}{20}$

19. $\frac{2}{25}$ 20. $\frac{11}{20}$ 21. 2.7   22. 3.8   23. 5.12   24. 0.113

25. 0.801   26. 0.0012   27. $\frac{5}{5}$ 28. $\frac{325}{325}$

Rename each of the following as a fraction.

29. 10%   30. 20%   31. 35%   32. 18%   33. 57%   34. 71%

WRITTEN EXERCISES 5.6

A   Rename each of the following as a per cent.

1. $\frac{19}{100}$ 2. $\frac{23}{100}$ 3. $\frac{256}{100}$ 4. $\frac{348}{100}$

5. $\frac{62\frac{1}{2}}{100}$ 6. $\frac{87\frac{1}{2}}{100}$ 7. $\frac{8.3}{100}$ 8. $\frac{13.6}{100}$

9. 0.98   10. 0.67   11. 0.08   12. 0.05

Use the Multiplication Property of One in renaming the following as per cents. Show steps.

13. $\frac{1}{4}$ 14. $\frac{1}{5}$ 15. $\frac{7}{10}$ 16. $\frac{9}{10}$

17. $\frac{9}{20}$ 18. $\frac{11}{20}$ 19. $\frac{13}{25}$ 20. $\frac{16}{25}$

21. 0.4   22. 0.7   23. 3.8   24. 7.2

25. 0.187   26. 0.309   27. 17.3   28. 25.1

Use proportions to express the following ratios as per cents.

Example: Express $\frac{3}{8}$ as a per cent.

Answer:
$$\frac{3}{8} = \frac{x}{100}$$
$$8x = 300$$
$$8(\tfrac{1}{8} \cdot 300) = 300$$
$$x = \tfrac{1}{8} \cdot 300$$
$$\tfrac{3}{8} = 37\tfrac{1}{2}\%$$

29. $\frac{5}{8}$ 30. $\frac{7}{8}$

31. $\frac{5}{6}$ 32. $\frac{1}{6}$

33. $\frac{2}{3}$ 34. $\frac{4}{3}$

5.7 Proportion and Per Cent

The following are examples of the three basic kinds of per cent problems.

1 A pro football quarterback completes 60% of his passes in the championship game. How many passes does he complete if he throws a total of 25 passes?

2 A pro football quarterback completes 21 passes out of a total of 35 that are thrown. What per cent does he complete?

3 A pro football quarterback completes 12 passes in a game. How many passes does he throw if he completes 75% of the number he throws?

Perhaps you learned different ways of solving problems like these. You may now use your knowledge of proportions to solve them by one general method.

Example 1: Let the variable x represent the number of passes completed in 1. You can write the proportion $\frac{60}{100} = \frac{x}{25}$, where the ratio 60% is expressed as the fraction $\frac{60}{100}$.

■ **P-1** Can the number of passes completed be greater than the number thrown?

Since $\frac{60}{100}$ is less than 1, you express the other ratio as $\frac{x}{25}$, not as $\frac{25}{x}$. The fraction $\frac{25}{x}$ would represent a number greater than 1.

$$\frac{60}{100} = \frac{x}{25}$$
$$100x = 60 \cdot 25$$
$$100x = 1500$$
$$100(\tfrac{1}{100} \cdot 1500) = 1500$$
$$x = 15$$

Therefore, the number of passes completed is 15.

Example 2: This time, in 2, the variable x represents the per cent of passes he completes. The proportion is $\frac{x}{100} = \frac{21}{35}$.

■ **P-2** Why is the ratio $\dfrac{x}{100}$ used?

■ **P-3** Why is $\frac{21}{35}$ used instead of $\frac{35}{21}$?

$$\frac{x}{100} = \frac{21}{35}$$
$$35x = 21 \cdot 100$$
$$35x = 2100$$

■ **P-4** How can you express the truth number of the sentence $35x = 2100$ as a product?

Therefore, the quarterback completes 60% of his passes.

Example 3: This time, in $\boxed{3}$, let the variable x represent the number of passes thrown. The proportion is $\dfrac{75}{100} = \dfrac{12}{x}$.

■ **P-5** Why is $\dfrac{12}{x}$ used rather than $\dfrac{x}{12}$ in the proportion?

$$\frac{75}{100} = \frac{12}{x}$$
$$75x = 12 \cdot 100$$
$$75x = 1200$$

■ **P-6** How can you express the truth number of the sentence $75x = 1200$ as a product?

The quarterback throws 16 passes.

You can summarize the steps in solving per cent problems by this method as follows.

$\boxed{1}$ Choose a variable to represent the unknown number in the problem.

$\boxed{2}$ Form a proportion. One ratio is indicated by the per cent and is named by a fraction with 100 as its denominator, or second term. The terms of the other ratio are the two numbers that are being compared.

$\boxed{3}$ Make sure both ratios are expressed in the right order.

$\boxed{4}$ Find the truth number of the open sentence. This number represents the solution to the problem.

ORAL EXERCISES 5.7

State a proportion that describes each of these sentences.

1. x is 25% of 36.   **2.** r is 12% of 512.   **3.** 17 is $y\%$ of 82.

4. 23 is $t\%$ of 156.   **5.** 10 is 15% of a.   **6.** 19 is 80% of b.

7. $t\%$ of 15 is 92.   **8.** $r\%$ of 156 is 37.   **9.** 8% of $90 = x$.

10. $33\frac{1}{3}\%$ of $y = 36$.   **11.** 25% of $t = 144$.   **12.** $y\%$ of $54 = 30$.

13. $26 = 15\%$ of a.   **14.** $w = 28\%$ of 156.

The following table gives some information about free-throw shooting for a basketball team. Tell what numbers can be used to complete the table.

	Team Members	Free Throws Attempted	Free Throws Made	Per Cent Made
15.	Bob	20	15	?
16.	Dick	12	?	25%
17.	Tom	?	9	60%
18.	Roy	18	?	$33\frac{1}{3}\%$
19.	Don	10	8	?
20.	Roger	?	2	40%

WRITTEN EXERCISES 5.7

A   Give an open sentence in the form of a proportion to describe each sentence. Find the truth set.

  1. 25% of $28 = x$.   **2.** 40% of $35 = y$.   **3.** $r\%$ of $92 = 69$.

  4. $y\%$ of $65 = 39$.   **5.** 15 is 20% of a.   **6.** 21 is 30% of b.

  7. 150 is $x\%$ of 100.   **8.** 250 is $y\%$ of 100.   **9.** 12% of 13 is n.

10. 8% of 72 is p.   **11.** 15 is $x\%$ of 40.   **12.** 30 is $y\%$ of 48.

Solve the following problems by using the proportion method.

13. Mickey got 7 hits in 30 times at bat one week. What is his batting average expressed as a per cent?

14. Henry got a hit in 32% of the times he batted. If he batted 75 times, how many hits did he get?

15. Wilt made 60% of his free throws in a game. How many did he shoot if he made 15?

16. The Hawks made 40 field goals in the game and shot 95 times. What per cent of their shots did they make?

The following table shows information for the winners of the primary election in a school. Copy and complete the table. Show your work.

	Candidates		Total Number Voting	Votes Received	Per Cent of Votes Received
17.	President	Bill	128	48	?
18.		John	128	32	?
19.	Vice-Pres.	Sue	120	?	40%
20.		Harry	120	?	55%
21.	Secretary	Mary	?	44	40%
22.		Jean	?	66	60%

5.8   Per Cent of a Number

In the last section, you found the truth sets of sentences involving per cents. One such sentence was $x = 25\%$ of 60. You saw that the truth number of such a sentence is easily found by using a proportion.

$$\frac{25}{100} = \frac{x}{60}$$
$$100x = 25 \cdot 60$$
$$100(\tfrac{1}{100} \cdot 25 \cdot 60) = 25 \cdot 60$$
$$x = \tfrac{1}{100} \cdot 25 \cdot 60$$
$$x = (\tfrac{1}{100} \cdot 25)60$$
$$x = (\tfrac{25}{100})60, \text{ or } x = 15$$

If you replace x in the original sentence by 15, it reads $15 = 25\%$ of 60.

In the example, you expressed 15 as $(\tfrac{25}{100})60$. This gives you a hint on how to work such a problem without a proportion. To find 25% of 60, find the product $(\tfrac{25}{100})60$.

■ **P-1**   How can you express the phrase 12% of 75 as a product?

Such problems can always be worked by the use of a proportion. However, because this type of per cent problem is so common, it is good to know this short cut. In fact, it is often useful to express the given per cent in decimal form.

$$5\% \text{ of } 1200 = 0.05(1200)$$
$$= 60$$

■ **P-2** What is 12% of 3?

In a previous chapter, you had some practice in changing word phrases to open phrases. Many problems in algebra involve the formation of a phrase that represents a certain per cent of an unknown number. Here are some examples of word phrases and the corresponding open phrases:

Word Phrase	Open Phrase
5% of some number	$\frac{5}{100}n$
8% reduction in cost	$0.08x$
annual interest at 6%	$0.06p$
3% gain in weight	$\frac{3}{100}w$
120% increase in the number of cars	$1.2y$

■ **P-3** Can you give two open phrases that describe the following word phrase?

15% of the number of students in a school

■ **P-4** How would you express the phrase $x\%$ of 36 as a product?

Of course, you know that $x\%$ means $\frac{x}{100}.$ In decimal form, however, you must express it as $0.01x$. Therefore, the phrase $x\%$ of 36 can also be changed to $0.01x(36)$.

ORAL EXERCISES 5.8

Express each of the following phrases as a product.

1. 14% of 25
2. 36% of 50
3. 120% of 83
4. 225% of 41
5. $x\%$ of 10
6. $y\%$ of 125
7. 12% of r
8. 27% of t
9. 10% of a
10. 1% of b

Change each of the following word phrases to an open phrase that expresses a product.

11. 15% of x players
12. 75% of y students

13. 28% of the number of cars
14. 50% of the number of soldiers
15. 5% of the number of dollars saved
16. 20% of the cost of the football
17. 63% of the number of passes
18. 48% of the number of field goals
19. 70% of the number of high school graduates
20. 125% of the number of newspapers

WRITTEN EXERCISES 5.8

A Express each of the following phrases as a product in two ways, first with a fraction and then with a decimal.

1. 5% of 25

2. 6% of 30

3. 12% of 225

4. 18% of 336

5. 17% of x

6. 72% of y

7. x% of 56

8. y% of 27

9. 135% of 85

10. 150% of 72

11. 0.8% of 12

12. 0.5% of 17

Change the following word phrases to open phrases that express products.

13. 12% of x dollars
14. 15% of y pounds
15. 53% of f free throws
16. 35% of t touchdowns
17. x% of $2500
18. y% of $4200
19. p% of 3000 students
20. r% of 95 points
21. 10% of the number of planes
22. 15% of the number of schools
23. 225% of the number of votes
24. 153% of the number of people
25. 0.7% of the number of players
26. 0.9% of the number of accidents

Express each of the following as "per cent of."

Example: $0.06(x)$ *Answer:* 6% of x

27. $\frac{2}{100}(33)$

28. $\frac{17}{100}(72)$

29. $0.15(a)$

30. $0.93(b)$

31. $0.013(x)$

32. $0.278(y)$

5.9 Interest

Per cent is commonly used in the banking and business world. In this section, you will study interest. When a person or business lends money to another person or business, the lender is usually paid for the use of this money. This charge for the use of money is called **interest.**

> **Interest** is a certain per cent of the amount loaned. The amount of money loaned is called the **principal.**

■ **P-1** A man borrows $500 from a bank to buy a car. What is the amount $500 called?

■ **P-2** A girl receives $1.25 from the bank because she had $25 in a savings account for one year. What is the amount $1.25 called?

Interest is usually expressed in terms of one year's use of the money. The phrase "5% of $600" represents the interest paid for the use of $600 for one year. As you know, this can be expressed as $\frac{5}{100}(600)$, or $30.

■ **P-3** What is the interest on $300 at 4% for one year?

The per cent that is used in an interest problem is called the **rate.**

> The interest earned for one year is the product of the rate and the principal.

■ **P-4** What phrase represents the annual interest on $200 at a rate of 8%?

In algebra, a variable is often used to represent an unknown quantity in an interest problem. Study the following table to make sure you understand the examples.

Principal	Rate	Interest
$500	5%	$\frac{5}{100}(500) = 25$
x	6%	$\frac{6}{100}x = 0.06x$
$200	y%	$0.01y(200) = 2y$
$400	8%	$0.08(400) = 32$

■ **P-5** What phrase represents the interest on d dollars at $5\frac{1}{2}\%$?

■ **P-6** What phrase represents the interest on $75 at $r\%$?

The period for which the money is borrowed may be different from one year. If the rate is for a period other than one year, it should be so stated.

■ **P-7** What is the interest on $100 at a rate of 4% for one year?

■ **P-8** What is the interest if the money is loaned for two years? for three years?

■ **P-9** What is the interest if the money is loaned for six months? for three months?

You can see that, in problems such as these, you multiply the interest for one year by the time expressed in years. Therefore, the interest earned on $800 invested for nine months ($\frac{9}{12}$ of a year) at a rate of 6% can be expressed as follows.

$$\frac{6}{100}(800) \cdot \frac{9}{12} = 48 \cdot \frac{9}{12}$$
$$= 36$$

The interest earned is $36.

■ **P-10** What phrase represents the interest on x dollars at an annual rate of 6% for two years?

■ **P-11** What phrase represents the interest on $250 at an annual rate of $x\%$ for six months?

ORAL EXERCISES 5.9

Find the yearly interest on
1. $100 loaned at 3%.
2. $100 loaned at 4%.
3. $100 loaned at 5%.
4. $100 loaned at 6%.
5. $200 loaned at 4%.
6. $200 loaned at 5%.
7. $10 loaned at 6%.
8. $20 loaned at 5%.

Give a phrase that represents the annual interest on
9. t dollars borrowed at 8%.
10. w dollars borrowed at 12%.
11. $5 invested at $x\%$.
12. $300 invested at $r\%$.
13. x dollars loaned at $5\frac{1}{2}\%$.
14. y dollars loaned at 7.8%.

Give a phrase that represents the amount of interest indicated.
15. $500 borrowed for 2 years at 5%
16. $300 invested for 5 years at 6%
17. $100 loaned for 3 months at 12%
18. $200 loaned for 6 months at 8%
19. x dollars borrowed for 3 years at 6%
20. $50 borrowed for 9 months at x%

21. What is interest?
22. What is meant by the principal?
23. For what period of time are interest rates usually given?
24. How can you compute interest?

WRITTEN EXERCISES 5.9

A Find the interest for one year for each of the following.

1. $500 at 8%	**2.** $800 at 12%	**3.** $225 at 10%
4. $275 at 6%	**5.** $100 at $8\frac{1}{2}$%	**6.** $100 at $5\frac{1}{2}$%
7. $200 at 5.6%	**8.** $300 at 6.2%	

For each of the following, write an open phrase that represents the interest.

9. x dollars at 5% for 1 year   **10.** y dollars at 8% for 1 year
11. r dollars at 4% for 2 years   **12.** s dollars at 6% for 3 years
13. n dollars at 5% for 6 months
14. m dollars at 4% for 3 months
15. t dollars at 3% for 1 month
16. w dollars at 12% for 9 months
17. $100 at x% for 1 year   **18.** $300 at y% for 12 months
19. $500 at r% for 2 months   **20.** $600 at w% for 8 months

In each of the following problems, first select a variable. Then write a proportion that can be used to solve the problem.
21. A man pays $18 interest on $300 that he borrows for one year. What is the rate of interest?
22. A bank pays $65 to each customer who has invested $1000 for one year. What is the rate of interest?
23. The interest on an 8% loan for one year is $64. How much is borrowed?
24. A girl's savings earn her $5.50 in one year at $5\frac{1}{2}$%. How much did she have in her savings account for the year?

5.10 Discount

In the business world, per cents are very common in working with discounts. A **discount** is the amount that an article of merchandise is reduced in price.

■ **P-1** A store has a sign which says: "All fishing rods $5 off." What do you call the $5?

The regular price of an article is called the **list price.** Very often, discounts are given by merchants in special sales. Other businesses give discounts on large purchases or for cash payment of a bill.

The price of an item after the discount is deducted is called the **net price,** or **sale price.**

■ **P-2** A merchant advertises as follows: "All $5 shirts reduced to $3." What is the list price? the net price? the discount?

Discounts are often expressed as a certain per cent of the list price. The per cent is often called the **rate of discount.** A 15% discount on a tennis racquet listed at $10 is represented by the phrase $\frac{15}{100}(10)$. The discount is $1.50.

■ **P-3** What is the net price?

You can see that the relation between discount, list price, and net price can be shown as follows.

$$\text{Net price} = \text{List price} - \text{Discount}$$

In this sentence, the discount represents an amount of money and not a per cent. If the rate of discount and the list price are given, you can compute the discount as you computed interest. The following are some examples.

List Price	Rate of Discount	Discount
$ 50	15%	$\frac{15}{100}(50) = \$\ \ 7.50$
$400	25%	$0.25(400) = \$100$
$500	20%	$\frac{20}{100}(500) = \$100$

■ **P-4** What is the sale price in each of these examples?

Problems in discounts sometimes require the use of open phrases. A variable is used to represent an unknown quantity in the problem. Here are some examples:

List Price	Rate of Discount	Discount	Net Price
x	15%	$\dfrac{15}{100}x$	$x - \dfrac{15}{100}x$
y	30%	$0.30y$	$y - 0.30y$
$500	r%	$\dfrac{r}{100}(500)$	$500 - \dfrac{r}{100}(500)$
■ P-5 $ 25	p%	$\underset{\sim}{?}$	$\underset{\sim}{?}$

ORAL EXERCISES 5.10

Tell what numbers or phrases can be used to complete the following table.

	List Price	Discount	Net Price			List Price	Discount	Net Price
1.	$30	$3	?		4.	$100	x	?
2.	$50	?	$48		5.	$ 55	?	n
3.	?	$10	$60		6.	?	d	$26

What is the discount on each of the following sales?
7. A $10 hat reduced by 25%
8. A ball glove listed at $12 with a discount rate of $33\tfrac{1}{3}$%
9. A $20 dress on sale at a 15% discount
10. A refrigerator listed at $500 but reduced by 20%

Give an estimate of the selling price to the nearest whole dollar.
11. A table marked $49.98 but reduced 10%
12. An automobile listed at $1995 with a 25% discount
13. A coat marked $19.95 but reduced by 40%
14. A radio listed at $99.99 with a 30% discount

Give the correct phrase to replace each question mark in this table.

	List Price	Rate of Discount	Discount	Net Price
15.	$ 25	15%	$3.75	?
16.	x	12%	?	?
17.	$150	r%	?	?
18.	$400	10%	?	?

State a proportion that describes each of the following relationships.

	List Price	Rate of Discount	Discount
19.	$300	5%	$15
20.	x	15%	$35
21.	$ 85	r%	$15
22.	$125	25%	y

WRITTEN EXERCISES 5.10

A Copy and complete the following table.

	List Price	Discount	Net Price
1.	$100	$15	?
2.	$125	$45	?
3.	$400	?	$370
4.	$750	?	$695
5.	$195	x	?
6.	$ 49	d	?
7.	?	$15	n
8.	?	$33	p
9.	x	0.15x	?
10.	y	0.25y	?
11.	$259	?	n
12.	$595	?	2x

For each of the following, find the discount and then the net price.

13. A house listed at $12,000 is reduced 20%.

14. A car listed at $2500 is sold at a discount of 10%.

15. A dress marked for $12 is reduced $33\frac{1}{3}$%.

16. A hat originally priced at $15 is reduced 40%.

Choose a variable and then state a proportion that can be used in solving each of the following problems. Then solve the problem.

17. What is the rate of discount on a purchase if the list price is $50 and the sale price is $37?

18. A lamp is listed at $27, but Mary buys it for $20 when it is on sale. What is the discount rate?

19. The discount on a set of golf clubs is $25, and the rate of discount is 15%. What is the list price?

20. At a rate of 20%, a stove is reduced by $50. Find the list price.

5.11 Per Cent and Chemical Solutions

The use of per cent is rather common in chemistry. When one chemical is mixed with another, the weight or volume of one chemical can be expressed as a certain per cent of the weight or volume of the mixture. Doctors, pharmacists, chemists, farmers, lab technicians, and many others must know how to use per cents in mixing chemicals.

A man buys some weed killer for his ranch. The directions say: "Mix with water to get a 10% solution." This means that the amount of weed killer should be 10% of the amount of the total mixture. If he wants 50 gallons of the mixture to use in spraying weeds, he must use $\frac{10}{100} \cdot 50$, or 5, gallons of the weed killer.

■ **P-1** How many gallons of water would he use?

The mixture of water and weed killer in this case is called a 10% solution. Chemicals are often mixed with water before they are used. The strength of the solution is often described by a per cent. This represents the ratio of the amount of the chemical to the amount of the total mixture. In the above problem, the mixture would not be called a 90% solution, but it could be said that it is 90% water.

■ **P-2** A pharmacist makes up 100 gallons of a 4% acid solution. How many gallons of acid does he use? How many gallons of water?

A nurse must mix a certain medicine with water. She first puts an amount of water in the graduate as shown. Then she fills it up with the medicine to the 100 mark.

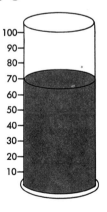

■ **P-3** How would you describe the mixture as a "per cent solution"?

Salt is mixed with water to obtain a salt solution. A 15% salt solution means that the weight of the salt in the mixture is 15% of the weight of the mixture.

■ **P-4** How much salt is in a 20% solution weighing 50 pounds?

In algebra, problems with mixtures of chemicals often involve finding an unknown quantity. A variable is chosen to represent the unknown quantity. The amount of salt in x pounds of a 12% solution is represented as $\frac{12}{100}x$, or $0.12x$.

■ **P-5** What phrase describes the amount of acid in y ounces of a 4% solution?

The following table shows some examples of acid solutions.

Amount of Mixture	Per Cent Solution	Amount of Acid
600 cc	5%	0.05(600), or 30, cc
x gallons	3%	$\frac{3}{100}x$, or 0.03x, gallons
15 quarts	x%	$\frac{x}{100} \cdot 15$, or $\frac{3x}{20}$, quarts
y ounces	8%	0.08y ounces

In a 60-ounce bottle of household vinegar, there are 3 ounces of acetic acid. Suppose $x\%$ represents the strength of the solution.

■ **P-6** How can this per cent be represented by a ratio?

■ **P-7** What proportion describes the problem?

The work should look like this:

$$\frac{x}{100} = \frac{3}{60}$$
$$60x = 300$$

■ **P-8** What is the truth number of the open sentence above?

■ **P-9** How would you describe the strength of the vinegar?

ORAL EXERCISES 5.11

Tell how much pure chemical is in each of the following solutions.
1. 10 pounds of a 40% solution
2. 30 quarts of a $33\frac{1}{3}\%$ solution
3. 80 grams of a 25% solution
4. 500 gallons of a 5% solution
5. 75 cubic centimeters of a 20% solution
6. 150 ounces of a 10% solution

Tell what numbers (or phrases) can be used to complete the following table.

	Weight of Salt	Per Cent Solution	Weight of Mixture
7.	?	10%	60 grams
8.	?	5%	x pounds
9.	?	r%	25 ounces
10.	20 pounds	20%	?

Tell what numbers (or phrases) can be used to complete the following table.

	Volume of Acid	Volume of Water	Per Cent Solution	Volume of Mixture
11.	?	?	4%	50 gallons
12.	?	35 quarts	5%	x
13.	25 cc	?	r%	x
14.	32 ounces	x	3%	?
15.	?	y	8%	231 cu in

WRITTEN EXERCISES 5.11

A 1. Suppose 18% of an 80-pound bag of fertilizer is nitrogen. How many pounds of nitrogen are there?

2. Suppose 5% of an acid solution is pure acid. How much pure acid is there in 200 cubic centimeters of the solution?

3. Five pounds of salt are dissolved in water. What is the weight of the water if the solution weighs 80 pounds?

4. A quantity of water is added to 1 quart of an insect spray to get 23 quarts of solution. How much water is added?

Copy and complete the following table for acid solutions.

	Amount of Acid	Per Cent Solution	Amount of Mixture		Amount of Acid	Per Cent Solution	Amount of Mixture
5.	?	3%	20 gallons	10.	20 ounces	?	80 ounces
6.	?	5%	30 quarts	11.	?	r%	56 cu in
7.	?	8%	x pounds	12.	?	t%	231 cu in
8.	?	12%	y grams	13.	20 grams	5%	?
9.	10 cc	?	100 cc	14.	35 gallons	10%	?

Give an open phrase for each of the following.

15. The total volume when x cubic centimeters of acid are mixed with 100 cubic centimeters of water

16. The total weight when 5 pounds of salt are dissolved in y pounds of water

17. The weight of water added to 5 pounds of fertilizer to get w pounds of mixture

18. The number of quarts of water to add to x quarts of antifreeze to fill the radiator to 15 quarts

CHAPTER SUMMARY

Important Terms

1. Two numbers are **reciprocals** if their product is 1. Each is said to be the reciprocal of the other.
2. A **ratio** is an indicated quotient of two numbers. It is used to compare the two numbers.
3. The **terms** of a ratio are the two numbers that are compared.
4. A **proportion** is a statement of equality of two ratios.
5. In a proportion the first and fourth terms are called the **extremes.** The second and third terms are the **means.**
6. **Per cent** means "per hundred." Per cent expresses a ratio in which the second term is 100. For example, $5\% = \frac{5}{100}$.
7. **Interest** is money paid for the use of money.
8. The amount of money borrowed or loaned is called the **principal.**
9. A **discount** is the amount by which the charges for merchandise or service are reduced.
10. The **list, or marked, price** is the regular price before the discount.
11. The **net, or sale, price** is the price after the discount is deducted.
12. **Rate of discount** is the per cent that expresses the ratio of the discount to the list price.

Important Ideas

1. Every number of arithmetic except 0 has a reciprocal.
2. If a is any number of arithmetic, then $(a)(0) = 0$.
3. The truth number of $ax = b$ is the reciprocal of a multiplied by b, where a and b are any numbers of arithmetic except $a \neq 0$.
4. The second term of a ratio cannot be 0.
5. A ratio does not have a label.
6. In a proportion the product of the means equals the product of the extremes.
7. If $\frac{a}{b} = \frac{c}{d}$ is a proportion, then the following are also true.
$$\frac{a}{c} = \frac{b}{d}; \quad \frac{b}{a} = \frac{d}{c}; \quad \frac{c}{a} = \frac{d}{b}$$
8. A number named by a decimal can be renamed as a per cent by the multiplication of the number by 100 and the use of the symbol for per cent, %. Thus, $0.05 = 5\%$.
9. 5% of 75 means $\frac{5}{100}(75)$.
10. Net price = list price − discount.

CHAPTER REVIEW

Give a name for the reciprocal of each of the following.

1. 23
2. $\frac{1}{9}$
3. $\frac{13}{16}$
4. 0.23

Express the truth number of each of these sentences as a product.

5. $13x = 25$
6. $\frac{1}{3}x = \frac{15}{16}$
7. $\frac{3}{5}x = 92$
8. $0.3x = 19$

Give a common name for each of the following ratios.

9. 10 to 80
10. 44 to 4
11. x inches to 2 feet
12. 1 gallon to q quarts

Use the cross-products property to find whether or not the following are proportions. Use *Yes* or *No* to indicate your answer.

13. $\frac{5}{6} = \frac{11}{12}$
14. $\frac{3}{4} = \frac{31}{44}$
15. $\frac{12}{17} = \frac{15}{21}$
16. $\frac{16}{12} = \frac{12}{9}$

Find the truth sets of the following open sentences.

17. $\frac{x}{5} = \frac{28}{35}$
18. $\frac{3}{5} = \frac{12}{x}$
19. $\frac{1}{x} = \frac{13}{16}$
20. $\frac{5}{12} = \frac{x}{72}$

Change each of the following proportions to three other forms.

21. $\frac{2}{4} = \frac{3}{6}$
22. $\frac{2}{3} = \frac{8}{12}$
23. $\frac{5}{6} = \frac{50}{60}$
24. $\frac{20}{3} = \frac{40}{6}$

Write a proportion describing each of the following problems.

25. 15 pages typed in 2 hours; x pages typed in 8 hours
26. 5 gallons of gas for $1.70; 16 gallons of gas for x cents

Express each of the following as a per cent.

27. $\frac{83}{100}$
28. $\frac{253}{100}$
29. 0.18
30. 3.7
31. $\frac{3}{5}$
32. 0.015

Express each of the following sentences in the form of a proportion.

33. x is 33% of 28.
34. $12 is r% of $35.
35. 3 is 15% of y.
36. a is 12% of b.

Express each of the following as a product.

37. 16% of 150
38. 12% of x
39. r% of 225
40. t% of b boys

Give an open phrase expressing each of the following.

41. Interest on $200 for 1 year at p%
42. Interest on x dollars for 6 months at 8%
43. Discount on a car listed at y dollars at a rate of 10%
44. Net price on a dress listed at $15 less t%
45. Amount of salt in a 12% solution weighing w pounds
46. Volume of mixture made up of x gallons of acid and 50 gallons of water

One glance at the instrument panel of an airplane tells you how important numbers are in measurement. The instruments in the cockpit measure the location, speed, and condition of the aircraft at any given moment. It would be very difficult, indeed, for the pilot to know these measurements without their numerical description. In this chapter, you will study the use of numbers in measurement.

Using Numbers
in Measurement

6

6.1 The Nature of Measurement

When you measure an object, you are trying to find a numerical description for the size of the object. A number that is assigned to the object to describe its size is called a **measurement.** Associated with each measurement is a **unit of measure.**

> Measurement shows a comparison of the size of the object to the unit of measure.

■ **P-1** What is the unit of measure for each of the following measurements?

15 inches; 36 pounds; 100 meters; 6 feet; 3 car lengths; 1 arm length

Units of measure such as the inch, foot, yard, centimeter, meter, pound, and so forth are **standard units.** These units have been clearly defined, and they do not change in value from one person to another or from one locality to another.

■ **P-2** What units listed in **P-1** are not standard? Why?

You are now going to look at some measurements using the inch as the standard unit. Suppose you want to measure the length of a block of wood with a ruler that has only the whole numbers of inches marked.

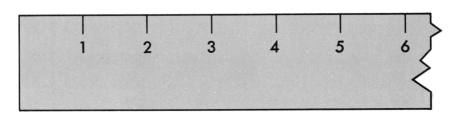

You can see that a ruler is like a number line. Usually 0 is not marked on the ruler. The next figure shows the block of wood being compared to the ruler in order to find the length of the block.

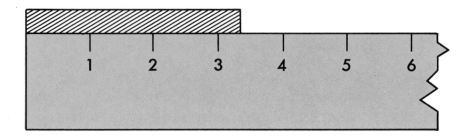

■ **P-3** What is the length of the block to the nearest inch?

The difference between the length of the block and the reported measurement is the **error.**

■ **P-4** What is your estimate of the error in the measurement for **P-3**?

Suppose you measure the same block of wood with a ruler that has each $\frac{1}{2}$ inch marked.

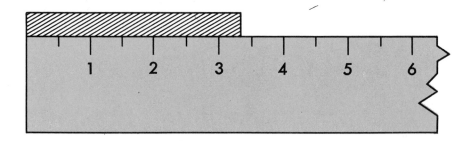

■ **P-5** What is the length of the block to the nearest $\frac{1}{2}$ inch? One-half inch is the unit of measure in this case.

■ **P-6** Is there still an error in the measurement? About how much?

■ **P-7** Is the length of the block greater or less than the measurement?

Again measure the same block of wood, but this time the ruler has each $\frac{1}{4}$ inch marked.

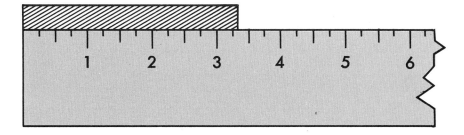

P-8 What is the length of the block to the nearest $\frac{1}{4}$ inch? In this case, $\frac{1}{4}$ inch is the unit of measure.

P-9 Is the length greater or less than the measurement?

From these examples, you should be able to see that the error in the measurement of the block of wood gets smaller as you use smaller and smaller units. No matter how small a unit you choose for your measurement, however, the length of the block will not be exactly the same as the measurement. There will always be an error. This basic idea of measurement is usually stated as follows.

Every measurement is an approximation.

ORAL EXERCISES 6.1

1. What do you call a number that is used to describe the size of an object?
2. Name ten standard units of measure.
3. Can you name some units of measure that are not standard?
4. What is meant by the error in a measurement?
5. How can the error of a measurement be made smaller?
6. Why is every measurement an approximation?

Tell whether the unit of measure in each of the following sentences is a standard unit.

7. The distance is 17.3 miles.
8. The horse is 16 hands high.
9. The container holds $1\frac{3}{4}$ quarts.
10. The meat weighs 2.7 pounds.
11. The width of the lawn is 25 steps.
12. The length of the floor is 18 tiles.
13. The track star ran 220 meters.
14. She put 2 pinches of pepper in the stew.

In each of the following, suppose the arrow by each letter indicates the point at which you would read a length. Tell the measurement corresponding to each letter, using the unit indicated.

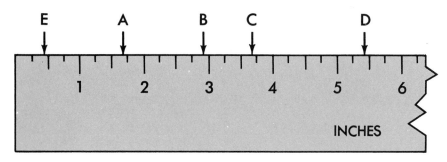

15. A; inch   **16.** B; $\frac{1}{2}$ inch   **17.** C; $\frac{1}{4}$ inch
18. D; $\frac{1}{2}$ inch   **19.** E; $\frac{1}{2}$ inch   **20.** A; $\frac{1}{2}$ inch
21. A; $\frac{1}{4}$ inch   **22.** B; inch   **23.** B; $\frac{1}{4}$ inch
24. C; $\frac{1}{2}$ inch   **25.** D; $\frac{1}{4}$ inch   **26.** D; inch
27. E; $\frac{1}{4}$ inch   **28.** E; inch

WRITTEN EXERCISES 6.1

A Three objects, A, B, and C, are weighed on the spring balance. Record each weight, using the indicated unit. The arrows in the figure point to the readings for the weights. The largest unit on the scale is 1 pound, and the smallest unit is $\frac{1}{8}$ pound.

1. A; pound   **2.** B; pound
3. A; $\frac{1}{2}$ pound   **4.** B; $\frac{1}{2}$ pound
5. A; $\frac{1}{4}$ pound   **6.** B; $\frac{1}{4}$ pound
7. A; $\frac{1}{8}$ pound   **8.** B; $\frac{1}{8}$ pound
9. C; pound   **10.** C; $\frac{1}{2}$ pound
11. C; $\frac{1}{4}$ pound   **12.** C; $\frac{1}{8}$ pound

In the following, the arrow at each letter indicates a point on the ruler at which you would read a length. Use the unit named in each exercise. Express each length in fraction form with the denominator indicating the unit used.

Example: T; $\frac{1}{4}$ inch   *Answer:* $\frac{6}{4}$ inches

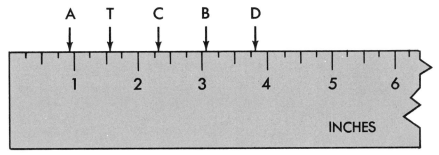

13. A; $\frac{1}{2}$ inch   14. B; $\frac{1}{2}$ inch   15. C; $\frac{1}{4}$ inch
16. D; $\frac{1}{4}$ inch   17. A; $\frac{1}{4}$ inch   18. B; $\frac{1}{4}$ inch
19. C; $\frac{1}{2}$ inch   20. D; $\frac{1}{2}$ inch

Record the measurements indicated by each of the following, using 0.5 centimeter as the unit.

Example: T   *Answer:* 8.0 (not 8)

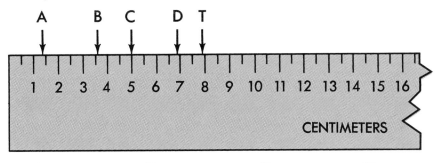

21. A   22. B   23. C   24. D

The following is a magnified portion of a ruler between 2 and 2.1 inches. Record each measurement indicated, using 0.01 inch as the unit.

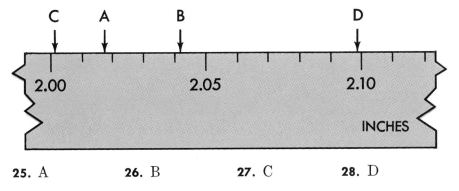

25. A   26. B   27. C   28. D

29. What is your estimate of the error in Exercise 25?

30. What is your estimate of the error in Exercise 26?

B   Suppose each of the following measurements of length were made to the nearest $\frac{1}{4}$ inch. What are the greatest and the least values possible for the lengths?

31. $3\frac{3}{4}$ inches   **32.** $2\frac{1}{4}$ inches   **33.** 5 inches   **34.** $4\frac{1}{2}$ inches

6.2   Greatest Possible Error

Suppose the length of a block of wood is measured as shown.

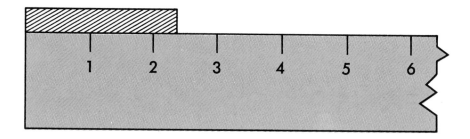

▪ **P-1**   What is the length measured to the nearest inch?

▪ **P-2**   What is your estimate of the error?

▪ **P-3**   Is the error less than $\frac{1}{2}$ inch?

Consider the following example.

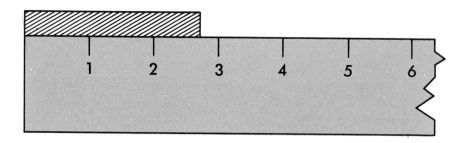

▪ **P-4**   What is this measurement to the nearest inch?

▪ **P-5**   Is the error less than $\frac{1}{2}$ inch?

Now look at the following example.

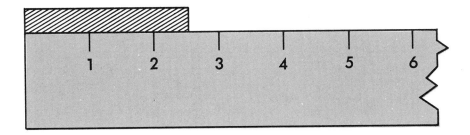

■ **P-6** What is the measurement to the nearest inch?

If the length is closer to 3 and you gave the measurement as 3, then the error is less than $\frac{1}{2}$ inch. If you state the measurement as 2, then the ruler has not been read correctly and the error would be slightly more than $\frac{1}{2}$ inch. There are few cases when it cannot be determined which measurement is closer to the length. In these cases the measurement you choose will depend upon your purpose for making the measurement, that is, whether it suits your purpose to overestimate or to underestimate the measure.

From these examples you probably can understand the following important fact.

> The **greatest possible error** in a measurement is one-half the smallest unit used, provided the instrument is correctly read.

■ **P-7** If you obtain the measurement $3\frac{3}{8}$ inches by using $\frac{1}{8}$ inch as the unit, what is the greatest possible error?

You can use your knowledge of multiplying fractions to obtain

$$\frac{1}{2}\left(\frac{1}{8}\right) = \frac{1}{16}.$$

The greatest possible error, $\frac{1}{16}$ inch, means that the length could be as large as $3\frac{3}{8} + \frac{1}{16}$, or $3\frac{7}{16}$, inches and it could be as small as $3\frac{3}{8} - \frac{1}{16}$, or $3\frac{5}{16}$, inches.

The following figure may help you to see this. If a block of wood that you are measuring ends at any point in the double-shaded region, then it has a measurement of $3\frac{3}{8}$ inches to the nearest $\frac{1}{8}$ inch.

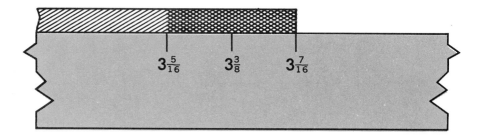

$3\frac{5}{16}$ $3\frac{3}{8}$ $3\frac{7}{16}$

■ **P-8**   A measurement is made to the nearest 0.01 inch and recorded as 3.56 inches. What is the greatest possible error?

Here are two ways to find it:

1   *Using decimal form,* you get

$$(0.5)(0.01) = 0.005 \quad \text{(in inches).}$$

2   *Using fractions,* you get

$$0.01 = \tfrac{1}{100} = \tfrac{10}{1000} \quad \text{(multiplying by } \tfrac{10}{10}\text{)},$$
$$\tfrac{1}{2} \cdot \tfrac{10}{1000} = \tfrac{5}{1000} = 0.005 \quad \text{(in inches).}$$

Sometimes it is important to have the measurement show the least unit that was used in obtaining it. Suppose the length of an object is measured with $\frac{1}{16}$ inch as the unit, and you observe that the object measures 3 inches. A measurement of 3 inches would not show that $\frac{1}{16}$ inch was used as the unit. You could, however, show the measurement as $\frac{48}{16}$ inches, or as $3\frac{0}{16}$ inches, and then the unit used would be clear.

The following examples will suggest what is meant.

Measurement	Unit
5.16 inches	0.01 inch
$2\frac{1}{4}$ inches	$\frac{1}{4}$ inch
$\frac{15}{16}$ inch	$\frac{1}{16}$ inch
5.3 inches	0.1 inch
6.0 inches	0.1 inch
6 inches	1 inch
$6\frac{0}{8}$ inches	$\frac{1}{8}$ inch
$\frac{8}{4}$ inches	$\frac{1}{4}$ inch
2 inches	1 inch

P-9 What is the least unit that is suggested by each of the following measurements?

$5\frac{4}{8}$ inches; $5\frac{1}{2}$ inches;   3.00 inches;   3.0 inches

Notice that 3 inches, 3.0 inches, and 3.00 inches do not mean exactly the same thing. You see that

the unit used in obtaining 3 inches is 1 inch,
the unit used in obtaining 3.0 inches is 0.1 inch,
the unit used in obtaining 3.00 inches is 0.01 inch.

ORAL EXERCISES 6.2

Indicate the least unit of measure that is suggested by each of the following measurements.

1. $2\frac{1}{4}$ feet
2. 5.3 yards
3. 152 meters
4. $5\frac{3}{8}$ inches
5. $\frac{8}{4}$ inches
6. 2 inches
7. 0.003 centimeter
8. 17.0 miles
9. 2.32 feet
10. $8\frac{3}{16}$ inches

Let each of the following be the smallest unit used in measuring lengths. What is the greatest possible error in each?

11. 1 foot
12. $\frac{1}{2}$ mile
13. $\frac{1}{4}$ yard
14. $\frac{1}{8}$ inch
15. $\frac{1}{16}$ rod
16. 10 miles
17. 1000 yards
18. 0.1 centimeter
19. 0.01 foot
20. 0.001 meter

Tell how you would correctly complete the following table.

Measurement	Greatest Possible Error	Greatest Possible Value for Length	Least Possible Value for Length
21. 26 feet	$\frac{1}{2}$ foot	$26\frac{1}{2}$ feet	?
22. $5\frac{1}{2}$ yards	$\frac{1}{4}$ yard	?	$5\frac{1}{4}$ yards
23. $1\frac{1}{4}$ inches	$\frac{1}{8}$ inch	$1\frac{3}{8}$ inches	?
24. 8.3 meters	0.05 meter	?	8.25 meters
25. 130 miles	?	135 miles	125 miles
26. 17.0 feet	?	?	?
27. 19.00 rods	?	?	?
28. $\frac{9}{8}$ centimeters	?	?	?

WRITTEN EXERCISES 6.2

A What is the least unit of measure that is indicated by each of these measurements?

1. 17 yards **2.** 256 miles **3.** $3\frac{3}{4}$ feet

4. $5\frac{2}{4}$ meters **5.** 7.01 inches **6.** 12.10 feet

7. $3\frac{5}{8}$ miles **8.** $\frac{13}{8}$ inches **9.** 12.0 meters

10. 10.7 centimeters

What is the greatest possible error in each of the following measurements?

11. 15.6 feet **12.** 135.8 yards **13.** $13\frac{1}{2}$ miles

14. $\frac{5}{2}$ meters **15.** $3\frac{3}{4}$ rods **16.** $17\frac{1}{8}$ miles

17. 2532 yards **18.** 2008 meters **19.** $\frac{13}{8}$ inches

20. $7\frac{1}{8}$ feet

Copy and complete the following table.

	Measurement	Greatest Possible Error	Upper Bound of Length	Lower Bound of Length
Example:	$15\frac{7}{8}$ feet	$\frac{1}{16}$ foot	$15\frac{15}{16}$ feet	$15\frac{13}{16}$ feet
21.	$5\frac{1}{2}$ miles	$\frac{1}{4}$ mile	$5\frac{3}{4}$ miles	?
22.	$3\frac{1}{4}$ yards	$\frac{1}{8}$ yard	?	$3\frac{1}{8}$ yards
23.	1700 meters	50 meters	?	?
24.	240,000 miles	5,000 miles	?	?
25.	5.0 inches	?	?	4.95 inches
26.	13.00 meters	?	?	12.995 meters
27.	$\frac{17}{2}$ feet	?	?	?
28.	$\frac{9}{4}$ centimeters	?	?	?

B The symbols $\leq$ and $\geq$ can be used to express the relationship between a measurement and the upper and lower bounds for a length.

Example: For $3\frac{1}{4}$ inches, the greatest possible error is $\frac{1}{8}$ inch. Let X represent the length. Thus, $3\frac{1}{8} \leq X$ *and* $X \leq 3\frac{3}{8}$. This compound sentence is sometimes written as

$$3\frac{1}{8} \leq X \leq 3\frac{3}{8}.$$

Write sentences of the form shown above for each of the following measurements.

29. $8\frac{1}{2}$ miles **30.** 3.7 inches **31.** $13\frac{1}{4}$ feet **32.** 3.018 meters

6.3 Precision

You learned in the last section how the recorded measurement can be used to show the least unit used in the measurement. For example, the measurement 10.6 inches shows that the measurement was made to the nearest 0.1 inch.

You also saw that the error in a measurement can be made less by using smaller and smaller units for the measurement. The greatest possible error in $9\frac{1}{2}$ feet is $\frac{1}{4}$ foot. For the measurement $13\frac{3}{8}$ feet, however, the greatest possible error is $\frac{1}{16}$ foot. The second measurement is made with a smaller unit, and the possible error is less.

A measurement such as $13\frac{3}{8}$ feet is more **precise** than the measurement $9\frac{1}{2}$ feet.

> The **precision** of a measurement is given by the least unit used in the measurement. The more **precise** of two measurements is the one using the smaller unit.

The precision of the measurement 3.115 meters is 0.001 meter.

■ **P-1** Which of the two measurements is more precise, 13.9 inches or 15.85 inches?

■ **P-2** How can you describe the precision of the measurement $5\frac{5}{8}$ feet?

■ **P-3** Which of the measurements is more precise, $13\frac{1}{4}$ yards or $17\frac{3}{4}$ feet?

Sometimes certain measurements are made with greater precision than is needed in the problem. In these cases the numbers are **rounded** to the precision desired. Here are some examples:

Measurement	Precision	Precision Desired	Rounded Measurement
$3\frac{1}{4}$ miles	$\frac{1}{4}$ mile	1 mile	3 miles
5.123 feet	0.001 foot	0.1 foot	5.1 feet
3.728 meters	0.001 meter	0.01 meter	3.73 meters
371 miles	1 mile	10 miles	370 miles
11.5 yards	0.1 yard	1 yard	12 yards
$5\frac{5}{8}$ inches	$\frac{1}{8}$ inch	$\frac{1}{4}$ inch	$5\frac{3}{4}$ inches

In rounding a measurement, you find the number that the given measurement is nearer to and that has the precision desired.

■ **P-4** How would you round 13.49 feet to the nearest foot?

You can see that 13.49 is nearer to 13 than it is to 14. A common error is to round 13.49 first to 13.5 and then to round 13.5 to 14. You can see that this is incorrect.

When there is not a value that is nearer to the given measurement, you may choose the greater value. For example, if you want to round 12.65 meters to the nearest 0.1 meter, choose 12.7 meters.

■ **P-5** What is 2.0475 inches rounded to the nearest 0.001 inch? to the nearest 0.01 inch? to the nearest 0.1 inch?

ORAL EXERCISES 6.3

1. What does the precision of a measurement depend upon?

2. How do you determine which is the more precise of two measurements?

Tell which of the two measurements is more precise in each case.

3. $2\frac{1}{4}$ inches and $3\frac{5}{8}$ inches
4. 258 miles and 13.6 miles
5. 5.6 centimeters and 7.18 centimeters
6. 0.005 foot and 0.09 foot
7. $3\frac{5}{16}$ yards and $2\frac{3}{8}$ yards
8. 0.56 meter and 0.560 meter
9. 11.0 feet and 11 feet
10. 15.6 miles and 13.8 miles

Round each measurement to the precision indicated.

11. $3\frac{5}{16}$ inches; $\frac{1}{2}$ inch
12. 1728 miles; 100 miles
13. $2\frac{1}{2}$ yards; 1 yard
14. 5.057 feet; 0.1 foot
15. 8.35 centimeters; 0.1 centimeter
16. 5.048 centimeters; 0.1 centimeter
17. $3\frac{3}{4}$ inches; $\frac{1}{2}$ inch
18. 578 yards; 5 yards
19. 585,276 miles; 10,000 miles
20. 1.95 feet; 0.1 foot

WRITTEN EXERCISES 6.3

A Indicate which of the two measurements is more precise in each of the following cases. Write *Neither* if the two measurements have the same precision.

1. $3\frac{3}{4}$ inches and $5\frac{6}{8}$ inches
2. $4\frac{1}{2}$ feet and $5\frac{4}{8}$ feet
3. 2.73 centimeters and 5.18 centimeters
4. 4.7 feet and 2.3 feet
5. 8.50 meters and 7.6 meters
6. 18.0 yards and 256 yards
7. $3\frac{1}{2}$ yards and 37 feet
8. $5\frac{3}{16}$ feet and 23 inches
9. 2.005 meters and 17.1340 meters
10. 1.00 miles and 13.178 miles

Suppose that each of the following numbers represents a measurement without a given name for the standard unit. Copy both tables and complete them by rounding each number to the degree of precision indicated.

	Measurement	$\frac{1}{4}$ unit	$\frac{1}{2}$ unit	1 unit
11.	$3\frac{9}{16}$	?	?	?
12.	$5\frac{3}{8}$	?	?	?
13.	$12\frac{11}{32}$	?	?	?
14.	$10\frac{3}{16}$	?	?	?
15.	$\frac{15}{8}$	?	?	?
16.	$\frac{19}{16}$	?	?	?

	Measurement	0.01 unit	0.1 unit	1 unit	10 units
17.	13.176	?	?	?	?
18.	156.019	?	?	?	?
19.	255.0472	?	?	?	?
20.	9.30495	?	?	?	?
21.	1003.0005	?	?	?	?
22.	56,298.1545	?	?	?	?
23.	23.9532	?	?	?	?
24.	118.1516	?	?	?	?

6.4 Accuracy

Two measurements such as 3.6 inches and 5.3 inches have the same degree of precision because the unit is 0.1 inch in both. Often, you can compare two such measurements by finding the **relative error** of each.

> The **relative error** of a measurement is the ratio of the greatest possible error to the measurement itself.

Since the greatest possible error in each of the measurements 3.6 inches and 5.3 inches is 0.05 inch, $\frac{0.05}{3.6} \left(\text{or } \frac{5}{360} \right)$ and $\frac{0.05}{5.3} \left(\text{or } \frac{5}{530} \right)$ represent the relative errors of the two measurements. Since $\frac{5}{530} < \frac{5}{360}$, you can see that the relative error of the measurement 5.3 inches is less than the relative error of the measurement 3.6 inches. The measurement 5.3 inches is more accurate than the measuremement 3.6 inches.

> The **accuracy** of a measurement depends upon its relative error. The more accurate of two measurements is the one with the smaller relative error.

■ **P-1** What is the greatest possible error in the measurement 16 feet?

■ **P-2** What is the relative error in the measurement 16 feet?

■ **P-3** What is the greatest possible error in the measurement 17 feet?

■ **P-4** What is the relative error in the measurement 17 feet?

■ **P-5** Which is the more accurate measurement, 16 feet or 17 feet?

In a measurement such as 160 feet, there may be doubt as to the smallest unit used. Perhaps the measurement 160 feet was obtained by the use of a steel tape that has marks at intervals of only 10 feet. On the other hand, maybe the smallest unit used was 1 foot, and the measured length was closer to 160 feet than to either 159 feet or 161 feet.

To remove doubt, a special symbol is sometimes used. The symbol $15\bar{0}$ feet indicates that the unit is 1 foot. The symbol 150 feet without the bar over 0 indicates that 10 feet is the unit. In the measurement $15,7\bar{0}0$ miles, the unit is 10 miles.

■ **P-6** What unit is assumed in the measurement 15,70$\bar{0}$ miles? in the measurement 15,700 miles?

The following table shows some interesting results.

Measurement	Unit of Measure	Greatest Possible Error	Relative Error
15,400 feet	100 feet	50 feet	$\dfrac{50}{15,400}$
1,540 feet	10 feet	5 feet	$\dfrac{5}{1540} = \dfrac{50}{15,400}$
154 feet	1 foot	0.5 foot	$\dfrac{0.5}{154} = \dfrac{50}{15,400}$
15.4 feet	0.1 foot	0.05 foot	$\dfrac{0.05}{15.4} = \dfrac{50}{15,400}$
1.54 feet	0.01 foot	0.005 foot	$\dfrac{0.005}{1.54} = \dfrac{50}{15,400}$
0.154 foot	0.001 foot	0.0005 foot	$\dfrac{0.0005}{0.154} = \dfrac{50}{15,400}$

■ **P-7** Which of the measurements in the table is the most precise? the least precise?

■ **P-8** What can you say about the accuracy of the measurements?

You can see a pattern in the table. Given a measurement such as 15.4 feet, any measurement obtained from it by moving just the decimal point will have the same degree of accuracy.

You can see that precision and accuracy do not mean the same thing in measurement. Precision is determined by the least unit used in the measurement. Accuracy is determined by the relative error.

ORAL EXERCISES 6.4

1. What is relative error?
2. How can you tell which of two measurements is more accurate?
3. Do the words *precision* and *accuracy* mean the same thing?

What is the least unit of measure that is suggested by each of the following measurements?

4. 13,500 yards
5. 13,50$\bar{0}$ yards
6. 13,5$\bar{0}$0 yards
7. 13,000 miles
8. 13,$\bar{0}$00 miles
9. 60 feet
10. 8$\bar{0}$ feet

Tell how you would complete the following table.

Measurement	Unit of Measure	Greatest Possible Error	Relative Error
11. 320 feet	10 feet	5 feet	?
12. $32\bar{0}$ feet	?	0.5 foot	?
13. 10.0 yards	0.1 yard	?	?
14. $1\bar{0}$ yards	1 yard	?	?
15. $3\frac{2}{4}$ inches	$\frac{1}{4}$ inch	?	$\frac{\frac{1}{8}}{\frac{14}{4}} = \frac{1}{8}\left(\frac{8}{14}\right) = \frac{1}{28}$
16. $3\frac{1}{2}$ inches	?	?	$\frac{\frac{1}{4}}{\frac{14}{4}} = \frac{1}{14}$
17. 256.9 meters	?	?	?
18. 25.69 meters	?	?	?

Which is more accurate in each of the following? Use the above table.

19. 320 feet or $32\bar{0}$ feet?   **20.** 10.0 yards or $1\bar{0}$ yards?

21. $3\frac{2}{4}$ inches or $3\frac{1}{2}$ inches?   **22.** 256.9 meters or 25.69 meters?

WRITTEN EXERCISES 6.4

A What is the least unit of measure suggested by each of the following?

1. 12,700 miles   **2.** 8,900 yards   **3.** $86\bar{0}$ yards

4. $11,7\bar{0}0$ meters   **5.** 170.0 feet   **6.** 90.00 yards

7. 186,000 miles   **8.** 240,000 miles   **9.** 800,000 meters

10. 3,100,000 miles   **11.** $25\bar{0},000$ miles   **12.** $29,\bar{0}00$ yards

Copy and complete the following table.

Measurement	Unit of Measure	Greatest Possible Error	Relative Error
13. $5\frac{1}{2}$ inches	$\frac{1}{2}$ inch	?	$\frac{\frac{1}{4}}{\frac{11}{2}} = \frac{1}{4}\left(\frac{4}{11}\right) = \frac{1}{22}$
14. $5\frac{2}{4}$ inches	$\frac{1}{4}$ inch	?	$\frac{\frac{1}{8}}{\frac{22}{4}} = \frac{1}{8}\left(\frac{8}{22}\right) = \frac{1}{44}$
15. 0.9 mile	0.1 mile	?	$\frac{0.05}{0.9} = \frac{?}{?}$
16. 0.5 meter	0.1 meter	?	?
17. 360 yards	?	?	?
18. 700 miles	?	?	?
19. $36\bar{0}$ yards	1 yard	?	?
20. $70\bar{0}$ miles	1 mile	?	?

For each of the following pairs of measurements, state (a) the greatest possible error in each, (b) the relative error of each, (c) the more accurate measurement.

21. 123 yards; 124 yards   **22.** 560 miles; 550 miles

23. 11.4 inches; 1.14 inches   **24.** 3.08 feet; 30.8 feet

6.5 Conversion of Standard Units of Measure

The standard units of measure such as the inch, foot, yard, mile, pound, ounce, quart, gallon, etc., make up the so-called English system of weights and measures. This system is the one familiar to most persons in the United States.

A very real problem that arises in working with measurements is in changing the form of the measurement from one standard unit to another. You know the relation that exists between the inch and the foot. In many books you will see this sentence: 12 inches = 1 foot.

You know that " = " in mathematics means that two numerals so related are names for the same number. It is evident that "12 inches" and "1 foot" do not name the same number. However, it is generally meant that "12 inches" and "1 foot" are two different ways of describing the same length.

The symbol for a correspondence, ↔, may be used to show this relation. Thus,

$$12 \text{ inches} \leftrightarrow 1 \text{ foot}$$

is true and may be read as the sentence "Twelve inches corresponds to one foot."

Here are some other examples:

$$3 \text{ feet} \leftrightarrow 1 \text{ yard}$$
$$36 \text{ inches} \leftrightarrow 1 \text{ yard}$$
$$5280 \text{ feet} \leftrightarrow 1 \text{ mile}$$

■ **P-1** Complete the following correspondence.

$$\underline{?} \text{ quarts} \leftrightarrow 1 \text{ gallon}$$

■ **P-2** Complete the following correspondence.

$$16 \text{ ounces} \leftrightarrow 1 \ \underline{?}$$

For your convenience, some of the more common correspondences between standard English units are summarized with their abbreviations on the following page.

Length and Distance

12 inches (in) $\leftrightarrow$ 1 foot (ft)
36 inches (in) $\leftrightarrow$ 1 yard (yd)
3 feet (ft) $\leftrightarrow$ 1 yard (yd)
5280 feet (ft) $\leftrightarrow$ 1 mile (mi)
1760 yards (yd) $\leftrightarrow$ 1 mile (mi)

Weight

16 ounces (oz) $\leftrightarrow$ 1 pound (lb)
2000 pounds (lb) $\leftrightarrow$ 1 ton (T)

Capacity

2 pints (pt) $\leftrightarrow$ 1 quart (qt)
8 pints (pt) $\leftrightarrow$ 1 gallon (gal)
4 quarts (qt) $\leftrightarrow$ 1 gallon (gal)

You may use your knowledge of proportion to change a measurement to its corresponding measurement in a different unit.

Example: Express the measurement 5 yards as the corresponding measurement in feet.

$3 \text{ ft} \leftrightarrow 1 \text{ yd}$ (This is the correspondence that defines these units.)
$x \text{ ft} \leftrightarrow 5 \text{ yd}$ (This is the correspondence that is wanted.)
$\dfrac{3}{x} = \dfrac{1}{5}$ (Remember that ratios have no labels.)
$1(x) = 3(5)$ (The cross-products rule is used.)
$x = 15$ (Common names are used.)

Therefore, 5 yd $\leftrightarrow$ 15 ft, and 15 feet is the answer to the problem.

Complete the steps in the following problem: "Express the measurement 21 pints in terms of gallons."

■ **P-3**

$$\underline{\;?\;} \text{ pt} \leftrightarrow 1 \text{ gal}$$
$$21 \text{ pt} \leftrightarrow x \text{ gal}$$

■ **P-4**

$$\frac{?}{21} = \frac{1}{?}$$

■ **P-5**

$$(\underline{\;?\;})x = 21$$

■ **P-6**

$$8(\underline{\;?\;} \cdot 21) = 21$$

■ **P-7**

$$x = \underline{\;?\;}$$

The steps used for converting a measurement from one unit to another are as follows.

1 Write a basic correspondence between the two standard units.
2 Write the correspondence that is desired, using a variable in naming the unknown measurement.
3 Write an open sentence in proportion form, using the terms of the two correspondences. Make sure each ratio compares measurements of the same kind of unit.
4 Find the truth number of the sentence and attach the correct label.

ORAL EXERCISES 6.5

Complete each correspondence without writing a proportion.

1. 24 in ↔ ? ft
2. 9 ft ↔ ? yd
3. 3 ft ↔ ? in
4. 4 yd ↔ ? ft
5. 4 ft ↔ ? yd
6. 5 pt ↔ ? qt
7. 12 qt ↔ ? gal
8. 3 qt ↔ ? pt
9. 2 gal ↔ ? qt
10. 16 pt ↔ ? gal
11. 3 gal ↔ ? pt
12. $2\frac{1}{2}$ qt ↔ ? pt
13. 32 oz ↔ ? lb
14. 3 lb ↔ ? oz
15. 3000 lb ↔ ? T
16. 2 T ↔ ? lb
17. 440 yd ↔ ? mi
18. 2640 ft ↔ ? mi

WRITTEN EXERCISES 6.5

A Complete each correspondence without writing a proportion.

1. 4 ft ↔ ? in
2. 5 yd ↔ ? ft
3. 60 in ↔ ? ft
4. 21 ft ↔ ? yd
5. 72 in ↔ ? yd
6. 3 yd ↔ ? in
7. 3 gal ↔ ? qt
8. 5 qt ↔ ? pt
9. 14 pt ↔ ? qt
10. 24 pt ↔ ? gal
11. 64 oz ↔ ? lb
12. 3 T ↔ ? lb
13. 6000 lb ↔ ? T
14. 5 lb ↔ ? oz

Complete each of the following correspondences by using a proportion and the method shown in this section. Show all steps.

15. 21 in ↔ ? ft
16. 11 ft ↔ ? yd
17. 27 in ↔ ? yd
18. 7040 ft ↔ ? mi
19. $\frac{7}{8}$ mi ↔ ? in
20. $\frac{15}{4}$ yd ↔ ? in
21. 3200 lb ↔ ? T
22. 12,800 oz ↔ ? T
23. 23 pt ↔ ? gal
24. 23 qt ↔ ? gal
25. $3\frac{5}{16}$ gal ↔ ? pt
26. 7.8 gal ↔ ? qt
27. 3.2 mi ↔ ? yd
28. 1980 yd ↔ ? mi

6.6 Metric Units

The metric system of measure is the system that is most common throughout the world. It is popular because conversion can be made from one standard unit to another very easily. In the United States the metric system is used in scientific work and in some industries. It is important that you learn about this system because its use in this country will probably increase in the future.

The basic standard unit of the metric system is the **meter.** The measurement 1 meter is slightly greater than the measurement 1 yard. The correspondence 1 meter ↔ 39.37 inches is true.

You will consider only the most commonly used metric units. The names of the units suggest how they compare with the basic unit.

Millimeter means *one thousandth* of a meter.
Centimeter means *one hundredth* of a meter.
Decimeter means *one tenth* of a meter.
Kilometer means *one thousand* meters.

The basic unit of mass in the metric system is the **gram.** The *mass* of an object corresponds to its weight on the earth's surface. An object weighing 1 ounce has a mass of about 28 grams.

Centigram means *one hundredth* of a gram.
Kilogram means *one thousand* grams.

■ **P-1** What does milligram mean?

The basic unit of capacity in the metric system is the **liter.** The liter is slightly greater than the quart. A capacity of 1 liter expressed in quarts is about 1.06 quarts.

Milliliter means *one thousandth* of a liter.
Kiloliter means *one thousand* liters.

■ **P-2** What does centiliter mean?

The following tables show some correspondences between metric units of measure along with the abbreviations.

Length and Distance
1000 millimeters (mm) ↔ 1 meter (m)
100 centimeters (cm) ↔ 1 meter (m)
10 decimeters (dm) ↔ 1 meter (m)
1000 meters (m) ↔ 1 kilometer (km)

Weight

100 centigrams (cg) ↔ 1 gram (g)

1000 grams (g) ↔ 1 kilogram (kg)

Capacity

1000 milliliters (ml) ↔ 1 liter (l)

1000 liters (l) ↔ 1 kiloliter (kl)

Complete each of the following correspondences.

■ **P-3**	$\underline{?}$ mm ↔ 1 cm
■ **P-4**	$\underline{?}$ mm ↔ 1 dm
■ **P-5**	$\underline{?}$ cm ↔ 1 dm
■ **P-6**	$\underline{?}$ cm ↔ 1 km

A measurement that is given in one metric unit can easily be changed to the corresponding measurement in a different unit. You will use proportions again to show this.

Example: Change the measurement 27 centimeters to the corresponding measurement expressed in meters.

$$100 \text{ cm} \leftrightarrow 1 \text{ m}$$
$$27 \text{ cm} \leftrightarrow x \text{ m}$$
$$\frac{100}{27} = \frac{1}{x}$$
$$100x = 27$$
$$100(\tfrac{1}{100} \cdot 27) = 27$$
$$x = \tfrac{27}{100}, \text{ or } 0.27$$

Therefore, 0.27 m ↔ 27 cm.

■ **P-7** How could you make the conversion easily in the above example without using proportion?

Here is another example. Convert 5.3 centimeters to millimeters.

$$10 \text{ mm} \leftrightarrow 1 \text{ cm}$$
$$x \text{ mm} \leftrightarrow 5.3 \text{ cm}$$
$$\frac{10}{x} = \frac{1}{5.3}$$
$$x = 10(5.3)$$
$$x = 53$$

Therefore, 53 mm ↔ 5.3 cm.

■ **P-8** How could you make the above conversion of centimeters to millimeters without using a proportion?

Sometimes it is necessary to convert a measurement in metric units to a measurement in English units.

Example: The distance to be run in a track event is 100 meters. What is the distance in yards?

$$1 \text{ m} \leftrightarrow 39.37 \text{ in}$$

$$100 \text{ m} \leftrightarrow 3937 \text{ in}$$

$$36 \text{ in} \leftrightarrow 1 \text{ yd}$$

$$3937 \text{ in} \leftrightarrow x \text{ yd}$$

$$\frac{36}{3937} = \frac{1}{x}$$

$$36x = 3937$$

$$36(\tfrac{1}{36} \cdot 3937) = 3937$$

$$x = \tfrac{3937}{36}, \text{ or } 109\tfrac{13}{36}$$

$$100 \text{ m} \leftrightarrow 109\tfrac{13}{36} \text{ yd}$$

The distance for the track event is approximately 109 yards.

ORAL EXERCISES 6.6

Complete the following correspondences of measurements.

1. 2 m ↔ ? mm
2. 5 m ↔ ? cm
3. 4 m ↔ ? dm
4. 300 m ↔ ? km
5. 3000 mm ↔ ? m
6. 900 cm ↔ ? m
7. 70 dm ↔ ? m
8. 5 cm ↔ ? mm
9. 3 kl ↔ ? l
10. 6 g ↔ ? cg
11. 5 kg ↔ ? g
12. 3 l ↔ ? ml
13. 25 mm ↔ ? cm
14. 15 cm ↔ ? dm
15. 23 dm ↔ ? cm
16. 150 cm ↔ ? m

What does each of the following prefixes mean?

17. centi-   18. kilo-   19. milli-   20. deci-

21. What is the basic metric unit of length?
22. What is the basic metric unit of weight?
23. What is the basic metric unit of capacity?

WRITTEN EXERCISES 6.6

A Complete the following correspondences. Use proportions if necessary.

1. 5.2 m ↔ ? mm
2. 3.4 m ↔ ? cm
3. 178 cm ↔ ? m
4. 1728 mm ↔ ? m
5. 13.5 dm ↔ ? m
6. 178 dm ↔ ? m
7. 83 mm ↔ ? cm
8. 57 cm ↔ ? dm
9. 13.6 dm ↔ ? cm
10. 5.8 cm ↔ ? mm
11. 35.7 mm ↔ ? dm
12. 5280 mm ↔ ? dm
13. 13.6 dm ↔ ? mm
14. 3.09 dm ↔ ? mm
15. 25.8 g ↔ ? kg
16. 13.6 g ↔ ? cg
17. 1.56 cg ↔ ? g
18. 3.8 kg ↔ ? g
19. 23.8 liters ↔ ? ml
20. 5.17 kl ↔ ? liters

C Convert each of the given measurements to the indicated unit. You may use these correspondences:

1 meter ↔ 39.37 inches
1 meter ↔ 3.28 feet
1 inch ↔ 2.54 centimeters

21. 20 meters ↔ ? feet
22. 12 inches ↔ ? centimeters
23. 100 feet ↔ ? meters
24. 60 centimeters ↔ ? inches

6.7 Square Units of Measure

In previous sections, you reviewed some of the standard units for measuring length. Now you are going to work with square units that are used in measuring **area.**

> The **area** of a plane figure is a number that shows a comparison of the size of the region enclosed by the figure to a unit of measure. The unit that is used is a square region such that each side has one of the standard units for its length.

One of the most common units for measuring area is the square region that is 1 inch on each side. This unit is called the **square inch.** It is shown in Figure 1 on the following page.

The area of the rectangle in Figure 2 can be described as 6 square inches. It can be abbreviated as 6 in². This measurement gives a comparison of the size of the region enclosed by the rectangle to the size of the region enclosed by the unit square.

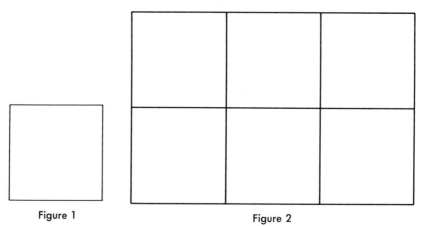

Figure 1   Figure 2

Other common square units for measuring area are the **square foot** (ft²), **square yard** (yd²), **square mile** (mi²), and so forth.

■ **P-1** How can you describe the unit called the *square foot?*

Again it is necessary in many problems to be able to change a measurement of area from one standard unit to another. Suppose the square region shown here in Figure 3 represents a square foot. Now mark off 12 units of equal length on each side and form smaller square regions as shown in Figure 4.

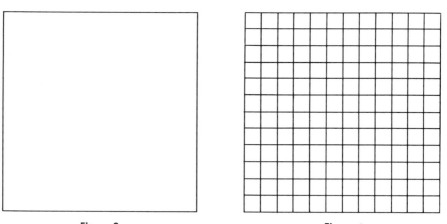

Figure 3   Figure 4

■ **P-2** What do you call each of the 12 units into which each side of Figure 4 has been marked off?

You can find the number of small squares by finding the product of the number of rows of squares times the number of columns of squares.

■ **P-3** What is each small square in Figure 4 called?

■ **P-4** How many small squares are there?

You can describe the area as 1 square foot or as 144 square inches. Again this relation can be shown as a correspondence.

$$1 \text{ ft}^2 \leftrightarrow 144 \text{ in}^2$$

Other correspondences between standard units of square measure can be derived in a similar manner. For example, since 1 square yard can be separated into $(36)(36)$ square inches, the following correspondence is true.

$$1296 \text{ in}^2 \leftrightarrow 1 \text{ yd}^2$$

■ **P-5** Complete the following correspondence.

$$\underline{?} \text{ ft}^2 \leftrightarrow 1 \text{ yd}^2$$

Here is a summary of the correspondence between some common English square units:

$$144 \text{ in}^2 \leftrightarrow 1 \text{ ft}^2$$
$$1296 \text{ in}^2 \leftrightarrow 1 \text{ yd}^2$$
$$9 \text{ ft}^2 \leftrightarrow 1 \text{ yd}^2$$
$$640 \text{ acres} \leftrightarrow 1 \text{ mi}^2$$

In like manner, square units can be expressed using the metric system. The units in this system are the square millimeter, square centimeter, square meter, and so forth.

Consider a square that has a length of 1 centimeter on each side.

■ **P-6** What is such a square called?

■ **P-7** What is the length of each side in millimeters?

■ **P-8** How can the measure of the area of the square region be expressed in square millimeters?

The following correspondence expresses the relation for **P-8**.

$$1 \text{ cm}^2 \leftrightarrow 100 \text{ mm}^2$$

Here is a summary of the most common correspondences between square metric units:

$$1{,}000{,}000 \text{ mm}^2 \leftrightarrow 1 \text{ m}^2$$
$$100 \text{ mm}^2 \leftrightarrow 1 \text{ cm}^2$$
$$10{,}000 \text{ mm}^2 \leftrightarrow 1 \text{ dm}^2$$
$$10{,}000 \text{ cm}^2 \leftrightarrow 1 \text{ m}^2$$
$$100 \text{ cm}^2 \leftrightarrow 1 \text{ dm}^2$$
$$100 \text{ dm}^2 \leftrightarrow 1 \text{ m}^2$$
$$1{,}000{,}000 \text{ m}^2 \leftrightarrow 1 \text{ km}^2$$

ORAL EXERCISES 6.7

Complete the following correspondences.

1. $2 \text{ yd}^2 \leftrightarrow \underline{?} \text{ ft}^2$
2. $2 \text{ ft}^2 \leftrightarrow \underline{?} \text{ in}^2$
3. $27 \text{ ft}^2 \leftrightarrow \underline{?} \text{ yd}^2$
4. $\frac{1}{2} \text{ yd}^2 \leftrightarrow \underline{?} \text{ in}^2$
5. $2592 \text{ in}^2 \leftrightarrow \underline{?} \text{ yd}^2$
6. $2 \text{ mi}^2 \leftrightarrow \underline{?} \text{ acres}$
7. $3 \text{ cm}^2 \leftrightarrow \underline{?} \text{ mm}^2$
8. $2 \text{ m}^2 \leftrightarrow \underline{?} \text{ cm}^2$
9. $1000 \text{ mm}^2 \leftrightarrow \underline{?} \text{ m}^2$
10. $500 \text{ dm}^2 \leftrightarrow \underline{?} \text{ m}^2$

Indicate whether each of the following statements is *True* or *False*.

11. A square foot is larger than a square inch.
12. The number of square feet in a given area is larger than the number of square inches.
13. A square centimeter is larger than a square meter.
14. The number of square centimeters in a given area is larger than the number of square millimeters.
15. A square meter is larger than a square yard.
16. A square centimeter is larger than a square inch.
17. The number of square feet in a given region is larger than the number of square yards.
18. The larger the unit that is used in expressing a measurement the smaller the number of units required.

Read each sentence and replace the question mark with a word that makes the sentence true.

19. A square centimeter is $\underline{?}$ times larger than a square millimeter.
20. A square foot is $\frac{1}{9}$ as large as a square $\underline{?}$.
21. A square foot is $\underline{?}$ times as large as a square inch.
22. A square meter is 10,000 times as large as a square $\underline{?}$.
23. One square mile is 640 times as large as an $\underline{?}$.
24. One square millimeter is $\underline{?}$ times as large as a square meter.

A Complete these correspondences. Use proportions if necessary.

1. $24 \text{ ft}^2 \leftrightarrow \underline{?} \text{ yd}^2$
2. $30 \text{ ft}^2 \leftrightarrow \underline{?} \text{ yd}^2$
3. $5 \text{ ft}^2 \leftrightarrow \underline{?} \text{ in}^2$
4. $5 \text{ yd}^2 \leftrightarrow \underline{?} \text{ ft}^2$
5. $10 \text{ yd}^2 \leftrightarrow \underline{?} \text{ ft}^2$
6. $7 \text{ ft}^2 \leftrightarrow \underline{?} \text{ in}^2$
7. $13.6 \text{ mm}^2 \leftrightarrow \underline{?} \text{ cm}^2$
8. $158 \text{ dm}^2 \leftrightarrow \underline{?} \text{ m}^2$
9. $2.3 \text{ km}^2 \leftrightarrow \underline{?} \text{ m}^2$
10. $0.28 \text{ m}^2 \leftrightarrow \underline{?} \text{ mm}^2$
11. $3.75 \text{ m}^2 \leftrightarrow \underline{?} \text{ cm}^2$
12. $1728 \text{ cm}^2 \leftrightarrow \underline{?} \text{ m}^2$

13. The area of one floor tile is 18 in^2. About how many will cover a floor with an area of 168 ft^2?

14. The area of a floor is 480 ft^2. How much will it cost to tile the floor if it costs $1.60 per yd^2?

15. One pound of fertilizer is to be used for each 25 ft^2 of lawn. How many pounds will it take to fertilize a lawn of 450 yd^2?

16. One gallon of paint will cover 50 yd^2. How many gallons will cover 900 ft^2?

6.8   Cubic Units of Measure

The size of a solid figure or object is usually best described by its **volume.**

> The **volume** is a number that shows a comparison of the size of the space enclosed by the figure with a unit of measure. The unit that is used is a cube with each edge having a standard unit for its length.

The **cubic inch** is shown in Figure 1. Each edge has a length of 1 inch.

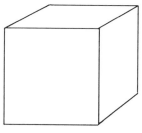

Figure 1

■ **P-1** How would you express the volume of the object in Figure 2, using cubic inches?

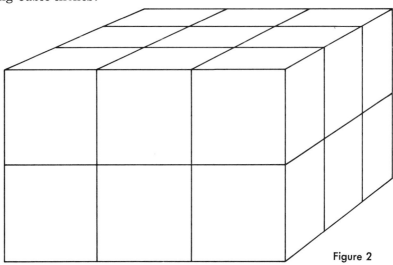

Figure 2

Some other common cubic units of measure are the **cubic foot, cubic yard, cubic millimeter, cubic centimeter,** and **cubic meter.**

■ **P-2** What is meant by a cubic foot? a cubic yard? a cubic centimeter?

■ **P-3** Which is larger, a cubic foot or a cubic yard?

■ **P-4** Which is larger, a cubic yard or a cubic meter?

These cubic units of measure can be abbreviated in much the same way as the square units. For example, 10 cubic inches can be abbreviated 10 in^3, and 13 cubic centimeters can be abbreviated 13 cm^3. It so happens that *cubic centimeter* is also often abbreviated cc.

■ **P-5** What do each of the following abbreviations represent?

$$ft^3; \quad yd^3; \quad mm^3; \quad m^3$$

■ **P-6** Why is it not desirable to abbreviate *cubic millimeter* as cm?

It is necessary to set up correspondences between pairs of cubic units of different kinds. Consider the cubic foot and the cubic inch. Figure 3 represents a region measuring one cubic foot that has been subdivided into cubic inches. You can find the number of cubic inches without counting each one. Find the number that make up the top layer and multiply by the number of layers.

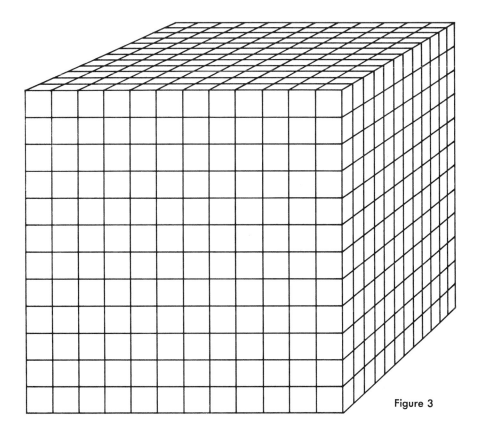

Figure 3

■ **P-7** How many cubic inches are there in the top layer?

■ **P-8** How many layers are there?

The number of cubic inches is 12(144), or 1728. Therefore, the correspondence 1728 in³ ↔ 1 ft³ is true.

By a similar process, you could work out other correspondences. Here is a summary of the most common ones for your use:

$$1728 \text{ in}^3 \leftrightarrow 1 \text{ ft}^3$$
$$27 \text{ ft}^3 \leftrightarrow 1 \text{ yd}^3$$
$$1000 \text{ mm}^3 \leftrightarrow 1 \text{ cm}^3$$
$$1000 \text{ cm}^3 \leftrightarrow 1 \text{ dm}^3$$
$$1{,}000{,}000 \text{ cm}^3 \leftrightarrow 1 \text{ m}^3$$

■ **P-9** How could you find the number of in³ corresponding to 1 yd³?

■ **P-10** How could you find the number of mm³ corresponding to 1 m³?

Recall that the basic unit of capacity is the liter. The cubic centimeter can also be used to measure capacity. In fact, the cubic centimeter can be used to describe the unit called the liter. This approximate correspondence between the cubic centimeter and the liter may be useful:

$$1 \text{ liter} \leftrightarrow 1000 \text{ cubic centimeters}$$

The basic unit of weight in the metric system, the gram, is the weight of 1 cubic centimeter of pure water measured at sea level with a temperature of 39.2° F. You can see that the cubic centimeter is used to describe the units of weight.

ORAL EXERCISES 6.8

1. What is the unit of measure that is used in expressing volume?
2. Name some standard cubic units.

Complete the following correspondences.

3. $\frac{1}{2}$ ft^3 $\leftrightarrow$ _?_ in^3

4. 54 ft^3 $\leftrightarrow$ _?_ yd^3

5. 2000 mm^3 $\leftrightarrow$ _?_ cc

6. 3 yd^3 $\leftrightarrow$ _?_ ft^3

7. 2 ft^3 $\leftrightarrow$ _?_ in^3

8. 3 dm^3 $\leftrightarrow$ _?_ cc

9. 1 liter $\leftrightarrow$ _?_ dm^3

10. 3000 cc $\leftrightarrow$ _?_ liters

11. 1 cc $\leftrightarrow$ _?_ ml

12. 3 liters $\leftrightarrow$ _?_ dm^3

13. About what is the weight in grams of 1 liter of water?
14. About what is the weight in grams of 1 milliliter of water?

Do you think the following are correct correspondences? Explain.

15. 1 cc $\leftrightarrow$ 1 g

16. 1 ml $\leftrightarrow$ 1 g

17. Does 1 cubic inch of water weigh 1 ounce?
18. Does 1 quart of water weigh 1 pound?

WRITTEN EXERCISES 6.8

A Indicate whether each of the following is *True* or *False*.

1. A cube that is 2 inches along each edge has twice the volume of a cubic inch.
2. A cube that is 2 centimeters along each edge can be subdivided into 8 cubic centimeters.
3. A cubic centimeter is smaller than a cubic inch.
4. A cubic foot is smaller than a cubic decimeter.
5. A kilogram of water has a capacity of about one liter.
6. A cubic decimeter of water weighs about one kilogram.

Using the correspondence 231 in³ ↔ 1 gal, complete the following.

7. 1 gal ↔ _?_ ft³   **8.** 1 ft³ ↔ _?_ gal

9. 1 qt ↔ _?_ in³   **10.** 1 pt ↔ _?_ in³

Solve the following problems.

11. If concrete costs $15 per cubic yard, how much will 18 cubic feet cost?

12. If a man pays $24 for 36 cubic feet of concrete, how much does it cost per cubic yard?

13. The volume of a classroom is 186 cubic yards. If there are 40 students, does each student have at least 30 cubic feet?

14. Suppose a room should have at least 50 cubic feet per person. What should be its volume in cubic yards to handle 30 people?

15. If 1 ounce of water weighs about 28 grams, what is the weight in ounces of 70 cubic centimeters of water?

16. If 1 ounce of water weighs about 28 grams, what is the volume in cubic centimeters of $10\frac{3}{4}$ ounces?

6.9 Formulas for Perimeters and Areas

In Chapter 2, you saw that a phrase such as $4n$ can represent the perimeter of any square. Of course, n is to be replaced by the length of a side of the square. Suppose you want to find the perimeters of squares whose sides have lengths as given by the numbers in the set

$$\{1, 2\tfrac{1}{2}, 5, 10\tfrac{1}{4}, 99\}.$$

You can associate any unit of length with each of these numbers.

■ **P-1**   Complete the following table.

Length of One Side	n	1	$2\frac{1}{2}$	5	$10\frac{1}{4}$	99
Perimeter	_?_	_?_	_?_	_?_	_?_	_?_

Since $4n$ represents the perimeter, you may give it the simpler name p, which is suggested by the word *perimeter*. The relation between the perimeter and the length of a side is given by the open sentence

$$p = 4n.$$

This kind of open sentence is called a **formula.**

You could make up many such open sentences by forming an open phrase and assigning a single variable for its name. However, a formula is usually considered to be an open sentence that is used to describe a commonly used rule.

You are probably familiar with the formula for finding the length of a diameter of a circle if the length of a radius is known:

$$d = 2r.$$

In this formula, r represents the length of a radius and $2r$ represents the length of a diameter.

■ **P-2** What value does d have when r equals 15?

■ **P-3** Can 0 be in the domain of the variable n in the formula $p = 4n$?

■ **P-4** Can {numbers of arithmetic} be the domain of r in the formula $d = 2r$?

It is possible that an open phrase that describes a rule can have several variables.

■ **P-5** What open phrase describes the perimeter of the rectangle in Figure 1?

If you let p be a simpler name for the perimeter, then you have the formula

$$p = 2l + 2w.$$

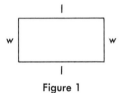

Figure 1

In this formula, l represents the length and w the width of the rectangle. Any number of arithmetic except 0 could be in the domain of each of these variables. The formula $p = 2l + 2w$ can be used to find the perimeter of any rectangle.

■ **P-6** What is the perimeter of a rectangle if l measures 10 inches and w measures 5 inches?

Formulas are used very much in the science and engineering fields. It is important that you be able to show your work clearly when using them. It will be easier both for you to check your own work and for others to follow what you have done.

Example 1: Find the perimeter of a rectangle whose length is 8.3 centimeters and whose width is 5.8 centimeters.

Write down the formula. ────────────────────▶ $p = 2l + 2w$
Replace the variables by
  their given values. ────────────────────▶ $p = 2(8.3) + 2(5.8)$
Show some steps — not
  just the answer. ────────────────────▶ $p = 16.6 + 11.6$
Obtain an answer and label
  with the proper unit. ────────────────────▶ $p = 28.2$ cm

Some other common formulas and their meanings are as follows.

Perimeter of a Triangle

$p = a + b + c$ a, b, and c represent the lengths of the three sides.

Circumference of a Circle

$c = 2\pi r$ r represents the length of a radius. $\pi \approx 3.14$. ("$\approx$" means "approximately equal to.")

Area of a Square

$A = s^2$ s represents the length of each side.

Area of a Rectangle

$A = lw$ l and w represent the length and width respectively.

Area of a Triangle

$A = \frac{1}{2}bh$ b represents the base and h the altitude.

Area of a Circle

$A = \pi r^2$ r represents the length of a radius.

Example 2: Find the area of a circle whose radius is 10 centimeters long. Use 3.14 as an approximation for π.

$$A = \pi r^2$$
$$\approx (3.14)10^2$$
$$= (3.14)100$$
$$\text{Therefore,} \quad A = 314 \text{ cm}^2.$$

Remember that the measurement of an area is expressed in square units. Notice that the approximation sign is used only once — when the approximation is introduced.

ORAL EXERCISES 6.9

Using the formula $p = 2l + 2w$ for the perimeter of a rectangle, find p for each of these rectangles.

1. $l = 10$ in; $w = 5$ in
2. $l = 5$ ft; $w = 3$ ft
3. $l = 8$ m; $w = 6$ m
4. $l = 15$ mm; $w = 12$ mm

Find the area of the rectangle in each of the following problems, using $A = lw$. Be sure to express A with the proper units.

5. $l = 5$ yd; $w = 3$ yd
6. $l = 12$ dm; $w = 4$ dm
7. $l = 6$ cm; $w = 3\frac{1}{2}$ cm
8. $l = \frac{1}{2}$ ft; $w = \frac{1}{4}$ ft

Find the area of the square in each problem, using $A = s^2$.

9. $s = 9$ ft
10. $s = 0.5$ cm
11. $s = \frac{1}{3}$ m
12. $s = 1.2$ in

WRITTEN EXERCISES 6.9

A Use $c = 2\pi r$ to find the circumference of each of the given circles. Show steps and label answers.

1. $r = 7$ in; $\pi \approx \frac{22}{7}$
2. $r = 14$ cm; $\pi \approx \frac{22}{7}$
3. $r = 5$ mm; $\pi \approx 3.14$
4. $r = 10$ ft; $\pi \approx 3.14$

Use $A = \frac{1}{2}bh$ to find the area of each triangle. Show steps and label answers.

5. $b = 10$ ft; $h = 5$ ft
6. $b = 12$ m; $h = 7$ m
7. $b = \frac{1}{3}$ m; $h = 12$ m
8. $b = \frac{1}{4}$ yd; $h = 16$ yd.
9. $b = 5$ cm; $h = 7$ cm
10. $b = 3$ dm; $h = 11$ dm

Use $A = \pi r^2$ to find the area of each circle. Show steps and label answers.

11. $r = 7$ ft; $\pi \approx \frac{22}{7}$
12. $r = 14$ cm; $\pi \approx \frac{22}{7}$
13. $r = 12$ dm; $\pi \approx 3.14$
14. $r = 8$ in; $\pi \approx 3.14$
15. $r = 2\frac{1}{3}$ mm; $\pi \approx \frac{22}{7}$
16. $r = 1\frac{2}{5}$ m; $\pi \approx \frac{22}{7}$

B A **micron** is defined as one millionth of a meter. Here are the correspondences:

$$1000 \text{ microns} \leftrightarrow 1 \text{ mm}$$
$$1,000,000 \text{ microns} \leftrightarrow 1 \text{ m}$$

17. If a diameter of a red blood cell is 7 microns long, what is the length of its radius?

18. What is its area in square microns? Use $A = \pi r^2$ and $\pi \approx \frac{22}{7}$.

19. What is the area of the red blood cell in square millimeters?

6.10 Formulas for Volumes and Rates

You learned about standard units for measuring volume in a previous lesson. These are cubic units. Some of the commonly used cubic units are the cubic inch, cubic foot, cubic yard, cubic centimeter, cubic meter, and so forth.

Here is a review of some of the formulas for finding volumes of familiar solids. One of the simplest solids is the cube. It is used as the basic unit to describe volume. You can find the volume of any cube by cubing the length of an edge. The formula

$$V = s^3$$

describes this rule, where s represents the length of a side and V represents the volume.

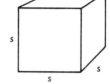

■ **P-1** What is the volume of a cube that measures 2 inches on each edge?

Some formulas for volumes and their meanings follow.

Volume of a Rectangular Solid

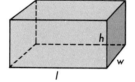

$$V = lwh$$

l, w, and h represent the length, width, and height respectively.

Volume of a Cylinder

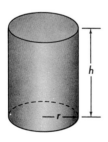

$$V = \pi r^2 h$$

r is the length of a radius of the base and h is the height.

Volume of a Cone

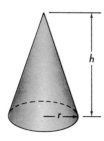

$$V = \tfrac{1}{3}\pi r^2 h$$

r is the length of a radius of the base and h is the height.

Example: Find the volume of a cone if a radius of the base is 7 centimeters long and the altitude is 9 centimeters. Let $\pi \approx \frac{22}{7}$.

$$V = \tfrac{1}{3}\pi r^2 h$$
$$\approx \tfrac{1}{3} \cdot \tfrac{22}{7} \cdot 7^2 \cdot 9$$
$$= \frac{22 \cdot 7 \cdot 7 \cdot 9}{3 \cdot 7}$$
$$= 22 \cdot 7 \cdot 3$$

Therefore, $V = 462 \text{ cm}^3$.

Another relationship that is easily described by a formula is that involving distance, rate (or speed) and time. If a train travels a distance of 2000 miles in 40 hours, its average speed is 50 miles per hour. This does not mean that it is going exactly 50 miles per hour for the entire trip. In climbing mountains it may go much slower, and on the plains it may go much faster.

The following formula describes the rule for finding the rate, or speed.

$$r = \frac{d}{t}$$

The variable d represents the distance traveled, and t represents the time. The speed is expressed in units that are determined by the distance unit and the time unit. **Miles per hour, feet per second, and meters per second** are common units of speed.

■ **P-2**   What is the speed of an object that travels 100 yards in 5 minutes?

■ **P-3**   What is the speed of an object that travels 120 kilometers in 3 hours?

Two other variations of this formula are used.

The formula $d = rt$ represents the rule for finding the distance traveled if r represents the speed and t represents the time. The unit of time used to express the speed must be the same as that for t in the formula.

The formula $t = \dfrac{d}{r}$ represents the rule for finding the time an object takes to move at a speed r and for a length of time t. Again, the same unit of distance must be used for both d and r.

■ **P-4**   How far will a plane travel in 3 hours at a speed of 600 miles per hour?

■ **P-5** How long will it take a runner to go 100 yards at a speed of 10 yards per second?

ORAL EXERCISES 6.10

Give the volume in the proper units of each of the cubes, using $V = s^3$.
1. $s = 3$ ft **2.** $s = 4$ mm **3.** $s = \frac{1}{2}$ yd **4.** $s = 2$ cm

Give the volume in the proper units of each rectangular solid. Use the formula $V = lwh$.
5. $l = 3$ ft; $w = 2$ ft; $h = 1$ ft
6. $l = 2$ cm; $w = 2$ cm; $h = 1$ cm
7. $l = \frac{1}{2}$ yd; $w = \frac{1}{3}$ yd; $h = \frac{1}{5}$ yd
8. $l = 10$ mm; $w = 5$ mm; $h = 2$ mm

Using $d = rt$, find the distance corresponding to each rate, or speed, and period of time.
9. $r = 10$ ft per sec; $t = 3$ sec **10.** $r = 8$ m per min; $t = 10$ min
11. $r = 30$ mi per hr; $t = 5$ hr **12.** $r = 50$ mi per hr; $t = 30$ min

WRITTEN EXERCISES 6.10

A Use $V = \pi r^2 h$ to find the volume of each cylinder. Let $\pi \approx 3.14$. Show steps.
1. $r = 2$ in; $h = 5$ in **2.** $r = 3$ cm; $h = 6$ cm
3. $r = 0.5$ m; $h = 4$ m **4.** $r = \frac{1}{2}$ ft; $h = 4$ ft

Use $V = \frac{1}{3}\pi r^2 h$ to find the volume of each cone. Let $\pi \approx \frac{22}{7}$. Show steps.
5. $r = 5$ dm; $h = 21$ dm **6.** $r = 3$ yd; $h = 14$ yd
7. $r = \frac{1}{2}$ ft; $h = 84$ ft **8.** $r = 0.1$ m; $h = 42$ m

Use $r = \dfrac{d}{t}$ to find the speed in each problem.

9. $d = 500$ mi; $t = 8$ hr **10.** $d = 800$ ft; $t = 3$ sec
11. $d = 400$ m; $t = 65$ sec **12.** $d = 400$ km; $t = 9$ hr

Use $t = \dfrac{d}{r}$ to find the length of time in each problem.

13. $d = 1000$ yd; $r = 6$ yd per sec
14. $d = 200$ km; $r = 35$ km per hr
15. $d = 2925$ mi; $r = 650$ mi per hr
16. $d = 20$ m; $r = 50$ cm per sec

CHAPTER SUMMARY

Important Terms

1. A **measurement** is a number that is assigned to an object to describe its size.
2. The **error** in measuring is the difference between the length, area, volume, or weight and the reported measurement.
3. The **greatest possible error** in a measurement is one-half the smallest unit used.
4. The **precision** of a measurement is defined by the least unit used.
5. The **relative error** of a measurement is the ratio of the greatest possible error to the measurement.
6. The **accuracy** of a measurement depends upon its relative error.
7. **Area** is a number assigned to describe the size of the region enclosed by a plane figure.
8. **Volume** is a number assigned to describe the size of the space enclosed by a figure.
9. A **formula** is an open sentence that describes a rule.

Important Ideas

1. Every measurement is an approximation.
2. The smaller the unit used, the more precise is a measurement.
3. The more accurate of two measurements is the one with the smaller relative error.
4. The unit used in expressing area is the unit square.
5. The unit used in expressing volume is the unit cube.

CHAPTER REVIEW

What is the least unit that is implied by each of these measurements?

1. $12\frac{3}{4}$ ft
2. 13.8 cm
3. $1\frac{5}{6}$ mi
4. 12.50 m
5. $2\frac{6}{8}$ in
6. 85,000 km

Give the greatest possible error in these measurements.

7. $3\frac{1}{4}$ lb
8. 13.6 cc
9. 9800 yd
10. 3.056 m
11. 157 ft
12. 15.82 g

Tell which of the two measurements is more precise in each pair.

13. 13.7 cm; 5.23 cm
14. $1\frac{3}{8}$ oz; $5\frac{3}{4}$ oz
15. 17,000 mi; 18,500 mi
16. 13.70 gal; 15.6 gal
17. $3\frac{4}{16}$ ft; $5\frac{1}{4}$ ft
18. 286.3 km; 2863 km

Round each measurement to the degree of precision indicated.
19. $15\frac{5}{8}$ ft; $\frac{1}{2}$ ft   **20.** 12.77 m; 0.1 m
21. 15,786 km; 1000 km   **22.** 13.7462 cm; 0.1 cm
23. 15.01 lb; 0.1 lb   **24.** $5\frac{1}{4}$ in; 1 in

Find the relative error for each of the following measurements.
25. 25 ft   **26.** 12.6 cm   **27.** 12,600 km   **28.** 156.26 m

Which is the more accurate measurement in each of the following pairs?
29. 123 mi; 124 mi   **30.** 13,500 yd; 13,5$\overline{0}$0 yd
31. 12.8 cm; 5.8 cm   **32.** 16 km; 16.0 km

Complete each of the following correspondences.
33. 36 in $\leftrightarrow$ _?_ ft   **34.** 36 ft^2 $\leftrightarrow$ _?_ yd^2
35. 13 m $\leftrightarrow$ _?_ cm   **36.** 56 mm $\leftrightarrow$ _?_ cm
37. 3 mi $\leftrightarrow$ _?_ yd   **38.** 5 ft^2 $\leftrightarrow$ _?_ in^2
39. 3 m^2 $\leftrightarrow$ _?_ cm^2 **40.** 3 gal $\leftrightarrow$ _?_ qt
41. 48 oz $\leftrightarrow$ _?_ lb   **42.** 5 cm^3 $\leftrightarrow$ _?_ ml
43. 3 ft^3 $\leftrightarrow$ _?_ in^3 **44.** 3 liters $\leftrightarrow$ _?_ ml

Use the formula and the values given to obtain an answer. Label answers.
45. $A = lw$; $l = 5$ cm; $w = 3$ cm
46. $p = 2l + 2w$; $l = 5.6$ yd; $w = 3.5$ yd
47. $c = 2\pi r$; $r = 42$ mm; $\pi \approx \frac{22}{7}$
48. $V = \pi r^2 h$; $r = 3$ dm; $h = 10$ dm; $\pi \approx 3.14$
49. $d = rt$; $r = 10$ ft per sec; $t = 25$ sec
50. $A = \pi r^2$; $r = 0.7$ cm; $\pi \approx \frac{22}{7}$

CUMULATIVE REVIEW   (CHAPTERS 4–6)

Write each of the following as a product of its prime factors.
1. 286   **2.** 96   **3.** 152   **4.** 1304

Indicate whether each of the following is divisible by (a) 2, (b) 3, (c) 4, (d) 5, (e) 10.
5. 15   **6.** 80   **7.** 90   **8.** 240

Indicate by *Yes* or *No* whether the first number is divisible by the second in each of the following. .
9. $3^5 \cdot 2^3 \cdot 5^2$; $3 \cdot 2^2 \cdot 5 \cdot 5$ **10.** $5 \cdot 7 \cdot 11$; $5^2 \cdot 7 \cdot 11$
11. $2 \cdot 3 \cdot 5 \cdot 7 \cdot 11$; $2 \cdot 5 \cdot 11$ **12.** $5^2 \cdot 7^3 \cdot 11$; $5 \cdot 3 \cdot 7$

Give a common name for each of the following fractions.

13. $\frac{12}{16}$ **14.** $\frac{22}{36}$ **15.** $\frac{35}{90}$ **16.** $\frac{112}{256}$

Supply the numerator to make each of the following sentences true.

17. $\frac{2}{3} = \frac{?}{45}$ **18.** $\frac{5}{8} = \frac{?}{72}$ **19.** $\frac{4}{5} = \frac{?}{60}$ **20.** $\frac{8}{7} = \frac{?}{21}$

Find the following products in reduced form.

21. $\frac{1}{12} \cdot \frac{1}{5}$ **22.** $\frac{2}{5} \cdot \frac{3}{4}$ **23.** $\frac{2}{3} \cdot \frac{15}{8}$ **24.** $\frac{5}{16} \cdot \frac{2}{35}$

Find the least common multiple of each of the following sets of numbers.

25. $\{15, 8, 9\}$ **26.** $\{16, 6, 9, 7\}$

Find common names for each of the following sums.

27. $\frac{3}{16} + \frac{11}{16}$ **28.** $\frac{x}{5} + \frac{3x}{5}$

29. $\frac{1}{4} + \frac{3}{8}$ **30.** $\frac{3}{7} + \frac{5}{11}$

Find the truth set of each of the following open sentences. The domain is {numbers of arithmetic}.

31. $\frac{1}{5}x = 1$ **32.** $8n = 1$ **33.** $\frac{3}{16}y = 1$
34. $0 \cdot x = 1$ **35.** $5x = 13$ **36.** $\frac{1}{3}x = 5$

Give the common name of each ratio.

37. 10 cm to 35 cm **38.** 5 dm to 3 m
39. $2x$ to $6x$ **40.** 1 pt to 1 gal

Find the truth set of each of the following proportions. The domain is {numbers of arithmetic}.

41. $\frac{x}{6} = \frac{2}{3}$ **42.** $\frac{4}{5} = \frac{8}{x}$

43. $\frac{2}{5} = \frac{7}{x}$ **44.** $\frac{1}{x} = \frac{5}{3}$

Express each of the following as a per cent.

45. $\frac{43}{100}$ **46.** 0.23 **47.** $\frac{3}{25}$ **48.** 5.6

Give a proportion that describes each of the following sentences.

49. a is 15% of 52. **50.** 12 is x% of 88.
51. 120 is 5% of y. **52.** 80% of 1600 is r.

53. Find the interest on $1500 loaned for one year at 6%.
54. What is the net price on a set of golf clubs listed at $120 if the rate of discount is 15%?

55. What is the rate of discount on an item listed at $25 if the sale price is $15?

56. How many cubic centimeters of acid are there in 50 cubic centimeters of a 4% solution?

Give the measurement of the block that is shown in the following figure to the degree of precision indicated.

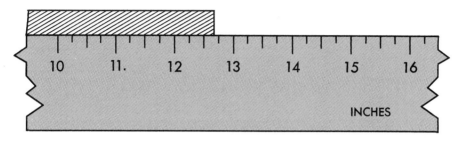

57. 5 inches   **58.** 1 inch   **59.** $\frac{1}{2}$ inch   **60.** $\frac{1}{4}$ inch

Use the following figure and the same directions as for Exercises 57–60.

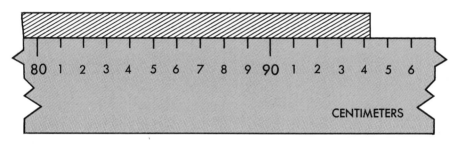

61. meter   **62.** decimeter   **63.** centimeter   **64.** $\frac{1}{2}$ decimeter

Two engineers stand in a wind tunnel at Langley Field, Virginia. The wind tunnel is used by engineers in studying complex problems in the aerodynamics of an aircraft flying at speeds near the speed of sound. Many of these problems must first be translated into algebra in order that they may be solved. You will learn some methods of solving problems in this chapter.

7.1 Word Phrases to Open Phrases

In a previous chapter, you learned what open phrases are. In algebra, open phrases are used to represent word phrases. In a sense, algebra is a language, and one of your important tasks will be to translate from English into algebra.

Suppose Bill wants to use a phrase to represent the age of each member of his family 8 years from now. He records the information in a table like this:

Member of Family	Age Now	Age 8 Years from Now
Father	45	$45 + 8$
Mother	42	$42 + 8$
Jane	9	$9 + 8$
Bill	14	$14 + 8$
Tom	19	$19 + 8$

■ **P-1** Could Bill use the variable a to represent the present age of *any* member of his family?

■ **P-2** What is the domain of a in **P-1**?

■ **P-3** What open phrase represents the age of any member of Bill's family 8 years from now?

You could start out with the word phrase "the age of any member of Bill's family 8 years from now." One translation of this word phrase is the open phrase

$$a + 8.$$

You will recall that, in Chapter 2, some expressions were listed that are used to suggest certain operations. The list is given again for your convenience on the following page.

Operation	Expressions
Addition	Sum, plus, increased by, more than
Subtraction	Less, less than, minus, difference, decreased by
Multiplication	Product, multiplied by, times, twice, tripled
Division	Quotient, divided by

In the translation of a word phrase to an open phrase, the following steps are usually used.

$\boxed{1}$ Select a variable to represent the unknown number in the word phrase.

$\boxed{2}$ Examine the word phrase to see what operation or operations are suggested.

$\boxed{3}$ Write an open phrase using the variable and symbols of operation.

Here are some examples:

Word Phrase: "10 pounds less than the weight of a football player"

Let w equal the weight of a player.

Open Phrase: $w - 10$

■ **P-4** Would $10 - w$ be a correct translation?

Word Phrase: "Number of square feet in a region whose area is given in square yards"

Let x equal the area in square yards.

Open Phrase: $9x$

■ **P-5** Where does 9 come from in this phrase?

In problems like the previous examples, it is sometimes helpful first to form a numerical phrase. This may help you see the pattern of the problem.

For example, consider the word phrase "interest on a five per cent loan for one year." Suppose the loan is $500. Then the interest is found by the phrase $0.05(500)$. So, let x equal the amount of the loan. Then the open phrase is $0.05x$.

■ **P-6** What open phrase could you use if the loan is for two years?

ORAL EXERCISES 7.1

Give an open phrase that is a translation of each of the following word phrases.

1. Three more than the number of fish
2. Five less than the number of swimmers
3. The product of 12 and the number of feet
4. The number of square inches divided by 144
5. 20 less the number of runs
6. The number of miles per hour increased by 5
7. The number of units in the length tripled
8. The difference of the perimeter of a rectangle and its length of 10 units
9. The price of the football decreased by $3
10. Three more than twice the number of centimeters

Translate each of the following to an open phrase using the variable that is suggested.

11. The number of pints in x gallons
12. The number of days in w weeks
13. The number of feet in y inches
14. The number of millimeters in t centimeters
15. The number of pounds in x ounces
16. The number of square inches in f square feet
17. The number of gallons in q quarts
18. The number of inches in y yards
19. The number of yards in i inches
20. The number of cubic feet in y cubic yards

WRITTEN EXERCISES 7.1

A Choose a variable, tell what it represents, and write an open phrase for each word phrase.

1. The sum of a number and three times that number
2. Twice a number minus the number itself
3. The perimeter of a square
4. The area of a square
5. Three less than five times a number
6. Six more than double a number
7. Twice the successor of a number
8. The sum of a number and its successor

Translate each of the following to an open phrase using the variable that is suggested.

9. The number of square centimeters in x square decimeters
10. The number of square feet in y square yards
11. The interest on d dollars loaned for 1 year at 6%
12. The interest on x dollars borrowed for 1 year at 8%
13. The interest on 500 dollars at r% for 1 year
14. The interest on 900 dollars at t% for 2 years
15. The discount on an article listed at d dollars at a rate of 20%
16. The discount on a dress listed at x dollars at a rate of 15%
17. The sale price on a car listed at n dollars with a discount of $200
18. The sale price on a TV set listed at $300 with a discount of d dollars
19. The number of ounces of salt in x ounces of a 12% solution
20. The number of grams of salt in 120 grams of an r% solution
21. The number of centimeters in m millimeters
22. The number of deciliters in y liters
23. The number of kilograms in g grams
24. The number of yards in t feet

7.2 Word Sentences to Open Sentences

You have learned what open sentences are, and you have found the truth sets of some open sentences. Many problems can be solved with the use of open sentences. In this section, however, you will be interested only in learning to translate word sentences to open sentences. You will learn more about finding truth sets later.

Example 1: The total score in a football game was 52 points. The winning team scored 6 more points than the losing team. How many did the winning team score?

You could work the problem by guessing. Your line of thought might go like this:

First Guess

Points by Losing Team: 20   (just a guess)

Points by Winning Team: 20 + 6, or 26

■ **P-1** Do these guesses add up to the correct total?

Points by Losing Team: ___22___ (just a guess)

■ **P-2** Points by Winning Team: ___?___

■ **P-3** Do these add up to the correct total?

You could go on guessing and probably find the correct answer. Here is how you might set up an open sentence to describe the problem:

Number of Points by Losing Team: ___p___

Number of Points by Winning Team: ___$p + 6$___

■ **P-4** What open sentence can you form using the total number of points for both teams?

Your thinking is correct if you see that

$$p + (p + 6) = 52$$

is the open sentence. The truth number for this sentence happens to be 23, which is the number of points scored by the losing team.

■ **P-5** How many points did the winning team score?

You are not expected to be able to find the truth sets of all open sentences at this point.

Example 2: The length of a rectangle is 3 centimeters more than the width, and the area is 60.16 square centimeters. What is the width?

First Guess

Width: ___5___ cm (just a guess)

■ **P-6** Length: ___?___ cm

■ **P-7** Does the product of the width and length give the correct area?

Second Guess

Width: ___6___ cm

■ **P-8** Length: ___?___ cm

■ **P-9** Does the product of the width and length give the correct area?

Using a Variable

Width: ___x___ cm

■ **P-10** Length: ___?___ cm

You can probably see that the open sentence

$$x(x + 3) = 60.16$$

describes the problem. When you learn to find truth sets of sentences like this, you will be able to solve such problems.

In your study of English grammar, you know that a sentence has a subject and a verb. A phrase does not.

> When you translate a word sentence into an open sentence, you must have a symbol for the verb. Some of the symbols that represent verbs are $=$, $\neq$, $>$, $<$, $\leq$, and $\geq$.

The word sentence "Five is equal to the sum of a number and 3" can be translated: $5 = n + 3$. Forming the open sentence is just a matter of replacing words by mathematical symbols. Of course, you must choose a variable to represent an unknown number in the problem.

ORAL EXERCISES 7.2

Translate these sentences into mathematical open sentences.
1. 15 equals the sum of x and 7. 2. 35 is 9 times as great as n.
3. t increased by 5 equals 32. 4. 51 less y is 39.
5. The sum of y and twice y is 14. 6. 12 is 5% of x.
7. The ratio of x to 5 equals the ratio of 7 to 12.
8. 26 less q is the same as q tripled.

Exercises 9–12 refer to the following problem: "The length of a rectangle is 10 inches more than its width, and the perimeter is 56 inches. What is the width?"
9. What variable can you use to represent the width?
10. What open phrase represents the length?
11. How do you find the perimeter of any rectangle?
12. What open sentence describes the problem?

Exercises 13–16 refer to the following problem: "A football player catches a pass and runs for a touchdown, the play covering 80 yards. If he runs 20 yards more than the pass covers, how many yards does the pass cover?"
13. What would you let the variable represent?

14. Let a variable represent the number of yards the pass covers. How can you represent the number of yards the player runs?
15. What open sentence describes the problem?
16. If you choose a variable to represent the number of yards the player runs, what phrase represents the length of the pass?

WRITTEN EXERCISES 7.2

A Solve the following problems.
  1. The perimeter of a rectangle is 50 feet. What is the sum of its length and width?
  2. The length of a rectangle is 15 decimeters and the width is 3 decimeters. What is its perimeter?
  3. The perimeter of a triangle is 35 inches, and its sides have lengths x inches, x inches, and 3 inches. What open sentence describes this problem?
  4. The lengths of the sides of a triangle are x centimeters, $(x + 1)$ centimeters, and 5 centimeters. If the perimeter is 38 centimeters, what open sentence describes the problem?
  5. The length of a baseball bat is 36 inches, and it breaks into two pieces. If one piece is x inches long, what is the length of the other piece?
  6. A mountain peak is 5000 feet high. If a climber reaches a point x feet high, how far is he from the top?

Translate the following into mathematical open sentences.
  7. 5 more than x is 72.   8. 3 less than y equals 97.
  9. 54 is the same as 7 less than n.   10. 13 less than r is 86.
 11. Twice the sum of q and 5 is 28.
 12. The sum of twice x and 13 is 58.
 13. Hester got 30 more votes than Chester. If there were 150 votes cast, how many did Chester get?
 14. Sandy won 3 fewer games than Juan. Together they won 39 games. How many did Juan win?
 15. Harry and Larry get on some scales at the same time, and they weigh 375 pounds. If Larry is 20 pounds heavier than Harry, how much does Harry weigh?
 16. Herbert and Hubert pick oranges for a day, and Herbert earns 35¢ more than Hubert. How much does Hubert earn if they earn $5.00 between them?

7.3 Number Problems

Students sometimes have difficulty in knowing when to use = and when to use < or > in forming open sentences. Consider these two word sentences:

$\boxed{1}$ Fifteen is two more than some number.

$\boxed{2}$ Fifteen is more than some number.

The first sentence can be translated into the open sentence

$$15 = x + 2.$$

The second sentence has this open sentence as its translation:

$$15 > x.$$

Notice that both sentences involve the words "is more than." These words seem to suggest the "is greater than" symbol, >. However, sentence $\boxed{1}$ tells how much greater one number is than another. That is why you can write it as an equality. You will have to be careful in making such translations.

Consider these sentences:

$\boxed{3}$ 17 is 5 less than n.

$\boxed{4}$ 35 is less than n.

■ **P-1** What open sentence is a translation of $\boxed{3}$?

■ **P-2** What open sentence is a translation of $\boxed{4}$?

Sentence $\boxed{3}$ tells how much less 17 is than n. Hence you can use =. Sentence $\boxed{4}$ says only that 35 is less than n. This involves <.

Example 1: The sum of two numbers is 56, and one of them is 42 more than the other. What are the two numbers?

You want to write an open sentence that is a translation of this problem.

■ **P-3** If you let n represent the smaller number, what open phrase represents the greater number?

■ **P-4** What open sentence states that the sum of the numbers is 56?

Every problem should be read carefully. The next step should be to choose a variable to represent an unknown number in the problem.

Often it is desirable for the variable to represent the smallest unknown in the problem.

There is another way that the last example can be translated:

Let n equal the smaller number.
Then $56 - n$ equals the greater number.

■ **P-5** What open sentence states that one of these is 42 more than the other?

You should be able to see that the open sentence

$$56 - n = n + 42$$

is also a correct translation of the problem.

Shown below is one more example that will be the form for the different kinds of problems in this chapter.

Example 2: One number is 3 more than twice another number. Their product is 65. What are the numbers?

Choose a variable; tell
what it represents. ——————→ Let x equal the smaller number.
Use open phrases to represent
other unknowns. ——————→ Then $2x + 3$ equals the greater number.
Write the open sentence. ——————→ $x(2x + 3) = 65$

■ **P-6** If you let x represent the greater number, can you find an open phrase to represent the smaller?

Here you can see the advantage of letting the variable represent the smaller number. However, this is not always necessary.

ORAL EXERCISES 7.3

Translate each of the following word sentences into a mathematical open sentence.

1. 5 is 7 more than y.
2. 5 is more than y.
3. 13 exceeds 5 by x.
4. 13 exceeds 5.
5. 28 is 10 less than r.
6. 28 is less than r.
7. 75 is equal to x less 20.
8. 95 less q equals 21.
9. 37 is greater than the product of 5 and t.
10. 95 is 17 greater than the sum of 3 and w.

11. The sum of two numbers is 23. If the smaller one is represented by x, what phrase represents the greater number?
12. The difference between two numbers is 5. If y represents the greater number, what phrase represents the smaller?
13. One number is 3 greater than another. If n represents the greater number, what phrase represents the smaller?
14. One number is 12 less than another. If s represents the smaller number, what phrase represents the greater?
15. One number is 3 less than 5 times another. How would you represent the numbers?
16. One number exceeds 10 times another number by 17. How would you represent the numbers?

WRITTEN EXERCISES 7.3

A In each of the following, (a) select a variable and identify it, (b) write an open phrase for each of the other unknowns, and (c) write an open sentence translating the problem. Do not find the truth sets.

1. One number is 8 more than another, and their sum is 45. What are the numbers?
2. One number is 5 less than another, and their sum is 56. What are the numbers?
3. One number is 3 less than twice another number. If the sum of the numbers is 28, what are the numbers?
4. One number is 1 more than 5 times another number, and their product is 76. What are the numbers?
5. The sum of a whole number and its successor is 83. What is the number?
6. The product of a whole number and its successor is 380. What is the number?
7. The square of a number increased by 3 equals 56. What is the number?
8. The square of a number is 1 more than twice the number. What is the number?
9. The sum of twice a number and three times the same number is 112. What is the number?
10. The product of a number and 3 more than the number is 88. What is the number?

7.4 Problems with Perimeters and Areas

Many algebra problems involve working with perimeters and areas of figures such as squares, rectangles, and triangles. You should be familiar with the list of formulas that are used in finding perimeters and areas that is given in Chapter 6. In translating such problems into open sentences, you should have a clear understanding of the rule that each formula represents.

Example 1: The length of a rectangle is 3 centimeters greater than the width. The perimeter is 50 centimeters. What are the length and width in centimeters? (Drawing a figure will probably help you.)

Let x equal the number of centimeters in the width. Then $x + 3$ equals the number of centimeters in the length.

■ **P-1**   What is the formula for the perimeter of a rectangle?

Using the idea expressed by the formula, you can form an open sentence using only the variable x.

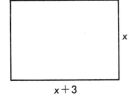

$$p = 2l + 2w \qquad \text{(Formula)}$$
$$50 = 2(x + 3) + 2x \qquad \text{(Open Sentence)}$$

Notice that $x + 3$ must be enclosed in parentheses.

■ **P-2**   What is the difference in meaning between $2(x + 3)$ and $2x + 3$?

Do not label the numerals in an open sentence with the units of measure. Label only the final answer.

Example 2: The base of a triangle is 2 inches less than the altitude. If the area of the triangle is 24 square inches, what is the altitude?

■ **P-3**   If you let x represent the altitude, what phrase represents the base?

■ **P-4**   What is the formula for the area of a triangle?

Here are the steps:

Let x equal the number of inches in the altitude.
Then $x - 2$ equals the number of inches in the base.

$$A = \tfrac{1}{2}bh \qquad \text{(Formula for the Area of a Triangle)}$$
$$24 = \tfrac{1}{2}(x - 2)x \qquad \text{(Open Sentence)}$$

Here is a summary of the formulas that will be helpful in this section:

Perimeter of a Square:	$p = 4s$
Perimeter of a Rectangle:	$p = 2l + 2w$
Perimeter of a Triangle:	$p = a + b + c$
Area of a Square Region:	$A = s^2$
Area of a Rectangular Region:	$A = lw$
Area of a Triangular Region:	$A = \frac{1}{2}bh$

Generally, you may abbreviate the expression "area of a rectangular region" to "area of a rectangle" with no loss of meaning.

ORAL EXERCISES 7.4

1. What is the perimeter of the rectangle in Figure 1?

2. What is the perimeter of the triangle in Figure 2?

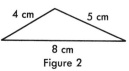
15 in

10 in

Figure 1

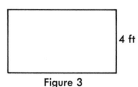
4 cm   5 cm
8 cm
Figure 2

3. If the length of the rectangle in Figure 3 is 3 feet more than its width, what is its perimeter?

4. What is the area of the rectangle in Figure 1?

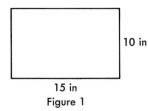
4 ft

Figure 3

5. What is the area of the rectangle in Figure 3?

6. What phrase represents the perimeter of the rectangle in Figure 4?

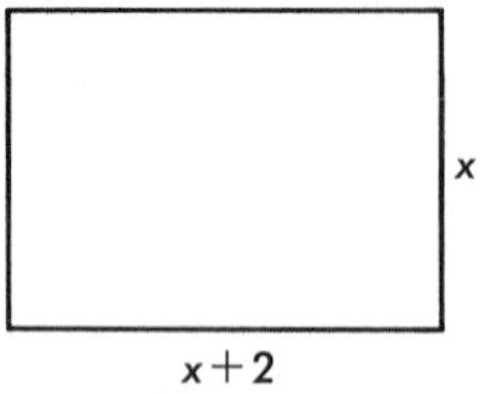

7. What phrase represents the length of the rectangle in Figure 5 if the length is 7 millimeters more than the width?

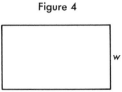
x

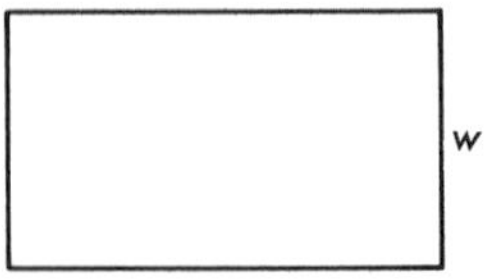

x+2

Figure 4

8. What phrase represents the area of the rectangle in Figure 4?

w

Figure 5

9. Give an open sentence that says the perimeter of the rectangle in Figure 6 is 72.

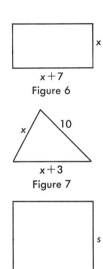

Figure 6

Figure 7

Figure 8

10. Give an open sentence that says the area of the rectangle in Figure 6 is 500.

11. Give an open sentence that says the perimeter of the triangle in Figure 7 is 29.

12. Give an open sentence that says the area of the square in Figure 8 is 152.

WRITTEN EXERCISES 7.4

A For each of the following problems, (a) draw a figure, (b) select a variable and show on the figure what it represents, (c) write open phrases for the other parts of the figure needed in the problem, and (d) write an open sentence translating the problem.

1. The length of a rectangle is 10 feet more than its width, and the perimeter is 100 feet. What are the width and length?

2. The width of a rectangle is shorter than the length by 3 centimeters. If the perimeter is 56 centimeters, what is the length?

3. The width of a rectangle is 6 meters less than the length. The area is 44 square meters. What is the length?

4. The length of a rectangle is 1 inch more than twice the width. If the area is 132 square inches, what is the width?

5. One side of a triangle is twice the length of another. The third side is 15 centimeters long, and the perimeter is 55 centimeters. What are the lengths that are not given?

6. Two sides of a triangle have the same length, and the third side has a measurement of 12 decimeters. If the perimeter is 45 decimeters, how long are the sides of equal length?

7. In a triangle the base is 15 inches long and the area is 75 square inches. What is the length of the altitude?

8. A triangle has an area of 68 square centimeters. If the altitude measures 20 centimeters, how long is the base?

C   **9.** In the figure at the right, what phrase represents the area of the unshaded region inside the rectangle?

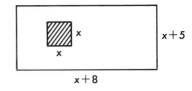

10. In the figure at the right, what phrase represents the area of the enclosed region?

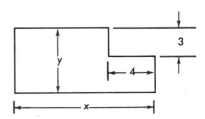

7.5   Problems in Costs

It is usually understood that the cost of merchandise is proportional to the amount purchased. For example, if one candy bar costs 10¢, you expect five candy bars to cost 50¢. Of course, some merchants reduce the price for sales of large amounts. In this section, assume that prices and numbers of items are proportional for the same merchandise.

■ **P-1**   What proportion could you use to solve the following problem?

How much will 20 reams of paper cost if one ream costs 85¢?

You can probably see that the following is one possible way of solving the problem.

$$\frac{x}{85} = \frac{20}{1}$$
$$x = 20 \cdot 85$$
$$x = 1700$$

■ **P-2**   In what unit of money is 1700 expressed?

In effect, you can find the answer by multiplying 20 and 85; that is, you multiply the number of items purchased by the cost per item. This is a standard rule in business, and it can be expressed by the formula

$$T = nc,$$

where n represents the number of items and c, the cost of each item. The phrase nc represents the total cost and is given the common name T.

■ **P-3** What phrase represents the total cost of 15 dresses at x dollars each?

■ **P-4** What is the total cost of n cars at $2200 each?

This same idea can be applied to coins. For example, to find the value in cents of 6 dimes, use the phrase $10 \cdot 6$. The number 10 is the number of cents in one dime, and 6 is the number of dimes.

■ **P-5** What is the value of 3 quarters expressed in cents?

■ **P-6** What is the value of 4 half dollars expressed in cents?

■ **P-7** What phrase represents the value of x nickels in cents? y quarters? n dimes?

■ **P-8** How would you express $1.80 in cents?

Here is a coin problem:

Example: A boy has a collection of nickels and dimes in his bank. There are 2 more dimes than nickels, and the total value is $1.25. How many nickels and how many dimes does he have?

Let x equal the number of nickels.

■ **P-9** $\underline{\ ?\ }$ equals the number of dimes.

■ **P-10** $\underline{\ ?\ }$ equals the value of nickels in cents.

$10(x + 2)$ equals the value of dimes in cents.
Thus, $5x + 10(x + 2) = 125$ is the open sentence for the problem.

■ **P-11** Why is 125 used instead of $1.25?

■ **P-12** As a translation for this problem, what is wrong with your using the sentence $x + (x + 2) = 125$?

ORAL EXERCISES 7.5

Translate the following into mathematical open sentences.
1. At 29¢ each, x cans of soup cost $2.03.
2. The cost of y admissions to the movie at 75¢ each is $6.75.
3. One dozen doughnuts at r cents each cost 78¢.
4. The total value of d dimes is $3.70.
5. x quarters have a value of $3.25.
6. In a collection of coins, there are x nickels and twice as many quarters. In all, there are 39 coins.

Exercises 7–11 refer to the following problem: "A man buys 5 gallons of regular gasoline for his lawn mower and 15 gallons of ethyl gasoline for his car. It costs $6.25 altogether. If ethyl gasoline costs 3¢ more per gallon than regular gasoline, how much is the cost of regular gasoline per gallon?"

7. How can you represent the cost of regular gasoline?

8. What phrase represents the cost of ethyl gasoline?

9. What phrase represents the cost of 5 gallons of regular gasoline?

10. What phrase represents the cost of 15 gallons of ethyl gasoline?

11. What open sentence is a translation of the problem?

Complete the following table for this problem: "A boy has 2 more quarters than nickels, and three times as many dimes as nickels. The collection is worth $4.10. How many nickels does he have?"

	Type of Coin	Number	Value in Cents
12.	Nickels	x	?
13.	Quarters	?	?
14.	Dimes	?	?

15. Do you know how many coins there are altogether?

16. What is the value in cents?

17. What open sentence describes the problem?

WRITTEN EXERCISES 7.5

A For each problem, (a) identify the variable, (b) write open phrases that are needed, and (c) write an open sentence to describe the problem.

1. Twelve reams of paper cost $13.15 including 55¢ tax. What is the price per ream, not including tax?

2. Twelve tennis balls cost the same as 9 golf balls. The cost of a golf ball is 25¢ more than the cost of a tennis ball. How much does a tennis ball cost?

3. Hurley buys 3 shirts costing $2.50 each and some socks costing 75¢ a pair. How many pairs of socks did he buy if his total bill was $11.25?

4. Mr. Smith buys 4 tires, 3 at the regular price and the other for $5.00 less. If the 4 tires cost $82.96, what was the regular price?

5. Roy has 5 more nickels than dimes. If he has $2.05, how many dimes does he have?

6. The number of dimes Elbert has is 20 more than the number of half dollars Delbert has. If their savings have the same value, how many dimes does Elbert have?

7. Kay has twice as many quarters as she has dimes. How many dimes does she have, if the collection is worth $1.20?

8. Randy has saved $1.70. He has 12 nickels and three times as many dimes as quarters. How many quarters does he have?

C 9. A bottle and a stopper cost $1.10, and the bottle cost $1.00 more than the stopper. How much did each cost?

10. Can you work this problem? In a collection of 100 coins worth $5.00, there are pennies, dimes, and half dollars. How many of each are there?

7.6 Problems Involving Distances and Lengths

Many problems involve the sum of two lengths or distances.

■ **P-1** If the sum of two distances is 500 miles and one distance is 150 miles, what is the other?

■ **P-2** The sum of two distances is 500 miles. If one distance is represented by x, what phrase represents the other?

Sometimes a diagram will help you to see these relationships.

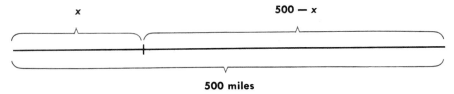

Example 1: A stick 27 inches long is broken into two pieces. Twice the length of one piece plus the length of the other equals 45. What is the length of each piece?

Let x equal the length of one piece. Then $27 - x$ equals the length of the other piece, and

$$2x + (27 - x) = 45$$

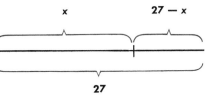

is the open sentence that you need.

■ P-3 Could $x - 27$ be used for the length of one of the two pieces in Example 1?

■ P-4 Do you think the sentence $x + (27 - x) = 27$ could be used to solve the problem in Example 1?

Example 2: Two planes take off in opposite directions, one flying at 500 mph and the other at 600 mph. How long will they have to fly until they are 2750 miles apart?

Let x equal the number of hours that they fly.

■ P-5 What phrase represents the distance traveled by the slower plane in x hours? by the faster plane? Recall that the formula for distance is

$$d = rt.$$

The following diagram may help you to understand the problem.

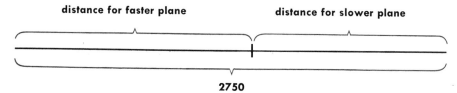

distance for faster plane   distance for slower plane

2750

The following open sentence describes the problem.

$$500x + 600x = 2750$$

Example 3: A man takes a trip in 25 hours. He travels by car part way at 60 mph and by train the remainder of the trip at 50 mph. How long did he travel by car if the entire trip was 1330 miles?

Let x equal the number of hours of traveling by car.

■ P-6 What phrase represents the number of hours of traveling on the train?

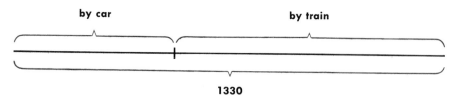

by car   by train

1330

■ P-7 What phrase represents the distance traveled by car? by train?

You should see that the following sentence describes the problem.

$$60x + 50(25 - x) = 1330$$

Translate the following into mathematical open sentences.

1. 500 miles is the distance traveled in x hours at 45 mph.
2. 230 miles is the distance traveled in 4 hours at r mph.
3. An object at a speed of 50 feet per second travels 950 feet in y seconds.
4. In 12 minutes, a jet can travel 135 miles at x mph.

Fill in the missing numerals in the table for this problem: "Henry and Mel run a race. Henry can run it in 10 seconds. Mel runs it 2 yards per second slower in 12.5 seconds. What is Henry's speed?"

Runner	Speed	Time	Distance = Speed · Time
5. Henry	x	10 sec	?
6. Mel	?	12.5 sec	?

7. Since they run the same distance, what open sentence describes the problem?

Fill in the following table for this problem: "Two cities are 3000 miles apart. A train leaves A toward B at the same time a train leaves B toward A. The train leaving A averages 50 mph and the train leaving B averages 55 mph. How far from A do they meet?"

Train	Speed	Distance	Time = $\dfrac{\text{Distance}}{\text{Speed}}$
8. Slower	50 mph	x	?
9. Faster	55 mph	?	?

10. Since the time each travels is the same, what open sentence describes the problem?

WRITTEN EXERCISES 7.6

A Translate the following into open sentences. Be sure to identify the variable in each case.

1. A halfback and a tackle are 60 yards apart, and they run toward each other. How many seconds will it take them to meet if the halfback runs 9 yards per second and the tackle runs 7 yards per second? (A diagram and a table for this problem are given on the following page.)

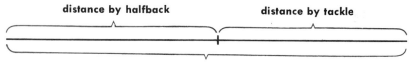

distance by halfback   distance by tackle

60 yards

	Time	Speed	Distance
Halfback	x	9 yd per sec	9x
Tackle	?	7 yd per sec	?

2. A tackler is 10 yards behind the ball carrier. How long will it take him to catch the ball carrier if the tackler runs at 10 yards per second, and the ball carrier runs at 8 yards per second?

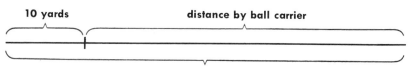

10 yards   distance by ball carrier

distance by tackler

	Time	Speed	Distance
Tackler	x	10 yd per sec	10x
Ball Carrier	?	8 yd per sec	?

3. A plane is 900 miles from its carrier. They move toward each other. The plane's speed is 500 mph, and the ship's speed is 30 mph. In how many hours will the plane reach the ship?

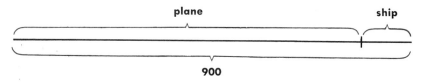

plane   ship

900

4. Two boys start on a cross-country bicycle hike. Ed arrives at their destination 2 days before Ned. Ed averages 100 miles per day, and Ned averages 95 miles per day. How long does it take them?

5. A board 16 feet long is to be cut into two pieces whose lengths are in the ratio 2 : 3. How long is each piece? (Let 2x equal the length of the shorter piece.)

6. A piece of wire one yard long is to be bent into the shape of a rectangle. The ratio of the length to the width is to be 4 : 3. What are the length and width of the rectangle in inches? (Let 4x equal the length in inches.)

7.7 Word Sentences and Inequalities

Now you will translate some word sentences to open sentences that require the use of the symbols $<$, $>$, $\leq$, and $\geq$. For your help, here are some of the word descriptions for these symbols:

Symbol	Word Description
$<$	is less than; is smaller than; is fewer than
$>$	is greater than; is larger than; is more than
$\leq$	is less than or equal to; is not greater than
$\geq$	is greater than or equal to; is not less than; is at least as large as

Example 1: The speed of sound is about 1100 feet per second. How many seconds will it take for sound to travel more than one mile?

First Guess

Number of Seconds: 3

Distance Traveled: 3300 ft

■ **P-1**   Is this distance more than one mile?

Second Guess

Number of Seconds: 4

■ **P-2**   Distance Traveled: ?

■ **P-3**   Is this distance more than one mile?

Third Guess

Number of Seconds: 5

■ **P-4**   Distance Traveled: ?

■ **P-5**   Is this distance more than one mile?

■ **P-6**   Are there any other answers to the problem?

Using a Variable

Number of Seconds: x

Distance Traveled: $1100x$

Open Sentence: $1100x > 5280$

■ **P-7**   Why is 5280 used for the distance instead of 1?

Example 2: The TV announcer estimated the number of people at the football game was not more than 50,000. About how many paid admissions were there if 1500 were admitted free?

First Guess

Number Paid: 49,000

Total Estimate: 49,000 + 1500

■ **P-8** Is this more than 50,000?

Second Guess

Number Paid: 48,000

Total Estimate: 48,000 + 1500

■ **P-9** Is this more than 50,000?

Third Guess

Number Paid: 48,500

Total Estimate: 48,500 + 1500

■ **P-10** Is this more than 50,000?

Using a Variable

Number Paid: x

Total Estimate: $x + 1500$

Open Sentence: $x + 1500 \leq 50,000$

ORAL EXERCISES 7.7

Translate each of the following into mathematical open sentences.

1. A board x inches long is shorter than a board 3 feet long.
2. The lengths of two sides of a triangle are x centimeters and $x + 1$ centimeters. The sum of their lengths is greater than the length of the third side, which is 35 centimeters.
3. The number of pints in x gallons is less than 27.
4. The value of x nickels is greater than 76¢.
5. The cost of n pencils at 5¢ each is not greater than $5.30.
6. The distance traveled in x hours by a motorcycle going 75 mph is greater than or equal to 450 miles.
7. The crowd of n people was at least 5000.
8. The cost of 100 pens at t cents each is not greater than $8.20.
9. The value of n quarters is not less than $15.00.
10. The number of millimeters in r centimeters is more than 370.

In each of the following choose a variable, tell what the variable represents, and give an open sentence that translates the word sentence.

11. The number of airplanes is greater than 50.
12. The number of points is at least 72.
13. Three more than the number of fish is less than 27.
14. There are not more than 5 TV stations in the area.
15. The length of the field is less than twice the width of 120 feet.
16. Twice the number of students is more than 5000.
17. Less than one half the students are boys, and there are 900 boys.
18. More than half the 35 players on the squad wanted to be halfbacks.
19. The population of Phoenix is not less than 500,000.
20. The list price less the discount of $5.00 was not more than $12.50.

WRITTEN EXERCISES 7.7

A   In each of the following choose a variable, tell what it represents, then write an open sentence that translates the problem.

1. The sum of a number and twice that number is more than 56. What numbers have this property?
2. One more than three times a number is less than or equal to 30. What whole numbers make this sentence true?
3. The product of a whole number and its successor is at least 12. What whole numbers make this sentence true?
4. The sum of a whole number and its successor is not more than 3. What whole numbers have this property?
5. The number of inches in a measurement is more than 52. What is the measurement in feet?
6. The number of quarts the radiator holds is not more than 15. How many pints does it hold?
7. The height of Humphrey's Peak is more than 12,000 feet. The hiking club started at 7000 feet and hiked to the top. How far did they climb?
8. The lake is less than 50 feet deep. Bruce's fishing lure is 10 feet from the surface. How far is it from the bottom?
9. The Dodgers got 16 runs, scoring more than twice as many in the game as the Cubs. How many did the Cubs score?
10. Joe scored more points on field goals in the basketball game than the other team. How many field goals did Joe make if the other team had 60 points?

11. How many quarters does Jean have in her bank if the value is at least $2.30?

12. What is the value in cents of a collection of dimes if there are not more than 29 dimes?

13. The discount on the purchase of a table is at least $25. What is the list price if the rate of discount is 15%?

14. The interest earned for one year on a 5% loan is less than $50. What is the principal?

15. The value of a certain number of nickels and three times as many dimes is at least $5.25. How many nickels are there?

16. Adult tickets to the game cost 75¢ each, and student tickets cost 50¢. Three times as many student tickets as adult tickets were sold. If the gate receipts were not more than $450, how many adult tickets were sold?

CHAPTER SUMMARY

1. Remember the steps in translating word sentences to open sentences:
   (a) Read the problem carefully.
   (b) Choose a variable to represent an unknown (often the smallest number).
   (c) Represent other unknowns, if there are any, by open phrases.
   (d) Write an open sentence using the operations that are suggested by the problem.
   (e) It may be helpful for you to guess some answers to help you see the pattern of the problem.

2. If the sum of two numbers is 50, one of the numbers can be represented by x and the other by $50 - x$.

3. A sentence must have a verb. In mathematical sentences the symbols $=$, $\neq$, $<$, $>$, $\leq$, $\geq$, and others represent verbs.

4. The symbol $=$ is used as the verb when the problem tells how much one number is greater than another.

5. The symbol $>$ or $<$ is used as the verb when the problem just tells that one number is greater than or is less than another.

6. When working with perimeters of rectangles, remember that the sum of the length and width is only half the perimeter.

7. The total cost of articles of merchandise is the product of the number of articles and the cost per article.

CHAPTER REVIEW

Translate each of the following word phrases into an open phrase. Tell what the variable represents.

1. The sum of a number and twice that number
2. Three times a number and the product increased by 5
3. The interest on savings for one year at 6%
4. The cost of a certain number of books at 75¢ each
5. The value in cents of a certain number of $1 bills and twice as many $5 bills
6. The number of grams of salt in a certain number of grams of 6% solution
7. The distance traveled by an object at 550 feet per second in a given number of seconds
8. The area of a rectangle whose length is 2 inches greater than its width
9. The area of a triangle whose base is twice its altitude
10. The circumference of a circle

Write an open sentence that is a translation of each problem. Tell what the variable represents.

11. Jeanie is 10 years older than Mary Ann. The sum of their ages is 22. How old is each?
12. The discount on a certain sale is $20, and the rate of discount is 15%. What is the list price?
13. The right guard on the football team weighs 10 pounds less than the left guard. What does each weigh if the sum of their weights is 380?
14. The number of eggs in a certain number of cartons is more than 1000. How many cartons are there if there are 12 eggs in a carton?
15. The width of a rectangle is 3 centimeters less than the length. If the perimeter is 96 centimeters, what is the length?
16. The length of a rectangle is 5 feet less than twice the width. If the area is 228 square feet, find the length.
17. The sum of a number and 18% of the number is 236. What is the number?
18. The perimeter of a triangle is not greater than 120 centimeters. The second side is twice the length of the first. The third side is 3 centimeters longer than the first. What is the length of each side?

At temperatures far below zero, most materials become brittle and can be shattered easily. A rubber ball that has been frozen in liquefied nitrogen at a temperature of 320° below zero, Fahrenheit, shatters when it is bounced. Many strange things happen to materials at temperatures near absolute zero (about 460° below zero, Fahrenheit), the temperature at which matter is wholly deprived of heat. How can you express temperatures below zero without using the words "below zero"? In this chapter, you will learn about numbers that are "below zero."

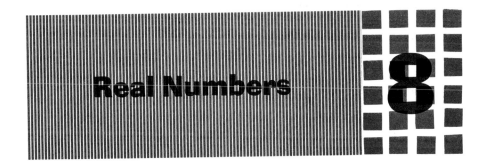

Real Numbers

8.1 Integers

In Chapter 1, you learned about the number line. You had practice in making number lines, and you saw that different sets of numbers can be defined by the number line. Some of the sets of numbers you have considered are the counting numbers, whole numbers, rational numbers of arithmetic, and numbers of arithmetic.

■ **P-1** Is there a number of arithmetic that is not a rational number?

Again you will use the number line to develop some new numbers. You will remember that, in constructing a number line, you first had to choose the points with coordinates 0 and 1. These two points determined a unit that was used in locating other points to the right of 1. (This really means points to the right of the point whose coordinate is 1. It is just easier to say "points to the right of 1.")

Now you will extend the number line to the left of 0. You will use the unit to locate points to the left of 0 as follows.

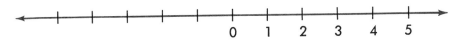

Mathematicians assign numbers to the points to the left of zero. Remember that the number associated with a point on the number line is called its **coordinate**. The first point to the left of 0 is labeled "⁻1." This is read "negative one." The next point is labeled "⁻2," the next "⁻3," and so forth. Here is the extended number line:

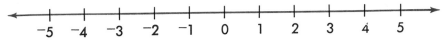

The arrows at each end of the line indicate that the line can be extended in both directions. You could locate points as far out either to the right or to the left as you wish.

■ **P-2** Where is the point located whose coordinate is ⁻10?

■ **P-3** Is there a point on the number line whose coordinate is ⁻10,000?

The numbers that are coordinates of points to the left of 0 are called **negative numbers.** The negative numbers shown on the number line on the previous page are members of the set of **negative integers.** Notice that you may obtain the numerals for the negative integers by placing the high dash, ⁻, before the numerals for the counting numbers.

The set of negative integers can be shown by the modified roster method in two ways.

$$\boxed{1}\ \{\cdots, ^-4, ^-3, ^-2, ^-1\} \quad \text{or} \quad \boxed{2}\ \{^-1, ^-2, ^-3, ^-4, \cdots\}$$

■ **P-4** Is the set of negative integers finite or infinite?

Remember that the three dots represent missing elements. Of course, you can find the missing elements by continuing the pattern. The set of counting numbers, $\{1, 2, 3, 4, 5, \cdots\}$, is often called the set of **positive integers.**

■ **P-5** Is 0 an element of either the set of positive integers or the set of negative integers?

> The set of integers is the set that is made up of the negative integers, zero, and the positive integers.

The set of integers can be shown as follows.

$$\{\cdots, ^-4, ^-3, ^-2, ^-1, 0, 1, 2, \cdots\}$$

■ **P-6** Is zero a whole number? Is zero an integer?

Give names for the sets that are graphed below. Recall that "etc." means that the graph extends infinitely in the same pattern.

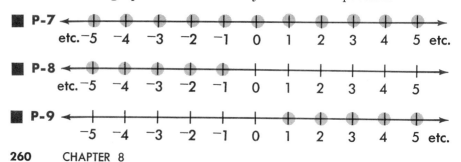

ORAL EXERCISES 8.1

1. How do you read the symbol ⁻15?
2. What do you call numbers that are coordinates of points to the left of 0?
3. What is another name for the set of counting numbers?
4. Is 0 a positive integer or a negative integer?
5. What is the set of integers?

Tell whether each of the following is *True* or *False*.
6. {negative integers} is a subset of {integers}.
7. {whole numbers} is a subset of {integers}.
8. {negative integers} is a subset of {whole numbers}.
9. {counting numbers} is a subset of {integers}.
10. {positive integers} is a subset of {whole numbers}.
11. {counting numbers} = {positive integers}.
12. {0} is a subset of {integers}.
13. {positive integers} is a subset of {negative integers}.
14. {numbers of arithmetic} is a subset of {integers}.

For each pair of points whose coordinates are given, tell which point is to the right of the other.
15. ⁻5; 3   16. 0; ⁻10   17. ⁻100; 100
18. 10; 0   19. ⁻3; ⁻7   20. 13; ⁻5

WRITTEN EXERCISES 8.1

A Use the roster method or the modified roster method to list elements of the following sets.
1. {positive integers}   2. {negative integers}
3. {whole numbers}   4. {counting numbers}
5. {integers}   6. {nonnegative integers}
7. {nonpositive integers}   8. {negative numbers of arithmetic}

Describe by the roster method or the modified roster method the sets that are graphed below.

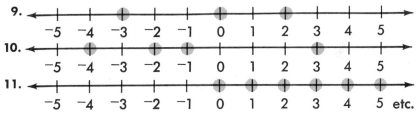

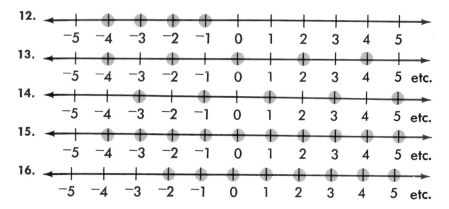

12.

−5 −4 −3 −2 −1 0 1 2 3 4 5

13.

−5 −4 −3 −2 −1 0 1 2 3 4 5 etc.

14.

−5 −4 −3 −2 −1 0 1 2 3 4 5 etc.

15.

−5 −4 −3 −2 −1 0 1 2 3 4 5 etc.

16.

−5 −4 −3 −2 −1 0 1 2 3 4 5 etc.

Draw graphs of the following sets.

17. $\{-3, -1, 0, 2\}$ **18.** $\{-2, -1, 3, 5\}$ **19.** $\{\cdots, -3, -2, -1\}$

20. $\{-1, -2, -3, -4, \cdots\}$ **21.** $\{\cdots, -6, -4, -2, 0, 2, 4, 6, \cdots\}$

22. $\{\cdots, -5, -3, -1, 1, 3, 5, \cdots\}$

8.2   Rational Numbers

In an earlier chapter you learned about the rational numbers of arithmetic. These are numbers each of which can be expressed as the quotient formed by dividing a whole number by a counting number.

■ **P-1**   What rational numbers of arithmetic are graphed here?

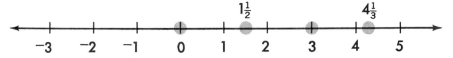

$1\frac{1}{2}$ $4\frac{1}{3}$

−3 −2 −1 0 1 2 3 4 5

■ **P-2**   How can each of the numbers graphed above be expressed as the quotient of a whole number divided by a counting number?

Of course, the rational numbers of arithmetic consist of 0 and those numbers associated with certain points to the right of 0. It seems reasonable that there should be numbers much like the rational numbers of arithmetic associated with points to the left of 0. These numbers are called the **negative rational numbers.**

The point halfway between the points with coordinates 0 and ⁻1 is given the coordinate ⁻$(\frac{1}{2})$ as shown:

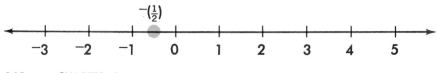

⁻$(\frac{1}{2})$

−3 −2 −1 0 1 2 3 4 5

■ **P-3** Where would you locate the point with coordinate $^-(1\frac{1}{2})$?

Below is shown the graph of the following subset of the set of negative rational numbers.

$$\{^-(\tfrac{2}{3}),\ ^-(1\tfrac{1}{4}),\ ^-(2\tfrac{1}{3}),\ ^-(\tfrac{11}{3})\}$$

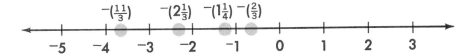

Notice that you can write the coordinates above the line to avoid crowding. Also notice carefully the location of each point with respect to the two points whose coordinates are successive integers. For example, $^-(2\tfrac{1}{3})$ is located a distance equal to one third of the unit to the left of the point with coordinate $^-2$.

You can see how the numerals for negative rational numbers are obtained. The numerals for the rational numbers of arithmetic are enclosed in parentheses with the raised dash, $^-$, placed before the parentheses.

■ **P-4** How would you read the symbol $^-(\tfrac{13}{4})$?

The rational numbers of arithmetic whose points are to the right of 0 are called the **positive rational numbers.**

■ **P-5** Is 0 a negative rational number? Is it a positive rational number?

> The set of **rational numbers** is the set that is made up of the negative rational numbers, zero, and the positive rational numbers.

■ **P-6** Is the set of positive rational numbers finite or infinite? What about the negative rational numbers?

You probably remember that you cannot describe the rational numbers of arithmetic by either the roster or the modified roster method. There is no pattern. Likewise, you can use only word descriptions for the set of negative rational numbers, the set of positive rational numbers, and the entire set of rational numbers.

ORAL EXERCISES 8.2

Indicate whether each of the following is *True* or *False*.
 1. {negative rational numbers} is a subset of {rational numbers}.
 2. {positive rational numbers} is a subset of {rational numbers}.
 3. {0} is a subset of {rational numbers}.
 4. {integers} is a subset of {rational numbers}.
 5. {negative rational numbers} is a subset of {negative integers}.
 6. {positive integers} is a subset of {positive rational numbers}.
 7. {whole numbers} is a subset of {positive rational numbers}.
 8. {counting numbers} is a subset of {rational numbers}.
 9. {rational numbers of arithmetic} = {positive rational numbers}.
 10. {0} is a subset of {positive rational numbers}.

For each pair of points whose coordinates are given, tell which point is to the right of the other.
 11. $^-(\frac{1}{3})$; $\frac{2}{5}$ **12.** $^-(2\frac{1}{3})$; $^-2$ **13.** $2\frac{1}{5}$; 3 **14.** $^-(3\frac{1}{4})$; $^-4$
 15. $^-(4\frac{1}{3})$; $\frac{1}{3}$ **16.** $\frac{7}{8}$; $\frac{7}{16}$ **17.** $^-(\frac{7}{8})$; $^-(\frac{7}{16})$ **18.** 0; $^-(\frac{1}{5})$
 19. $^-(2\frac{8}{9})$; $^-(3\frac{1}{9})$ **20.** $^-(1\frac{1}{3})$; $^-(1\frac{2}{3})$

WRITTEN EXERCISES 8.2

A Let $R = \{^-10, ^-(\frac{8}{2}), ^-(2\frac{2}{3}), ^-(\frac{7}{4}), ^-(0.1), 0, \frac{5}{8}, 3, \frac{13}{4}, \frac{8}{2}\}$. Use the roster method to name subsets of R whose elements are the following numbers.

   1. rational numbers   **2.** negative rational numbers
   3. integers   **4.** nonnegative rational numbers
   5. whole numbers   **6.** numbers of arithmetic
   7. nonnegative integers   **8.** negative integers
   9. positive rational numbers   **10.** counting numbers

Draw graphs of the following sets.
 11. $\{^-(\frac{1}{2}), 3, ^-(\frac{9}{3}), 0, ^-(\frac{5}{2})\}$ **12.** $\{\frac{3}{4}, ^-(1\frac{1}{4}), \frac{8}{4}, ^-(2\frac{2}{3})\}$
 13. $\{^-(\frac{5}{3}), ^-(3\frac{3}{5}), ^-(\frac{3}{4}), \frac{3}{4}\}$ **14.** $\{\frac{13}{3}, 0, ^-(\frac{2}{3}), ^-(1\frac{1}{3}), ^-5\}$
 15. $\{\cdots, ^-(3\frac{1}{2}), ^-(2\frac{1}{2}), ^-(1\frac{1}{2}), ^-(\frac{1}{2}), \frac{1}{2}, 1\frac{1}{2}, 2\frac{1}{2}, \cdots\}$
 16. $\{\cdots, ^-(\frac{7}{2}), ^-(\frac{6}{2}), ^-(\frac{5}{2}), ^-(\frac{4}{2}), ^-(\frac{3}{2}), ^-(\frac{2}{2}), ^-(\frac{1}{2})\}$

Find the coordinate of a point that is between the two points with coordinates given.
 17. $^-3$ and $^-4$ **18.** $^-5$ and $^-6$ **19.** $^-(\frac{1}{4})$ and $^-(\frac{1}{2})$
 20. $^-(\frac{1}{2})$ and $^-(\frac{3}{4})$ **21.** $^-(3\frac{1}{4})$ and $^-(3\frac{1}{8})$ **22.** $^-(2\frac{5}{8})$ and $^-(2\frac{1}{4})$
 23. 0 and $^-(\frac{1}{16})$ **24.** $^-(\frac{1}{10})$ and 0

8.3 Real Numbers

In working with the rational numbers, you have seen that there is a point on the number line for each rational number.

■ **P-1** Do you think that every point on the number line has a coordinate that is a rational number?

You may remember that the answer to this question was "no" when you were working with the rational numbers of arithmetic. There is a point on the number line whose coordinate is π, and π is not a rational number. The number π cannot be expressed as the quotient of two whole numbers.

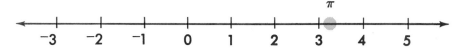

Many, many other points on the number line have coordinates that are not rational numbers. Look at the open sentence $x^2 = 2$. A truth number of this sentence is a number whose square is 2. If the domain of the variable is {rational numbers}, then the truth set of $x^2 = 2$ is empty. There is no rational number whose square is 2.

There are, however, two numbers that will make the sentence $x^2 = 2$ true. There are two points on the number line whose coordinates form the truth set of this open sentence. These numbers expressed in decimal form are $1.41421\cdots$ and $^-1.41421\cdots$. The three dots here mean that the numerals are nonending decimals. They are also nonrepeating. That is, there is no sequence of digits that is repeated infinitely many times.

> Numbers that can be expressed as nonending and nonrepeating decimals are called **irrational** numbers.

■ **P-2** How can you express the rational number $\frac{1}{3}$ as a decimal fraction?

You know that no matter how far you carry out the division, the digit 3 will continue to appear. You can represent $\frac{1}{3}$ in decimal form as $0.33333\cdots$. Here it is clear what the pattern of the continuing sequence of digits is. This is a repeating decimal that is nonending.

■ **P-3** What are the next two digits in the decimal 0.272727 · · · ?

You can see that 0.272727 · · · is also a repeating decimal that is nonending.

■ **P-4** What sequence of digits repeats in each of the following?

$$0.81234234234 \cdots; \quad 5.19999 \cdots; \quad 8.0000 \cdots$$

Any rational number can always be expressed as a repeating decimal. The irrational numbers are the numbers that can be represented as nonrepeating decimals, and the rational numbers are those that can be represented as repeating decimals.

■ **P-5** Is the following a numeral for a rational or an irrational number?

$$0.101001000100001 \cdots$$

You have now reached a very important point in your study of numbers. You now have a set that includes all the numbers that you will need to use in this course.

> The set of **real numbers** is made up of all the rational numbers and all the irrational numbers.

Every point on the number line has a real number for a coordinate. That number might be rational, it might be an integer, it might even be a positive integer. However, it can still be called a real number.

Also, for any real number, there is always a point on the number line associated with it.

> There is a one-to-one correspondence between points of the number line and the real numbers.

Because of this fact the number line is often called the real-number line.

■ **P-6** About where would you locate a point whose coordinate is $^-\pi$?

It should be clear from the discussion that every set of numbers you have studied so far is a subset of the set of real numbers.

ORAL EXERCISES 8.3

Tell whether each of the following is *True* or *False*.

1. {rational numbers} is a subset of {real numbers}.
2. {integers} is a subset of {irrational numbers}.
3. {negative real numbers}
   is a subset of
   {negative rational numbers}.
4. {positive rational numbers} is a subset of {real numbers}.
5. {irrational numbers} is a subset of {real numbers}.
6. {negative integers} is a subset of {negative real numbers}.
7. {nonnegative rational numbers}
   is a subset of
   {nonnegative real numbers}.
8. {negative real numbers} is a subset of {irrational numbers}.
9. {positive real numbers} is a subset of {real numbers}.
10. {0} is a subset of {real numbers}.

For each of the following numbers, indicate those sets of which it is a member.

$$R = \{\text{real numbers}\}$$
$$Q = \{\text{rational numbers}\}$$
$$I = \{\text{integers}\}$$
$$W = \{\text{whole numbers}\}$$

11. 16
12. $^-3$
13. $\frac{2}{3}$
14. $3.167167167\cdots$
15. $5.0000\cdots$
16. $^-\pi$
17. 0
18. $^-(\frac{3}{5})$
19. $^-(\frac{20}{5})$
20. $0.12345678910111213\cdots$

WRITTEN EXERCISES 8.3

A Express each of the following rational numbers as an infinite repeating decimal.

1. 9
2. 5
3. $3\frac{1}{2}$
4. $16\frac{1}{4}$
5. $\frac{3}{7}$
6. $\frac{5}{6}$

Round the value of π to the degree of precision given in each of the following.

$$\pi \approx 3.1415926536$$

7. 9 decimal places
8. 8 decimal places
9. 7 decimal places
10. 6 decimal places
11. hundred thousandths
12. ten thousandths
13. thousandths
14. hundredths

Make a table like the one below. If each number is an element of a particular set, write *Yes*. Otherwise, write *No*.

	real numbers	rational numbers	irrational numbers	integers	whole numbers
15. $^-13$	?	?	?	?	?
16. 12	?	?	?	?	?
17. $3\frac{1}{2}$	?	?	?	?	?
18. $^-\left(\frac{13}{5}\right)$	?	?	?	?	?
19. $2.3535\cdots$	?	?	?	?	?
20. $73.1818\cdots$	?	?	?	?	?
21. $^-\pi$	?	?	?	?	?
22. 0	?	?	?	?	?

23. Name an integer that is not a whole number.
24. Name a rational number that is not an integer.

C 25. Which is a closer approximation to π, $\frac{22}{7}$ or 3.14?
26. Which is a closer approximation to $1.414214\cdots$, $\frac{17}{12}$ or $\frac{29}{17}$?

8.4 Order of Real Numbers

You have had some practice in graphing subsets of the real numbers. To do this, of course, you need to find a point on the number line corresponding to each real number of the set you are graphing. Often, such points are located only by approximate methods. You are now going to see how the position of two points on the number line is related to the size of their coordinates. You have probably sensed this relationship already.

■ **P-1** Is a point with a positive coordinate to the right or to the left of 0?

■ **P-2** Is a point with a negative coordinate to the right or to the left of 0?

The real numbers that are coordinates of points to the right of 0 are called the positive real numbers. The coordinates of points to the left of 0 make up the set of negative real numbers.

■ **P-3** Is a point with a negative coordinate to the right or to the left of a point with a positive coordinate?

■ **P-4** Of the two numbers 2.1718 and 2.17181, which is greater? Which has its point to the right of the other?

■ **P-5** Of the two numbers ⁻1.81 and ⁻1.8, which has its point to the left of the other? Which number do you think is lesser?

This discussion should help you see a reasonable rule for relating order of points on the number line and size of their coordinates.

> The sentence $a > b$ means that the point with coordinate a is to the right of the point with coordinate b.

Often, points are named by capital letters and their coordinates by small letters. The above relation is shown on the number line below.

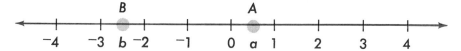

■ **P-6** Using the following number line, which of these is greater, x or y?

The **order of two real numbers** refers to the comparison of their positions on the number line. Since each point of the line has exactly one real number for its coordinate, the following property should be clear.

> If a is a real number and b is a real number, then exactly one of the following is true:
>
> $\boxed{1}\ a > b;\quad \boxed{2}\ a = b;\quad \boxed{3}\ a < b$

This is called the **comparison property** of real numbers.

How would you graph an open sentence for which the domain of the variable is {real numbers}? Consider the sentence $x > 3$. You know that any number that makes this sentence true will be to the right of 3 on the number line. Hence, the graph of the truth set of $x > 3$ will consist of all points on the number line to the right of the point with coordinate 3, as shown on the number line below.

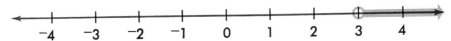

■ **P-7** Can you state an open sentence whose truth set is graphed as follows?

■ **P-8** How would you describe the graph of the truth set of the open sentence $x \leq {}^-2$?

You can also graph compound sentences, using {real numbers} as the domain. Below is the graph of the truth set of $x > {}^-(2\frac{1}{2})$ *and* $x \leq 3$.

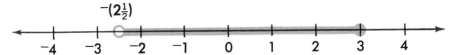

The following is the graph of the truth set of $x \leq {}^-2$ *or* $x > 1\frac{1}{2}$.

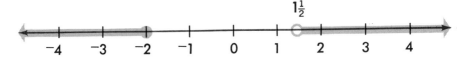

ORAL EXERCISES 8.4

For each pair of real numbers, tell which one is greater than the other.

1. $^-1$; 1	**2.** $^-(3\frac{1}{2})$; 2	**3.** 0; $^-5$
4. 10; 0	**5.** $^-3$; $^-4$	**6.** 5.6; $^-6.5$
7. $^-1.125$; $^-1.126$	**8.** 10; $^-100$	**9.** $1\frac{3}{4}$; $^-(1\frac{3}{4})$
10. $2\frac{1}{8}$; $^-(3\frac{5}{8})$	**11.** $^-17$; $^-1.5$	**12.** $^-1000$; 999

Tell whether or not the truth set of the given open sentence in each of the following is correctly graphed.

13. $x \leq {}^-1$

14. $y > {}^-2$

15. $^-5 \leq r$

16. $a \leq 0$

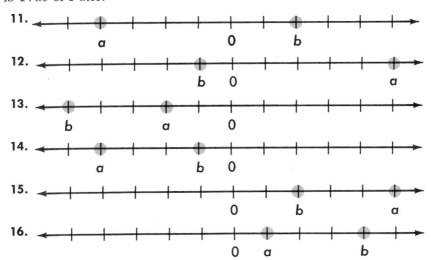

17. $x > {}^-3 \; and \; x \leq 1$

18. $x \leq {}^-3 \; or \; x > {}^-1$

WRITTEN EXERCISES 8.4

A Use $>$ and $<$ to form two true sentences with each pair of numbers.

1. $^-5; \; 5$ **2.** $10; \; ^-10$ **3.** $0; \; ^-3$ **4.** $0; \; 5$

5. $^-(3\frac{1}{4}); \; ^-(4\frac{1}{4})$ **6.** $^-10.2; \; ^-9.6$ **7.** $1.2; \; ^-2.1$

8. $^-8.9; \; 9.8$ **9.** $^-(\frac{1}{2}); \; ^-1$ **10.** $^-(\frac{3}{2}); \; ^-2$

From each of the following graphs, tell whether the sentence $a > b$ is *True* or *False*.

11.

        a   0   b

12.

        b   0   a

13.

     b   a   0

14.

     a   b   0

15.

           0   b   a

16.

         0   a   b

Make a graph of each of the truth sets of the following open sentences, using as the domain {real numbers}.

17. $x \geq {}^-3$ **18.** $x < {}^-2$ **19.** $x < {}^-(1\frac{1}{2})$ **20.** $x \geq {}^-(3\frac{1}{4})$

21. $x \leq 2$ **22.** $x < 3\frac{1}{2}$ **23.** $x \leq 0$ **24.** $x < 0$

25. $x < {}^-2 \; or \; x > 3$ **26.** $x \leq {}^-1 \; or \; x > 4$

27. $x > {}^-3 \; or \; x < 1$ **28.** $x > {}^-2 \; or \; x \leq 5$

29. $x \geq {}^-3 \; and \; x < 1$ **30.** $x > {}^-2 \; and \; x \leq 3$

31. $x \leq {}^-1 \; and \; x > 2$ **32.** $x < {}^-3 \; and \; x \geq 1$

8.5 Opposites

You have probably noticed that two numbers such as 3 and ⁻3 have their points on the number line at the same distance from 0.

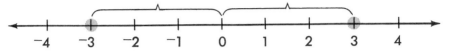

Two such numbers are said to be **opposites.** That is, 3 is the opposite of ⁻3, and ⁻3 is the opposite of 3.

You can find the opposite of any real number. Find the point on the number line that is the same distance from 0 as the point for the given number but in the opposite direction. Its coordinate is the opposite of the given number.

■ **P-1** What is the opposite of ⁻(2½)?

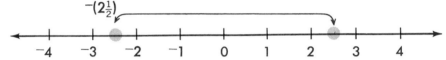

■ **P-2** What is the opposite of 3⅓?

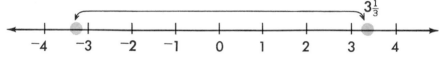

■ **P-3** What do you think is the opposite of 0?

Because the opposite of 0 is 0, each real number has exactly one opposite. To save writing, you may use a symbol to represent the opposite of a number. The dash symbol, −, placed before a numeral gives a symbol for the opposite of the number. Here are some examples:

> "−5" means "the opposite of 5."
> "−(⁻5)" means "the opposite of ⁻5."
> "−0" means "the opposite of 0."
> "−a" means "the opposite of a."

Notice that the dash symbol, −, for opposites looks like the minus sign used in subtraction. However, it does not mean subtraction here.

■ **P-4** What do the following numerals represent?

$$^-10; \quad -10; \quad -(^-10); \quad -\tfrac{1}{2}; \quad ^-(\tfrac{1}{2}); \quad -(^-\tfrac{1}{2})$$

You can use the meaning of opposites to find common names.

■ P-5 What number is the opposite of ⁻10?

The following sentence is true.

$$-(^-10) = 10$$

Hence, the numeral 10 is the common name for $-(^-10)$.

■ P-6 What is the common name for -10?

Since -10 represents a real number, $-(-10)$ also represents a real number. You may read this as "the opposite of the opposite of 10."

■ P-7 What do you think is the common name for $-(-10)$?

Look at it this way. First, locate the number 10 on the number line:

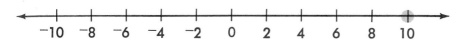

Then find "the opposite of 10," which is ⁻10:

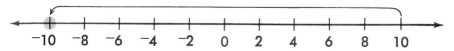

Then find "the opposite of ⁻10," which is 10:

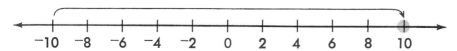

Thus, you see that $-(-10) = 10$.

■ P-8 What is the common name for $-(-^-3)$?

You can think of the problem this way. Start with ⁻3. Then find its opposite, which is 3. Then the opposite of 3 is ⁻3.

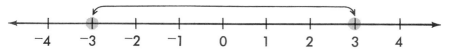

These examples suggest that "the opposite of the opposite of a number" is that given number.

> If x is any real number, then it is true that
> $$-(-x) = x.$$

ORAL EXERCISES 8.5

State each of the following in words. Then give a common name.

1. -7
2. $-(^-8)$
3. $^-(\frac{3}{4})$
4. $-\frac{3}{4}$
5. $-(^-(\frac{3}{4}))$
6. -0
7. $-(-100)$
8. $-(-^-100)$
9. $-(^-(\frac{1}{3}))$
10. $-(-t)$
11. $-(2+5)$
12. $^-(2+5)$
13. $-(-(-1))$
14. $-(-^-1)$

Tell whether the following sentences are *Always true*, *Sometimes true*, or *False*.

15. The opposite of a real number is a negative number.
16. The opposite of a positive number is a negative number.
17. The opposite of a negative number is a negative number.
18. A negative number cannot have a negative number as its opposite.
19. A real number has a different real number as its opposite.
20. A real number has exactly one real number as its opposite.

WRITTEN EXERCISES 8.5

A Give the common name for each of the following.

1. -15
2. -3.2
3. $-(^-11)$
4. $-(^-35)$
5. $-(-22)$
6. $-(-13)$
7. $-(^-(\frac{7}{8}))$
8. $-(^-(\frac{1}{5}))$
9. $-(-^-25)$
10. $-(-^-17)$
11. $-(-(-3))$
12. $-(-(-19))$
13. $^-(3\frac{1}{2})$
14. $^-(8.7)$
15. -0
16. $-(-0)$
17. $-(-r)$
18. $-(-y)$
19. $^-(8+5)$
20. $^-(13-7)$
21. $-(2\frac{1}{2}+\frac{1}{2})$
22. $-(3\frac{1}{4}+\frac{3}{4})$

Find the truth set of each of the following sentences. Let the domain be {real numbers}.

23. $-x = \frac{1}{2}$
24. $-y = ^-(\frac{2}{3})$
25. $-a = ^-(\frac{5}{2})$
26. $-r = ^-(\frac{7}{3})$
27. $-t = ^-(\frac{3}{4})$
28. $-x = ^-(.9)$

Indicate whether each of the following statements is *Always true*, *Sometimes true*, or *False*.

29. If x represents a real number, then $-x$ represents a negative number.
30. If $-y$ represents a positive number, y is a negative number.
31. If $-r$ represents a negative number, r is a positive number.
32. If x is a real number, then it is true that $x \neq -x$.

8.6 Order Property of Opposites

You know that a sentence such as $^-3 < 7$ is true. The point corresponding to $^-3$ is to the left of the point corresponding to 7 on the number line.

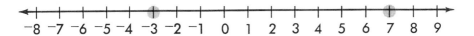

■ **P-1**   What is true about the order of the opposites of $^-3$ and 7?

$$-(^-3) = 3$$

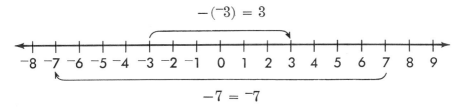

$$-7 = ^-7$$

Since 3 is the coordinate of the point that is to the right of the point corresponding to $^-7$, the sentence $3 > ^-7$ is true. This is what happened. You started with the true sentence $^-3 < 7$. You took the opposites of these two numbers and found that $-(^-3) > -7$, or $3 > ^-7$, was true.

Consider the sentence $^-8 < ^-2$.

■ **P-2**   What is the opposite of $^-8$?

■ **P-3**   What is the opposite of $^-2$?

■ **P-4**   What true sentence of order can you make using the opposites of $^-8$ and $^-2$?

Recall that $8 > 2$ and $2 < 8$ are sentences that show the same order relation between 2 and 8.

Consider the sentence $5 > 3$.

■ **P-5**   What is the opposite of 5?

■ **P-6**   What is the opposite of 3?

■ **P-7**   What true sentence using $<$ shows the order relation of $^-5$ and $^-3$?

These examples suggest that the order of the opposites of two real numbers is just the reverse of the order of the numbers themselves.

Thus, $^-8 < 3$ is true, and $-{}^-8 > -3$ is true.

> If a and b are any real numbers and $a < b$ is true, then $-a > -b$ is true. This is called the **Order Property of Opposites.**

■ **P-8** If $x > y$ is true for real numbers x and y, what true sentence shows the order of $-x$ and $-y$?

ORAL EXERCISES 8.6

From each of the following sentences, form a true sentence using the opposites of the given numbers.

1. $2 < 5$
2. $^-3 > {}^-8$
3. $^-1 < 7$
4. $10 > 8$
5. $^-7 < {}^-4$
6. $^-5 < 0$
7. $0 < 9$
8. $5 > {}^-11$
9. $0 > {}^-10$
10. $15 > 0$
11. $-7 > -9$
12. $-({}^-3) < 8$
13. $-5 < 5$
14. $^-3 < -(-7)$
15. $3\frac{1}{2} > {}^-(\frac{1}{2})$
16. $^-(\frac{3}{4}) < {}^-(\frac{1}{4})$

If a and b represent real numbers, tell whether each of the following is *True* or *False*.

17. If $-a > b$, then $a > -b$.
18. If $-a < -b$, then $b > a$.
19. If $a > -b$, then $-a < b$.
20. If $-b < -a$, then $b < a$.
21. If $b > a$, then $-a > -b$.
22. If $a < b$, then $-a > -b$.

WRITTEN EXERCISES 8.6

A Make a true sentence showing the order of the two numbers, using $<$. Then form a true sentence showing the order of their opposites, using $>$. Use common names for the opposites.

1. $8; \ 3$
2. $17; \ 5$
3. $^-3; \ {}^-10$
4. $^-1; \ {}^-12$
5. $^-7; \ 5$
6. $^-10; \ 3$
7. $0; \ {}^-7$
8. $^-12; \ 0$
9. $0; \ 8$
10. $12; \ 0$
11. $^-(1\frac{1}{2}); \ {}^-(3\frac{1}{4})$
12. $^-(5\frac{1}{8}); \ {}^-(7\frac{1}{4})$
13. $-({}^-3); \ -10$
14. $-17; \ -({}^-8)$
15. $^-(8 + 3); \ -(12 - 10)$
16. $-(8 + 7); \ {}^-(15 - 10)$

From each of the following sentences, form a true sentence showing the order of the opposites of the numbers given.

17. $^-15 < 2$
18. $5 > {}^-17$
19. $^-13 < {}^-11$
20. $^-56 < {}^-50$
21. $8 > 1$
22. $15 < 16$
23. $0 > -17$
24. $21 > 0$
25. $^-(5\frac{1}{8}) < {}^-(\frac{19}{4})$
26. $2\frac{5}{8} > {}^-(\frac{11}{8})$
27. $-5 < -({}^-7)$
28. $-({}^-10) > {}^-15$

B Choose the greater of each of the following numbers and its opposite.

29. $^-5$ **30.** 10 **31.** $-5\frac{1}{8}$

32. $-(^-6)$ **33.** $^-(8+9)$ **34.** $-\frac{1}{4}$

8.7   Opposites and Truth Sets

The Order Property of Opposites is helpful in making graphs of certain open sentences involving opposites. Consider the sentence $-x > 5$ with the domain {real numbers}.

■ **P-1**   How would you read the sentence $-x > 5$?

■ **P-2**   Is 2 an element of its truth set?

■ **P-3**   Is $^-6$ an element of its truth set?

Recall that a truth number makes the sentence true when it is used as a replacement for the variable. The variable in the sentence $-x > 5$ is x, not $-x$.

Now apply the Order Property of Opposites to the sentence $-x > 5$. Any truth number of $-x > 5$ is also a truth number of

$$-(-x) < -5, \quad \text{or} \quad x < {}^-5.$$

Likewise you can see that any truth number of $x < {}^-5$ is also a truth number of $-x > 5$. Therefore, the sentences $-x > 5$ and $x < {}^-5$ have the same truth sets. It is easy to see that the graph of the truth set using $x < {}^-5$ is as follows.

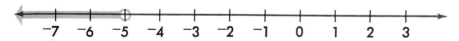

Example: Graph the truth set of the sentence $-x < {}^-3$.

■ **P-4**   What sentence do you get when you apply the Order Property of Opposites?

You should understand that the graph of the truth set of $x > 3$ is as shown below.

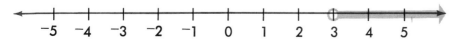

In a previous section, you found the truth sets of sentences such as $-x = 5$. Its truth set is $\{-5\}$. The truth set of $x = -5$ is also $\{-5\}$. The sentences $-x = 5$ and $-(-x) = -5$ have the same truth sets.

■ **P-5** What is the truth set of $-x = -(\frac{1}{2})$?

■ **P-6** What is the truth set of $x = \frac{1}{2}$?

These examples suggest that you can apply the Order Property of Opposites to sentences using $\leq$ and $\geq$. Any truth number of $-x \leq 3$ is also a truth number of $-(-x) \geq -3$, or $x \geq -3$. Likewise, any truth number of $x \geq -3$ is also a truth number of $-x \leq 3$.

The following is the graph of the truth set of

$$x \geq -3.$$

This, of course, is also the graph of $-x \leq 3$.

■ **P-7** What sentence results when you apply the Order Property of Opposites to $-5 \geq -x$?

You should see that the following is the graph of the truth set of

$$-5 > -x.$$

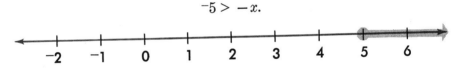

ORAL EXERCISES 8.7

Change each of the following open sentences so that it uses x instead of $-x$ but has the same truth set.

1. $-x \leq 5$
2. $-x > -6$
3. $-x < -(\frac{1}{2})$
4. $3 \leq -x$
5. $-10 \geq -x$
6. $-(\frac{1}{3}) < -x$
7. $10 > -x$
8. $-x < -8$ or $-x = -8$
9. $-x > 7$ or $-x = 7$
10. $-x > 3$ and $-x < 5$

Give two open sentences for each of the following graphs, one using x and the other $-x$.

11.
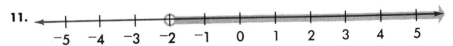

12.

13.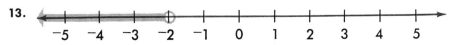

$1\frac{1}{2}$

14.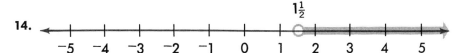

15.

16.

17.

18.

19.

20.

WRITTEN EXERCISES 8.7

A Make a graph of the truth set of each of the following open sentences. First apply the Order Property of Opposites to the sentence.

1. $-x > {}^{-}3$

2. $-x \leq 5$

3. $-x \leq 2$

4. $-x > {}^{-}1$

5. $-x < {}^{-}1$

6. $-x < {}^{-}3$

7. $-x \leq 0$

8. $-x > 0$

9. $0 < -x$

10. $0 \geq -x$

11. $-x > \frac{1}{2}$ or $-x = \frac{1}{2}$

12. $-x < {}^{-}3$ or $-x = {}^{-}3$

13. $-x < {}^{-}(\frac{3}{2})$ or $-x > 2$

14. $-x \leq 3$ or $-x > {}^{-}(\frac{5}{2})$

15. $-x < 2$ and $-x \geq 1$

16. $-x > {}^{-}2$ and $-x \leq {}^{-}5$

17. $x \neq 2$

18. $x \neq {}^{-}3$

19. $-x \neq 5$

20. $-x \neq {}^{-}1$

REAL NUMBERS 279

C Translate each of the following word sentences into an open sentence. Choose a variable, tell what it represents, and use a negative number for one of the quantities in the problem.

21. A team lost 5 yards on their first play. On the next play, their yardage was greater than on the first play. What was the team's yardage on the second play?

22. The low temperature for the year was 20° below zero on January 16th. What was the temperature on July 4th?

23. The lowest part of Death Valley is 280 feet below sea level. What is the altitude of the Imperial Valley if it has no part lower than the lowest part of Death Valley?

24. Jim is in debt to his friend for not more than 75¢. How much does he owe?

8.8 Absolute Value

You are now going to compare real numbers and their opposites to see which is greater.

■ **P-1** Which is greater, 10 or its opposite?

■ **P-2** Which is greater, ⁻10 or its opposite?

■ **P-3** Which is greater, ⁻($\frac{1}{3}$) or its opposite?

■ **P-4** Which is greater, ⁻1000 or its opposite?

The number that you chose as the answer to each of the above questions is called the **absolute value** of the given number.

> The **absolute value** of a real number, except 0, is the greater of that number and its opposite. The absolute value of 0 is 0.

Taking the absolute value of a number is a very important operation in mathematics.

■ **P-5** What is the absolute value of $\frac{3}{4}$?

■ **P-6** What is the absolute value of ⁻($1\frac{1}{2}$)?

There is a symbol in mathematics that means absolute value. Here are some examples:

| 100 | means "the absolute value of 100."
| ⁻3 | means "the absolute value of ⁻3."
| ⁻75½ | means "the absolute value of ⁻75½."
| 0 | means "the absolute value of 0."

■ **P-7** What is a common name for each of the following?

$$| \ 100 \ |; \quad | \ ^{-}3 \ |; \quad | \ ^{-}75\tfrac{1}{2} \ |; \quad | \ 0 \ |$$

Every real number has exactly one real number as its absolute value. Maybe you can imagine the absolute value operation as being performed by an absolute value machine.

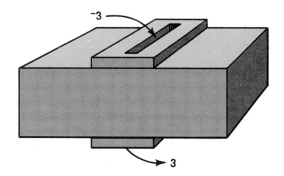

A real number is fed into the machine. Its absolute value is computed by the machine and comes out as a real number. Actually, this operation can be performed by modern digital computers.

■ **P-8** If you feed π into the absolute value machine, what number comes out?

■ **P-9** What is the distance (number of units) between the point with coordinate 5 and the point with coordinate 0? What is the common name for | 5 |?

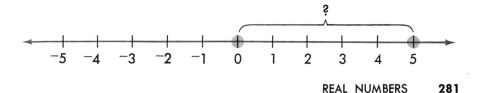

■ **P-10** What is the distance between ⁻5 and 0 on the number line? What is the common name for | ⁻5 |?

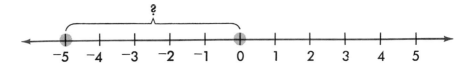

■ **P-11** What is the distance between ⁻(2½) and 0 on the number line? What is the common name for | ⁻(2½) |?

■ **P-12** What is the distance between 100 and 0? between ⁻100 and 0? What are the common names for | 100 | and | ⁻100 |?

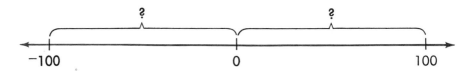

> **The absolute value of a nonzero number is the same as the distance on the number line between that number and 0.**

Distance refers only to the number of units, not to the direction from 0.

> **The absolute value of a real number can never be negative.**

The absolute value of a real number is always a positive number or zero.

ORAL EXERCISES 8.8

Give the common name for each of the following.

1. | 10 | **2.** | ⁻8 | **3.** | 1¾ | **4.** | ⁻(⅞) |
5. | 0 | **6.** | 2 | + | 3 | **7.** | ⁻2 | + | ⁻3 |
8. | 2 | + | ⁻3 | **9.** | ⁻2 | + | 3 | **10.** | ⁻3 |²

Tell whether each of the following sentences is *True* or *False*.

11. | 9 | = 9   **12.** | ⁻3 | ≤ 3   **13.** | ⁻2 | > 0
14. | ⁻(½) | = ½   **15.** ⁻2 > ⁻3   **16.** | ⁻2 | > | ⁻3 |
17. | ⁻100 | < 0   **18.** ⁻1 < | ⁻3 | **19.** | ⁻5 | ≠ | 5 |

Tell whether each of the following open sentences is correctly graphed.
Let {real numbers} be the domain for each sentence.

20. $|x| < 3$

21. $|x| \leq 2$

22. $|x| = 3$

23. $|x| > 2$

24. $|x| \geq 3$

WRITTEN EXERCISES 8.8

A   Find a common name for each of the following.

1. $|^-25|$ **2.** $|^-18|$ **3.** $|99|$ **4.** $|85|$

5. $|0|$ **6.** $-|0|$ **7.** $|2 + 7|$ **8.** $|\frac{1}{4} + \frac{3}{4}|$

9. $|12| + |8|$ **10.** $|8| + |10|$ **11.** $|^-3| + |10|$

12. $|7| + |^-13|$ **13.** $|^-2| + |^-11|$ **14.** $|^-5| + |^-16|$

15. $-|^-3|$ **16.** $-|^-(\frac{1}{2})|$ **17.** $-(|^-8| - 5)$

18. $-(12 - |^-4|)$ **19.** $-(|^-3| \cdot |^-2|)$ **20.** $-(|7| \cdot |^-21|)$

Graph each open sentence, using {real numbers} as the domain.

21. $|x| < 5$ **22.** $|x| \leq 4$ **23.** $|x| \geq 2$

24. $|x| > 3$ **25.** $|x| = 3$ **26.** $|x| = 2\frac{1}{2}$

27. $|x| > 0$ **28.** $|x| \geq 0$ **29.** $|x| = ^-1$

30. $|x| < 0$ **31.** $x < 5 \text{ and } x > -5$ **32.** $x \leq 4 \text{ and } x \geq ^-4$

Translate the following word sentences to open sentences.

33. The distance on the number line from a point to 0 is less than 10 units. What is the coordinate of the point?

34. The distance on the number line from a point to 0 is at least 5 units. What is the coordinate of the point?

B   For the following, let the domain of the variable be {real numbers}.

35. If x is a positive number, which is greater, x or $-x$?

36. If x is a negative number, which is greater, x or $-x$?

37. What is the truth set of the sentence $-x > 0$?

Give another name for $|x|$ in each of the following cases.

38. when $x > 0$ **39.** when $x < 0$ **40.** when $x = 0$

CHAPTER SUMMARY

Important Terms

1. The set of **integers** is described by $\{\cdots, {}^-3, {}^-2, {}^-1, 0, 1, 2, 3, \cdots\}$.

2. The set of **negative integers** is $\{\cdots, {}^-3, {}^-2, {}^-1\}$.

3. The set of **positive integers** is the same as the set of counting numbers, $\{1, 2, 3, \cdots\}$.

4. The set of **rational numbers** is made up of the rational numbers of arithmetic and the negative rational numbers.

5. The set of **real numbers** is made up of the rational numbers and the irrational numbers.

6. Two numbers are **opposites** if their points are located on the number line at equal distances from 0.

7. The **absolute value** of a real number is the greater of that number and its opposite.

Important Ideas

1. The set of rational numbers cannot be described by the roster method.

2. There is a one-to-one correspondence between points of the number line and the real numbers. The real numbers cannot be described by the roster method.

3. The sentence $a > b$ means that the point with coordinate a is to the right of the point with coordinate b.

4. *Comparison Property:* If a is a real number and b is a real number, then exactly one of the following is true:

$$\boxed{1}\ a > b, \quad \boxed{2}\ a = b, \quad \text{or} \quad \boxed{3}\ a < b.$$

5. *Order Property of Opposites:* If a and b are real numbers and $a < b$ is true, then $-a > -b$ is true.

6. The absolute value of a real number can never be negative. It can only be either positive or zero.

7. The set of integers is a subset of the set of rational numbers.

8. The set of rational numbers is a subset of the set of real numbers.

9. The absolute value of a real number is the distance on the number line between the number and 0.

10. Each real number has exactly one real number as its absolute value.

CHAPTER REVIEW

Use letters of the alphabet as names for sets of numbers; that is, let

N = {counting numbers}, Q = {rational numbers},
W = {whole numbers}, K = {irrational numbers},
I = {integers}, R = {real numbers}.

For each of the following numbers, list all the above sets of which the given number is an element.

Example: $\frac{1}{2}$; Q, R

1. 10   **2.** $^{-}15$ **3.** π **4.** $\frac{2}{3}$ **5.** $^{-}(\frac{3}{5})$ **6.** 0   **7.** $|2|$ **8.** $\frac{82}{7}$

Using the above names for sets, indicate whether each of the following is *True* or *False*.

9. Q is a subset of W.
10. K is a subset of R.
11. W is a subset of I.
12. Q is a subset of K.
13. I is a subset of R.
14. N is a subset of W.
15. I is a subset of W.
16. Each of the sets N, W, I, Q, K, R is a subset of every set listed after it.

Graph the truth set of each of the following open sentences, using {integers} as the domain.

17. $x \leq {}^{-}2$ **18.** $x > {}^{-}(3\frac{1}{2})$ **19.** $x < 3$ **20.** $x \leq 0$
21. $x > {}^{-}2$ *or* $x \leq {}^{-}4$ **22.** $x < 3$ *and* $x \geq {}^{-}3$
23. $x \leq 1$ *or* $x \geq {}^{-}5$ **24.** $x < {}^{-}2$ *and* $x \geq 0$

Graph the truth set of each of the following open sentences, but use {real numbers} as the domain.

25. $x \leq {}^{-}3$ **26.** $x > {}^{-}(2\frac{1}{2})$ **27.** $x > {}^{-}1$ *and* $x \leq 2$
28. $x \leq {}^{-}3$ *or* $x > 2$ **29.** $|x| < 1$ **30.** $|x| \geq 2$

Give the common name for each of the following.

31. $-({}^{-}30)$ **32.** $-|{}^{-}1|$ **33.** $|-({}^{-}3)|$ **34.** $-(-4.5)$
35. -0 **36.** $|0|$ **37.** $-(8+2)$ **38.** $-|7+3|$
39. $-(-{}^{-}12)$ **40.** $-(|{}^{-}3| + |3|)$

For each of the following true sentences, form another true sentence showing the order of the opposites of the numbers given.

41. $10 > 7$ **42.** $7 > {}^{-}3$ **43.** $-9 < -5$
44. $^{-}2 > {}^{-}10$ **45.** $-3 \leq 7$ **46.** $^{-}9 \leq {}^{-}1$

Using {real numbers} as the domain, graph each open sentence.

47. $-x \geq 4$ **48.** $-x < 3\frac{1}{2}$ **49.** $-x < {}^{-}(4\frac{1}{3})$ **50.** $-x > {}^{-}(\frac{3}{2})$

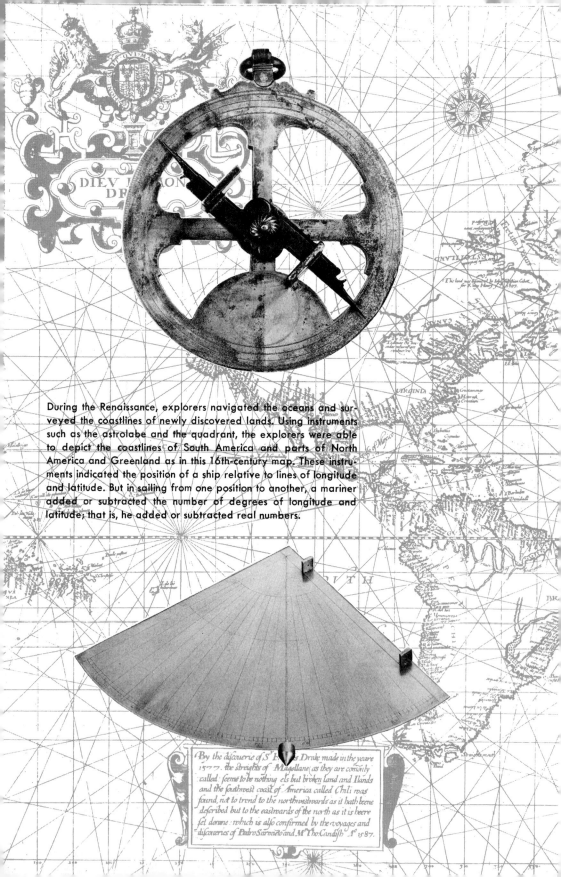

During the Renaissance, explorers navigated the oceans and surveyed the coastlines of newly discovered lands. Using instruments such as the astrolabe and the quadrant, the explorers were able to depict the coastlines of South America and parts of North America and Greenland as in this 16th-century map. These instruments indicated the position of a ship relative to lines of longitude and latitude. But in sailing from one position to another, a mariner added or subtracted the number of degrees of longitude and latitude; that is, he added or subtracted real numbers.

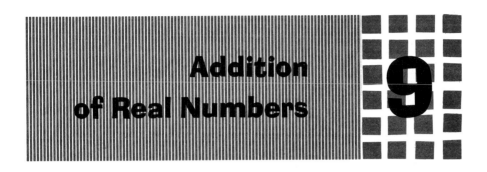

Addition of Real Numbers

9.1 Sums as Gains or Losses

Most of you know something about football. The game of football may be used as a means of learning about addition of real numbers.

A team makes a play. There may be a gain of yardage, there may be no gain, or there may be a loss. You may denote yardage gained by positive numbers and yardage lost by negative numbers. If there is no gain, the yardage will be denoted by 0.

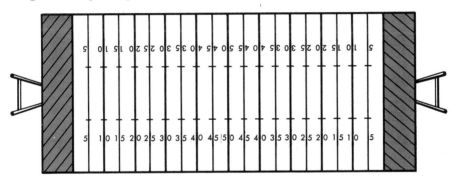

Consider these examples.

Example 1: A team gains 5 yards on the first play and loses 3 yards on the second play.

■ **P-1** What is the result of the two plays together?

This can be shown as $5 + (^-3) = 2$. There is a net gain of 2 yards on the two plays.

Example 2: A team loses 8 yards on the first play and gains 5 yards on the second play.

■ **P-2** What is the result of the two plays together?

The result can be shown by the sentence $(^-8) + 5 = ^-3$.

■ **P-3** Does the $^-3$ represent a net gain or a net loss of 3 yards?

Example 3: A team gains 4 yards on the first play and 6 yards on the second play.

■ **P-4** What is the result of the two plays together?

■ **P-5** What sum represents these two plays together?

Example 4: A team loses 6 yards on the first play and 7 yards on the second play.

■ **P-6** What is the result of the two plays together?

■ **P-7** What sum represents these two plays together? What does the answer mean?

Example 5: A team has no gain on the first play and loses 7 yards on the second play.

■ **P-8** $$0 + (^-7) = \underline{\ ?\ }$$

Example 6: A team loses 4 yards and then gains 4 yards on the next play.

■ **P-9** $$(^-4) + 4 = \underline{\ ?\ }$$

The examples above are now summarized.

$$5 + (^-3) = 2$$
$$(^-8) + 5 = ^-3$$
$$4 + 6 = 10$$
$$(^-6) + (^-7) = ^-13$$
$$0 + (^-7) = ^-7$$
$$(^-4) + 4 = 0$$

ORAL EXERCISES 9.1

Find the following sums by thinking of the positive numbers as yards gained and the negative numbers as yards lost.

1. $8 + 1$ 2. $(^-6) + 8$ 3. $3 + (^-5)$
4. $8 + (^-1)$ 5. $(^-3) + (^-5)$ 6. $0 + (^-10)$
7. $8 + 0$ 8. $(^-12) + 9$ 9. $(^-17) + 0$
10. $(^-15) + (^-12)$ 11. $5 + 1\frac{1}{2}$ 12. $3\frac{1}{2} + (^-3\frac{1}{2})$
13. $8 + (^-5\frac{1}{2})$ 14. $(^-4\frac{1}{2}) + (^-5\frac{1}{2})$ 15. $2\frac{1}{2} + 7\frac{1}{2}$
16. $(^-8) + 8$ 17. $(^-3 + ^-2) + 7$ 18. $(5 + ^-1) + 6$
19. $(^-1 + ^-5) + (^-4)$ 20. $(3 + ^-5) + (2 + ^-3)$

21. When you added two positive numbers, was the sum positive or negative?

22. When you added two negative numbers, was the sum positive or negative?

23. When you added a positive and a negative number, how did you decide whether the sum was positive or negative?

24. When you added 0 to a number, how did you decide whether the sum was positive or negative?

WRITTEN EXERCISES 9.1

A Give the common name for each of the following sums. Think of the numbers as gains or losses.

1. $13 + (^-12)$ **2.** $(^-7) + (^-11)$ **3.** $0 + (^-15)$

4. $2\frac{1}{2} + 3\frac{1}{2}$ **5.** $(^-17) + 13$ **6.** $(^-21) + 8$

7. $(^-10) + (^-10)$ **8.** $12 + (^-15)$ **9.** $(^-25) + 25$

10. $(^-12) + 0$ **11.** $21 + (^-18)$ **12.** $14 + (^-14)$

13. $(^-2) + 5 + (^-1)$ **14.** $10 + (^-3) + (^-2)$ **15.** $2 + (^-5) + 1$

16. $5 + (^-8) + 1$ **17.** $(^-2 + ^-3) + ^-4$ **18.** $(^-1 + ^-3) + ^-5$

19. $(^-1 + 5) + (0 + ^-2)$ **20.** $(^-3 + 0) + (^-1 + 7)$

Find the truth set of each of the following sentences. Use {real numbers} as the domain.

21. $x + 2 = 7$ **22.** $x + 5 = 8$ **23.** $x + 1 = ^-5$

24. $x + 3 = ^-9$ **25.** $x + (^-1) = 10$ **26.** $x + (^-3) = 12$

27. $x + (^-2) = ^-9$ **28.** $x + (^-3) = ^-12$

29. $^-2.3 + x = 5.3$ **30.** $^-8.7 + x = 5.7$

Solve each of the following problems by writing the sum of a positive and a negative number.

31. The temperature rose 25° from midnight to 5:00 P.M. It dropped 21° from 5:00 P.M. to midnight. What was the net change for 24 hours?

32. On the stock market the value of certain stocks gained two points one day and lost four points the next. What was the change for the two days?

33. The plane took off and climbed 3000 feet and then descended 500 feet. How high off the ground was it after descending?

34. A submarine descended 200 feet below the surface of the ocean and then ascended 40 feet. How far was it below the surface after it ascended?

9.2 Number-line Addition

In this section, you will use the number line to demonstrate addition of real numbers. Again, the game of football can be used to help you in this demonstration.

Think of a football team as moving from left to right along the number line. The "line of scrimmage" will be at 0. A motion to the right will be a gain, and a motion to the left will be a loss.

Consider again the net yardage after two plays by a football team. This time it will be shown on the number line.

Example 1: 1st Play, 2 yards gain; 2nd Play, 5 yards loss.

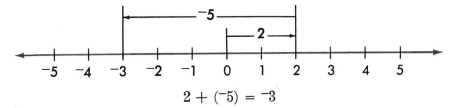

$$2 + (^-5) = ^-3$$

The team is at $^-3$ after two plays.

Example 2: 1st Play, 3 yards loss; 2nd Play, 7 yards gain.

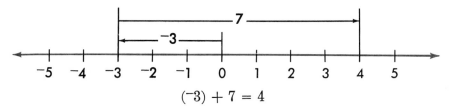

$$(^-3) + 7 = 4$$

The team is at 4 after two plays.

■ **P-1** Is the first play $|\ ^-3\ |$ units to the left?

Example 3: 1st Play, 2 yards loss; 2nd Play, 4 yards loss.

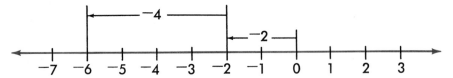

■ **P-2** Where is the team after two plays?

■ **P-3** How can you represent this problem as a sum?

■ **P-4** Is the first move $|\ ^-2\ |$ units to the left?

Example 4: 1st Play, 5 yards gain; 2nd Play, 3 yards gain.

■ **P-5**   Did the team move | 5 | units to the right on the first play?

■ **P-6**   Where does the second play end?

■ **P-7**   What sum represents the problem?

Example 5: 1st Play, 3 yards loss; 2nd Play, no gain.

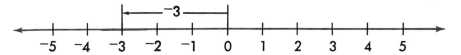

■ **P-8**   Where does the second play end?

■ **P-9** $(^-3) + 0 = ?$

The following is a summary of the number-line method of adding two real numbers a and b.

1   Start at 0.

2   Move | a | units to the right if a is positive. Move | a | units to the left if a is negative.

3   From this second point move | b | units to the right if b is positive. Move | b | units to the left if b is negative.

4   The coordinate of the point where the second motion ends is the sum of a and b.

ORAL EXERCISES 9.2

Tell how you would find the following sums on the number line.

1. $8 + (^-3)$
2. $(^-6) + 10$
3. $(^-12) + 5$
4. $6 + (^-11)$
5. $(^-3) + (^-5)$
6. $(^-7) + (^-12)$
7. $(^-1\frac{1}{2}) + 0$
8. $0 + (^-10)$
9. $(^-1\frac{1}{4}) + ^-(\frac{3}{4})$
10. $3\frac{1}{2} + ^-(1\frac{1}{2})$
11. $6.8 + ^-(3.2)$
12. $(^-1.6) + (^-5.1)$
13. $(2 + ^-5) + 7$
14. $(^-3 + ^-2) + (^-1)$
15. $(^-5 + 6) + (^-3)$
16. $(^-10 + 5) + 7$

Tell what sums are shown by these number-line examples.

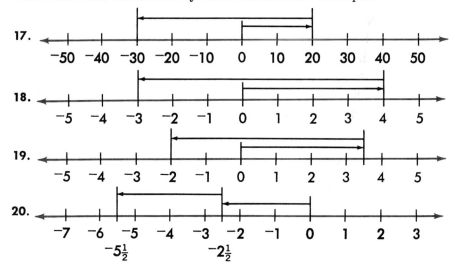

17.

18.

19.

20.

$-5\frac{1}{2}$ $-2\frac{1}{2}$

WRITTEN EXERCISES 9.2

A Find the following sums. Illustrate each with the number line.

1. $(^-5) + (^-5)$
2. $(^-3) + (^-4)$
3. $3 + 6$
4. $2 + 5$
5. $(^-2) + 7$
6. $6 + (^-3)$
7. $5 + (^-9)$
8. $(^-7) + 10$
9. $0 + (^-6)$
10. $(^-7) + 0$
11. $(^-2) + (^-2) + (^-2)$
12. $(^-1) + (^-1) + (^-1)$

Think of the following as gains or losses, and find the sums.

13. $\frac{1}{2} + (^-1\frac{1}{2})$
14. $2\frac{1}{2} + (^-4)$
15. $(^-2\frac{1}{2}) + (^-3\frac{1}{2})$
16. $(^-4\frac{1}{2}) + (^-1\frac{1}{2})$
17. $(^-2 + ^-3) + 7$
18. $(^-5 + ^-8) + 6$
19. $(10 + ^-2) + 7$
20. $(^-5 + 6) + ^-12$

Indicate whether each of the following is *True* or *False*.

21. $(^-7) + (^-10) = 17$
22. $(^-5) + 7 = ^-2$
23. $12 + (^-3) > 14$
24. $(^-5) + 13 < 8$
25. $(^-2) + 7 \neq 7 + (^-2)$
26. $(^-3) + (^-8) = (^-8) + (^-3)$
27. $(^-3 + 4) + (^-1) = (^-3) + (4 + ^-1)$
28. $5 + (^-1 + 3) = (5 + ^-1) + 3$
29. $2 \cdot 3 = 3 + 3$
30. $2 \cdot 3 = (^-3) + (^-3)$

B Indicate whether each of the following is *True* or *False*.

31. $(^-3) + (^-5) = -(|^-3| + |^-5|)$
32. $(^-5) + 3 = -(|^-5| - |3|)$
33. $5 + (^-3) = |5| - |^-3|$
34. $5 + (^-5) = |5| - |^-5|$
35. $0 + (^-5) = 0 + |^-5|$
36. $5 + 3 = |5| + |3|$

9.3 Addition of Real Numbers

You have added real numbers by treating them as gains and losses in yardage by a football team. You have also learned to use the number line in addition.

By now you should be able to see some patterns to these sums. See if you can apply your understanding of absolute value and the process of adding and subtracting numbers of arithmetic to form some rules.

■ **P-1** What is the common name for the sum $(^-3) + (^-5)$?

■ **P-2** What is the common name for the following phrase?

$$-(|^-3| + |^-5|)$$

This suggests that you can find the **sum of two negative numbers** by adding their absolute values and taking the opposite of that sum.

■ **P-3** What is the common name for the sum $5 + (^-3)$?

■ **P-4** What is the common name for the phrase $|5| - |^-3|$?

■ **P-5** What is the common name for the sum $(^-5) + 3$?

■ **P-6** What is the common name for the phrase $-(|^-5| - |3|)$?

Here is the summary of these last two examples:

$$5 + (^-3) = 2 \qquad\qquad (^-5) + 3 = ^-2$$
$$|5| - |^-3| = 2 \qquad\qquad -(|^-5| - |3|) = ^-2$$

These results suggest the following rule for **adding a positive and a negative number** when their absolute values are not equal.

> Subtract the lesser absolute value from the greater. If the greater absolute value is that of the positive number, the result is a positive number. If the greater absolute value is that of the negative number, the result is negative.

The following examples further demonstrate the rule.

$$(^-12) + 17 = |17| - |^-12| \quad \text{and} \quad 12 + (^-17) = -(|^-17| - |12|)$$
$$= 5 \qquad\qquad\qquad\qquad\qquad = ^-5$$

■ **P-7** What is the sum $5 + (^-5)$?

This suggests that the sum of a positive number and a negative number whose absolute values are equal is 0.

■ **P-8** What is the sum $(^-5) + 0$?

■ **P-9** What is the sum $5 + 0$?

Since the positive real numbers along with 0 make up the numbers of arithmetic, you have nothing new to learn to add two nonnegative real numbers. That is, $5 + 3 = 8$, whether you consider 5 and 3 as real numbers or as numbers of arithmetic.

You should keep the following simple facts in mind when adding real numbers.

[1] The sum of two positive numbers is a positive number.

[2] The sum of two negative numbers is a negative number.

[3] The sum of any real number and 0 is that real number.

[4] The sum of a positive number and a negative number may be positive, negative, or zero, depending upon the order of their absolute values.

All possible sums of two real numbers have been covered. You see that any two real numbers have a sum and that their sum is a real number. The real numbers have the **Closure Property of Addition.**

The rules for adding real numbers are summarized now for your convenience:

[1] To find the sum of two positive real numbers, add the numbers as numbers of arithmetic.

[2] To find the sum of two negative real numbers, add their absolute values and take the opposite of the result.

[3] To find the sum of a positive number and a negative number
   (a) find the difference between the absolute values if the positive number has the greater absolute value or if the absolute values are equal;
   (b) find the opposite of the difference between the absolute values if the negative number has the greater absolute value.

[4] The sum of any real number and 0 is that real number.

ORAL EXERCISES 9.3

Explain how to find each of the following sums by the rules just given.

1. $12 + 8$
2. $(^-9) + (^-8)$
3. $(^-12) + 3$
4. $(^-5) + 16$
5. $(^-10) + 0$
6. $25 + 0$
7. $(^-15) + 15$
8. $100 + (^-100)$

9. Is the sum of two positive numbers positive or negative?
10. Is the sum of two negative numbers positive or negative?
11. When is the sum of a positive and a negative number zero?
12. How can you tell whether the sum of a positive and a negative number is positive or negative?
13. What is the sum of any real number and zero?
14. What do you mean when you say the real numbers are closed under addition?
15. Is the opposite of a negative real number always a negative number?
16. Is the opposite of a positive number equal to a negative number?

WRITTEN EXERCISES 9.3

A Express each of the following sums by using absolute value symbols; then find the common name.

Example: $10 + (^-7) = |\,10\,| - |\,^-7\,| = 3$

1. $35 + 41$
2. $56 + 28$
3. $(^-32) + 18$
4. $12 + (^-41)$
5. $(^-35) + (^-17)$
6. $(^-29) + (^-55)$
7. $42 + (^-19)$
8. $38 + (^-23)$
9. $56 + (^-56)$
10. $(^-89) + 89$
11. $(^-13.8) + (^-3.7)$
12. $(^-19.3) + (^-7.2)$
13. $17.5 + (^-12.7)$
14. $19.6 + (^-14.9)$
15. $23.8 + (^-35.6)$
16. $(^-42.7) + (31.9)$

Find the truth set of each of the following open sentences. Let the domain be {real numbers}.

17. $x + 0 = ^-5\frac{1}{2}$
18. $0 + x = ^-(\frac{15}{8})$
19. $x + (^-7) = 0$
20. $x + ^-(\frac{2}{3}) = 0$
21. $12.3 + x = 0$
22. $\pi + x = 0$
23. $0 + x = 17$
24. $0 + x = \frac{3}{4}$
25. $x + (^-\pi) = 0$
26. $x + (^-17.4) = 0$

Graph the truth set of each of the following sentences. Let the domain be {real numbers}.

27. $x + 2 < 0$ 28. $3 + x \leq 0$
29. $x + (^-5) \leq 0$ 30. $x + (^-2) < 0$
31. $x + 3 > 0$ 32. $x + 3 \geq 0$

B Indicate whether each of the following sentences is *True* or *False*.

33. $(^-7) + 3 = 3 + (^-7)$
34. $12 + (^-5) = (^-5) + 12$
35. $(^-7) + ((^-5) + 8)) = ((^-7) + (^-5)) + 8$
36. $8 + ((^-3) + (^-10)) = ((8) + (^-3)) + (^-10)$

9.4 Addition Properties of Real Numbers

You have learned that, if you add 0 to any real number, the sum is that same real number. Thus, there is an **Addition Property of Zero** for real numbers.

> For any real number a, it is true that
>
> $$a + 0 = a.$$

■ **P-1** Can a equal 0 when you apply this property?

You have also seen that the sum of a positive number and a negative number, having equal absolute values, is 0. Every nonzero real number and its opposite have equal absolute values; and, of course, one number must be positive and the other negative. Hence, their sum must be 0. You remember that 0 is equal to -0. Using this and the Addition Property of Zero, you know that the following sentence is true.

$$0 + (-0) = 0$$

This discussion is summarized by the **Addition Property of Opposites.**

> For any real number a, it is true that
>
> $$a + (-a) = 0.$$

■ **P-2** How does the sentence $a + (-a) = 0$ read when a is equal to 0?

■ **P-3** Are the following sentences true or false?

$$^-5 + ^-3 = ^-3 + ^-5$$
$$^-5 + 3 = 3 + ^-5$$
$$5 + ^-3 = ^-3 + 5$$

■ **P-4** What property of addition of real numbers is suggested by the above sentences?

The **Commutative Property of Addition** applies to the set of real numbers as well as to the set of numbers of arithmetic. It is stated as follows.

> For any real numbers a and b, it is true that
>
> $a + b = b + a.$

■ **P-5** How can you show that each of the following sentences is true?

$$(^-5 + 7) + ^-3 = ^-5 + (7 + ^-3)$$
$$(8 + ^-4) + 3 = 8 + (^-4 + 3)$$
$$(^-3 + ^-4) + (^-5) = ^-3 + (^-4 + ^-5)$$

These examples suggest that the **Associative Property of Addition** is also true for real numbers. It is stated as follows.

> For any real numbers a, b, and c, it is true that
>
> $(a + b) + c = a + (b + c).$

■ **P-6** Is the following sentence an example of the Associative Property of Addition?

$$(^-2 + 5) + ^-3 = ((^-2) + 5) + (^-3)$$

ADDITION OF REAL NUMBERS   **297**

ORAL EXERCISES 9.4

Tell what property of addition is illustrated by each of the following true sentences.

1. $^-7 + 0 = ^-7$
2. $0 + ^-9 = ^-9 + 0$
3. $5 + ^-5 = 0$
4. $(^-1 + 3) + 5 = ^-1 + (3 + 5)$
5. $^-(\frac{1}{2}) + \frac{1}{3} = \frac{1}{3} + ^-(\frac{1}{2})$
6. $^-13 + 10 = 10 + ^-13$
7. $0 + ^-(\frac{1}{5}) = ^-(\frac{1}{5})$
8. $(8 + ^-12) + ^-5 = 8 + (^-12 + ^-5)$

Find a truth number for each of the following sentences. Let the domain be {real numbers}.

9. $x + ^-5 = ^-5 + 7$
10. $\frac{1}{2} + x = 0$
11. $^-(\frac{1}{3}) + x = ^-(\frac{1}{3})$
12. $(x + 7) + ^-3 = ^-10 + (7 + ^-3)$
13. $(^-9 + x) + ^-8 = ^-9 + ^-6$
14. $x + (^-3 + 20) = ^-3 + 20$
15. $(0 + 0) + x = ^-(\frac{1}{9})$
16. $6 + (^-6 + x) = \frac{1}{3}$

17. State the Addition Property of Zero for real numbers.
18. State the Addition Property of Opposites for real numbers.
19. Do the addition properties of real numbers also apply to numbers of arithmetic? Why or why not?
20. What addition property for real numbers does not apply to the numbers of arithmetic?

WRITTEN EXERCISES 9.4

A Give the common name for each of the following. Any variable represents a real number.

1. $x + (5 + ^-5)$
2. $(^-10 + 10) + a$
3. $\frac{1}{2} + ^-(\frac{1}{2}) + y$
4. $^-(\frac{1}{3}) + \frac{1}{3} + x$
5. $x + (-x) + 2$
6. $y + (-y) + ^-5$
7. $(^-8 + 5) + x$
8. $(^-10 + ^-5) + y$
9. $(^-3 + 3) + (x + -x)$
10. $(-y + y) + (8 + ^-8)$

Show that the sentence $a + b = b + a$ is true for each of the following cases.

Example: $a = {}^-5; \quad b = 12$

$$a + b = b + a$$
$$\begin{array}{c|c} {}^-5 + 12 & 12 + {}^-5 \\ 7 & 7 \end{array}$$

11. $a = {}^-13; \quad b = {}^-21$

12. $a = {}^-19; \quad b = {}^-26$

13. $a = 42; \quad b = {}^-37$

14. $a = 75; \quad b = {}^-31$

15. $a = \frac{1}{2}; \quad b = {}^-(\frac{1}{3})$

16. $a = {}^-(\frac{1}{4}); \quad b = \frac{1}{2}$

Show that the sentence $(a + b) + c = a + (b + c)$ is true for each of the following cases.

Example: $a = {}^-2; \quad b = 3; \quad c = {}^-5$

$$(a + b) + c = a + (b + c)$$
$$\begin{array}{c|c} ({}^-2 + 3) + {}^-5 & {}^-2 + (3 + {}^-5) \\ 1 + {}^-5 & {}^-2 + {}^-2 \\ {}^-4 & {}^-4 \end{array}$$

17. $a = 5; \quad b = {}^-4; \quad c = {}^-1$

18. $a = 8; \quad b = {}^-5; \quad c = {}^-2$

19. $a = {}^-3; \quad b = 10; \quad c = 7$

20. $a = {}^-11; \quad b = 6; \quad c = 8$

21. $a = {}^-5; \quad b = {}^-8; \quad c = {}^-13$

22. $a = {}^-6; \quad b = {}^-13; \quad c = {}^-15$

Find the truth set of each of the following open sentences. Let {real numbers} be the domain.

23. ${}^-12 + x = 8 + {}^-12$

24. $x + 7 = 7 + {}^-13$

25. $({}^-3 + x) + {}^-10 = {}^-3 + {}^-4$

26. $(12 + {}^-8) + x = 12 + {}^-10$

27. $(x + {}^-12) + 8 = (8 + {}^-12) + {}^-3$

28. $({}^-6 + 8) + x = (5 + {}^-6) + 8$

29. ${}^-6 + a + 6 = 8 + {}^-8$

30. $12 + {}^-12 + y = 13 + {}^-13$

31. $x + (-x) = \frac{1}{2} + {}^-(\frac{1}{2})$

32. $a + (-a) = \frac{2}{3} + {}^-(\frac{2}{3})$

33. $x + |{}^-6| = 6$

34. $23 = |23| + x$

35. $(16 + -y) + {}^-7 = (-y + {}^-7) + 16$

36. $(-r + 25) + {}^-(\frac{1}{2}) = (25 + {}^-(\frac{1}{2})) + (-r)$

9.5 Common Names for Phrases

Earlier, it was stated that a phrase such as $2 + 3 + 4$ has the meaning $(2 + 3) + 4$. You found that you add the terms of the phrase by pairs from left to right. In this way, the phrase $2 + 3 + 4$ is found to have the common name 9.

■ **P-1** What is the common name for the phrase $5 + {}^-8 + 2$?

■ **P-2** What is the common name for the phrase ${}^-2 + 13 + {}^-5 + 8$?

You can make use of the commutative and associative properties of real numbers to find the common name in different ways. Take the phrase $5 + {}^-13 + 7$ as an example.

By agreement⟶ $5 + {}^-13 + 7 = (5 + {}^-13) + 7$

■ **P-3** $= 7 + (5 + {}^-13)$ What property?

■ **P-4** $= (7 + 5) + {}^-13$ What property?

Using common names ⟶ $\begin{cases} = 12 + {}^-13 \\ = {}^-1 \end{cases}$

In effect, you first add the two positive numbers; then you add this result and ${}^-13$. The commutative and associative properties give you complete freedom in changing the order and grouping of terms to be added in a phrase.

■ **P-5** What is the common name for the phrase ${}^-5 + x + 7$?

You cannot get a common name by treating this phrase as $({}^-5 + x) + 7$. The number ${}^-5$ cannot be added to x unless you know the number that is the replacement for x. But you can again make use of the commutative and associative properties of addition to get the common name.

■ **P-6** $({}^-5 + x) + 7 = 7 + ({}^-5 + x)$ What property?

■ **P-7** $= (7 + {}^-5) + x$ What property?

$= 2 + x$

The phrase ${}^-5 + x + 7$ has the common name $2 + x$.

It will not be necessary for you to put down all these steps in getting common names for open phrases. However, you should be aware of the properties that are used.

■ **P-8** What is the common name for the phrase $^-3 + x + {}^-8$?

■ **P-9** What is the common name for the phrase $5 + {}^-7 + x + {}^-8$?

ORAL EXERCISES 9.5

Tell the property of addition that is illustrated by each of the following true sentences.

1. $(^-2 + x) + 5 = {}^-2 + (x + 5)$
2. $(7 + x) + {}^-3 = {}^-3 + (7 + x)$
3. $(x + {}^-3) + 7 = x + (^-3 + 7)$
4. $(^-5 + x) + 8 = (x + {}^-5) + 8$
5. $(-x + x) + 7 = 0 + 7$
6. $x + (8 + {}^-8) = x + 0$
7. $x + 0 = x$
8. $(^-3 + x) + {}^-9 = {}^-9 + (^-3 + x)$
9. $^-9 + (^-3 + x) = (^-9 + {}^-3) + x$
10. $(^-9 + {}^-3) + x = {}^-12 + x$

Give the common name for each of the following phrases.

11. $1 + x + 2$ 12. $x + 5 + 6$
13. $8 + {}^-3 + x$ 14. $^-5 + 2 + x$
15. $x + {}^-7 + {}^-3$ 16. $x + 10 + {}^-2$
17. $12 + x + {}^-4$ 18. $15 + x + {}^-1$
19. $3 + (-x) + 5$ 20. $^-3 + (-x) + {}^-7$

WRITTEN EXERCISES 9.5

A   Give the number property or rule that is used for each step in finding common names for the following phrases.

Example: $(8 + x) + 10 = 10 + (8 + x)$ $\underline{\ ?\ }$
$= (10 + 8) + x$ $\underline{\ ?\ }$
$= 18 + x$ $\underline{\ ?\ }$

Answer: In order, the number properties used are

the Commutative Property of Addition,
the Associative Property of Addition,
the rule for adding real numbers.

1. $(x + 13) + 5 = x + (13 + 5)$ $\underline{\ ?\ }$
$= x + 18$ $\underline{\ ?\ }$
2. $(x + {}^-2) + 7 = x + (^-2 + 7)$ $\underline{\ ?\ }$
$= x + 5$ $\underline{\ ?\ }$

ADDITION OF REAL NUMBERS   **301**

3. $(^-3 + x) + 7 = 7 + (^-3 + x)$ $\underline{\quad?\quad}$
$= (7 + ^-3) + x$ $\underline{\quad?\quad}$
$= 4 + x$ $\underline{\quad?\quad}$

4. $(9 + x) + ^-5 = (x + 9) + ^-5$ $\underline{\quad?\quad}$
$= x + (9 + ^-5)$ $\underline{\quad?\quad}$
$= x + 4$ $\underline{\quad?\quad}$

5. $(x + 7) + (-x) = -x + (x + 7)$ $\underline{\quad?\quad}$
$= (-x + x) + 7$ $\underline{\quad?\quad}$
$= 0 + 7$ $\underline{\quad?\quad}$
$= 7$ $\underline{\quad?\quad}$

6. $(-x + ^-9) + x = (^-9 + -x) + x$ $\underline{\quad?\quad}$
$= ^-9 + (-x + x)$ $\underline{\quad?\quad}$
$= ^-9 + 0$ $\underline{\quad?\quad}$
$= ^-9$ $\underline{\quad?\quad}$

7. $(^-3 + x) + 9 = ^-3 + (x + 9)$ $\underline{\quad?\quad}$
$= ^-3 + (9 + x)$ $\underline{\quad?\quad}$
$= (^-3 + 9) + x$ $\underline{\quad?\quad}$
$= 6 + x$ $\underline{\quad?\quad}$

8. $(x + 8) + ^-10 = (8 + x) + ^-10$ $\underline{\quad?\quad}$
$= ^-10 + (8 + x)$ $\underline{\quad?\quad}$
$= (^-10 + 8) + x$ $\underline{\quad?\quad}$
$= ^-2 + x$ $\underline{\quad?\quad}$

Give the common name for each of the following phrases. It is not necessary to show each step.

9. $^-2 + 5 + ^-7$

10. $10 + ^-1 + 3$

11. $4 + ^-3 + ^-1 + 7$

12. $^-8 + 5 + ^-1 + 6$

13. $2 + x + ^-7$

14. $^-3 + x + 8$

15. $^-5 + ^-6 + x$

16. $x + ^-15 + ^-3$

17. $5.2 + x + ^-4.1$

18. $9.8 + x + ^-5.3$

19. $2 + x + ^-9 + ^-1$

20. $^-3 + 5 + x + ^-1$

21. $-x + ^-5 + x + 2$

22. $-x + 7 + ^-3 + x$

23. $^-3 + 5 + x + ^-5$

24. $^-7 + 2 + x + ^-5$

25. $^-3 + (-x) + ^-8$

26. $-x + ^-9 + ^-4$

27. $3.7 + x + ^-5.2$

28. $^-8.7 + x + 3.9$

29. $\frac{5}{8} + x + ^-(\frac{3}{8})$

30. $^-(\frac{3}{11}) + x + ^-(\frac{5}{11})$

9.6 Addition Property of Equality

> **Equivalent** open sentences are sentences that have the same truth set.

■ **P-1** What is the truth number of $x + 2 = 5$ in the domain of real numbers?

■ **P-2** What is the truth number of $x + {}^-9 = {}^-6$ in the domain of real numbers?

■ **P-3** Are the sentences $x + 2 = 5$ and $x + {}^-9 = {}^-6$ equivalent?

■ **P-4** If the domain is {real numbers}, are the following sentences equivalent?

$$\boxed{1} \quad x < 6$$
$$\boxed{2} \quad x \le 5$$

■ **P-5** Are the two sentences in **P-4** equivalent if the domain is {integers}?

In the following discussion, use {real numbers} as the domain.

■ **P-6** What is the truth set of $x + 1 = 5$?

Now you may obtain another sentence by adding 3 to $x + 1$ and to 5 in the sentence in **P-6**.

$$(x + 1) + 3 = 5 + 3$$

Using the Associative
 Property of Addition $\longrightarrow$ $x + (1 + 3) = 5 + 3$
Using common names $\longrightarrow$ $x + 4 = 8$

■ **P-7** What is the truth set of $x + 4 = 8$?

You can see that the following sentences are equivalent.

$$\boxed{1} \quad x + 1 = 5$$

and

$$\boxed{2} \quad (x + 1) + 3 = 5 + 3$$

Sentences that have $=$ to represent the verb are often called **equalities,** or **equations.** The two phrases separated by $=$ are often called the **sides** of the equation.

■ **P-8** What is the truth set of the following sentence?

$$x + {}^-1 = 5$$

Adding $^-3$ to both sides ───────────→ $(x + {}^-1) + {}^-3 = 5 + {}^-3$

By the Associative
  Property of Addition ───────────→ $x + ({}^-1 + {}^-3) = 5 + {}^-3$

Using common names ───────────→ $x + {}^-4 = 2$

■ **P-9** What is the truth set of $x + {}^-4 = 2$?

Hence, the sentences $x + {}^-1 = 5$ and $(x + {}^-1) + {}^-3 = 5 + {}^-3$ are equivalent.

These examples lead to a most important property in algebra, which is called the **Addition Property of Equality.**

> If any real number is added to both sides of an open equation, then the new equation is equivalent to the first.

ORAL EXERCISES 9.6

Indicate whether or not the open sentences in each pair are equivalent. Let {real numbers} be the domain.

1. $5 + x = 16$; $x = 11$
2. $x + 2 = 9$; $x + 3 = 10$
3. $^-3 + x = {}^-8$; $x = 5$
4. $x = {}^-3$; $10 + x = 13$
5. $x + 3 = 3 + x$; $x + 0 = x$
6. $x + {}^-10 = 27$; $x = 37$
7. $3 + x = 19$; $(3 + x) + 8 = 19 + 8$
8. $x + {}^-2 = 188$; $(x + {}^-2) + 10 = 198$

Tell what real number can be added to each open phrase so that the result is x.

9. $x + 2$
10. $5 + x$
11. $\frac{1}{2} + x$
12. $x + {}^-6$
13. $^-10 + x$
14. $x + {}^-(\frac{1}{3})$
15. $^-3 + x + 5$
16. $6 + x + {}^-10$

For each open sentence, tell what real number can be added to each side to get an equivalent sentence with the variable alone on one side.

Example: $x + {}^-3 = 5$ *Answer:* Add 3.

$$(x + {}^-3) + 3 = 5 + 3$$
$$x + ({}^-3 + 3) = 5 + 3$$
$$x + 0 = 8$$
$$x = 8$$

17. $x + 2 = 7$
18. $3 + x = 9$
19. $x + {}^-5 = 10$

20. $8 + x = 17$

21. $x + \frac{1}{2} = 3$

22. $x + {}^-(\frac{1}{3}) = 12$

23. ${}^-10 + x + 10 = 3$

24. $5 + x + {}^-3 = 10$

WRITTEN EXERCISES 9.6

A Indicate whether or not the open sentences in each pair are equivalent. Let {real numbers} be the domain.

1. $x + 15 = 25; \quad x = 10$

2. $x + 19 = 23; \quad x = 4$

3. $2 + x = 31; \quad 5 + x = 34$

4. $5 + x = 18; \quad 7 + x = 20$

5. $x + 7 = 10; \quad x + {}^-7 = {}^-10$

6. $x + {}^-5 = {}^-12; \quad x + 5 = 12$

7. $x + 5 = 7; \quad (x + 5) + 2 = 7 + 2$

8. $8 + x = 5; \quad (8 + x) + 1 = 5 + 1$

9. $x + {}^-3 = {}^-8; \quad x = 11$

10. $x + {}^-6 = 10; \quad x = 4$

11. $x + 8 = 8 + x; \quad x + (-x) = 0$

12. $x + 0 = x; \quad x + {}^-5 = 0$

13. $x + {}^-3 = x; \quad 0 + x = 0$

14. ${}^-7 + x = x; \quad x + (-x) = 1$

Indicate the real number that can be added to the given open phrase so that the result is x.

15. $13 + x$

16. $27 + x$

17. $x + {}^-3$

18. $x + {}^-8$

19. $2 + x + {}^-3$

20. ${}^-5 + x + 6$

21. $\frac{1}{2} + x$

22. $x + \frac{2}{5}$

23. ${}^-3 + {}^-5 + x$

24. $x + {}^-9 + {}^-1$

25. $5 + x + 8$

26. $10 + x + 21$

For each of the following, write the equivalent sentence obtained by adding the given real number to each side of the given sentence.

Example: $x + {}^-6 = 10; \quad$ add 6

$\qquad (x + {}^-6) + 6 = 10 + 6$

27. $x + 8 = 20; \quad$ add ${}^-8$

28. $x + 13 = 15; \quad$ add ${}^-13$

29. $x + {}^-21 = 12; \quad$ add 21

30. $x + {}^-15 = 2; \quad$ add 15

31. $3 + x = 18; \quad$ add ${}^-3$

32. $12 + x = 3; \quad$ add ${}^-12$

33. $3 + x + {}^-8 = 10; \quad$ add 5

34. $12 + {}^-5 + x = 3; \quad$ add ${}^-7$

9.7 Truth Sets of Open Sentences

In finding truth sets of open sentences so far, you have used mainly a "guessing" method. Most of the sentences have been simple enough that truth numbers could be found rather easily. If you were given an open sentence such as the following, you would not have much luck in guessing its truth number.

$$x + {}^-5 + 3x + \tfrac{1}{3} + 28 = 99x + {}^-(\tfrac{3}{5})$$

You are now going to learn more general methods that will help you solve such sentences.

Keep in mind that you will be learning a method. It is important that you go through the steps in each problem. Otherwise, you will not learn how to handle the more difficult ones. From now on unless otherwise stated, use {real numbers} as the domain of the variable.

Example 1: Find the truth set of

$$x + {}^-(\tfrac{1}{5}) = 3.$$

Using the Addition Property of Equality, you can add $\tfrac{1}{5}$ to each side and obtain an equivalent sentence.

$$x + {}^-(\tfrac{1}{5}) + \tfrac{1}{5} = 3 + \tfrac{1}{5}$$

If you replace the phrase on each side by its common name, you will have another sentence that is equivalent to the first. By the Addition Property of Opposites, you get

$$x + 0 = 3\tfrac{1}{5},$$

and by the Addition Property of Zero, you have

$$x = 3\tfrac{1}{5}.$$

■ **P-1** What is the truth number of the last sentence, $x = 3\tfrac{1}{5}$?

Since $x + {}^-(\tfrac{1}{5}) = 3$ is equivalent to the sentence $x = 3\tfrac{1}{5}$, the truth set of $x + {}^-(\tfrac{1}{5}) = 3$ is $\{3\tfrac{1}{5}\}$.

■ **P-2** Why did you choose $\tfrac{1}{5}$ to add to each side as the first step?

Example 2: Find the truth set of

$$x + 5 = {}^-1.$$

■ **P-3** What number would you add to each side?

Here are the steps:

$$x + 5 + {}^-5 = {}^-1 + {}^-5$$
$$x + 0 = {}^-6$$
$$x = {}^-6$$
$$\{{}^-6\}$$

The truth set of $x + 5 = {}^-1$ is $\{{}^-6\}$.

You should always check your work.

■ **P-4** How can you check to see if $^-6$ is a truth number of

$$x + 5 = {}^-1?$$

Here is a plan for the check:

Check: $x + 5 = {}^-1$
$$\begin{array}{c|c} {}^-6 + 5 & \\ {}^-1 & \end{array}$$

Since both sides of the sentence $x + 5 = {}^-1$ name the same number, $^-6$ must be a truth number.

Example 3: Find the truth set of

$$^-3 + x = {}^-7.$$

■ **P-5** What number would you add to both sides?

Here are the steps:

$$^-3 + x = {}^-7$$
$$^-3 + x + 3 = {}^-7 + 3$$
$$x + 0 = {}^-4$$
$$x = {}^-4$$
$$\{{}^-4\}$$

Check: $^-3 + x = {}^-7$
$$\begin{array}{c|c} {}^-3 + {}^-4 & \\ {}^-7 & \end{array}$$

■ **P-6** What would you add to both sides of the sentence

$$x + a = b,$$

where x is the variable and a and b are real numbers?

Example 4: Find the truth set of

$$^-6 = {}^-10 + x.$$

Your aim is to get an equivalent sentence with x alone on one side.

■ **P-7** What number would you add to both sides to get x by itself?

Here are the steps:

$$^-6 = {}^-10 + x$$
$$^-6 + 10 = {}^-10 + x + 10$$
$$4 = x$$

■ **P-8** What is the truth number for the last sentence, $4 = x$?

Always indicate the truth set as $\{4\}$, *not as* $x = \{4\}$.

Check: $^-6 = {}^-10 + x$
$\qquad\quad \Big|\ {}^-10 + 4$
$\qquad\quad \Big|\ {}^-6$

ORAL EXERCISES 9.7

For each of the open sentences listed in Written Exercises 9.7, tell what number you would add to each side to get x by itself.

WRITTEN EXERCISES 9.7

A Find the truth set of each of the following open sentences. Show the steps and check.

1. $x + {}^-12 = 15$ 2. $x + {}^-6 = 23$ 3. $x + 9 = 13$
4. $x + 12 = 21$ 5. $x + 7 = {}^-8$ 6. $x + 20 = {}^-3$
7. $23 + x = 7$ 8. $29 + x = 13$ 9. $38 + x = {}^-27$
10. $51 + x = {}^-28$ 11. $^-13 = 2 + x$ 12. $^-17 = 5 + x$
13. $17.2 = x + {}^-3.8$ 14. $19.7 = x + {}^-8.5$ 15. $^-6.4 = {}^-9.6 + x$
16. $^-13.8 = {}^-3.9 + x$ 17. $x + {}^-(\frac{2}{3}) = 5$ 18. $x + {}^-(\frac{3}{4}) = 12$
19. $\frac{3}{5} = x + {}^-(\frac{4}{5})$ 20. $^-(\frac{5}{7}) + x = \frac{4}{7}$

9.8 More Open Sentences

In finding the truth set of an open sentence in the last section, you added a real number to both sides of the open sentence as the first step. When it is possible, you should usually replace the phrase on each side by its common name as the first step.

Example 1: Find the truth set of

$$^-3 + x + 5 = ^-10 + 7.$$

■ **P-1** What is the common name for the phrase on the left side? on the right side?

The equivalent sentence is as follows.

$$x + 2 = ^-3$$

■ **P-2** What is the next step?

The next step gives the following.

$$x + 2 + ^-2 = ^-3 + ^-2$$
$$x = ^-5$$
$$\{^-5\}$$

The truth set of $^-3 + x + 5 = ^-10 + 7$ is $\{^-5\}$.

Check:
$$
\begin{array}{c|c}
^-3 + x + 5 = ^-10 + 7 & \\
^-3 + ^-5 + 5 & ^-10 + 7 \\
^-3 + 0 & ^-3 \\
-3 &
\end{array}
$$

Example 2: Find the truth set of

$$\tfrac{1}{2} + 3 = ^-5 + x + \tfrac{3}{2}.$$

■ **P-3** What fraction names $\tfrac{1}{2} + 3$?

■ **P-4** What is the common name for the phrase on the right side?

Using common names, you get the equivalent sentence

$$\tfrac{7}{2} = x + ^-\left(\tfrac{7}{2}\right).$$

■ **P-5** What is the next step?

You should get the following.

$$\tfrac{7}{2} + \tfrac{7}{2} = x + ^-\left(\tfrac{7}{2}\right) + \tfrac{7}{2}$$
$$\tfrac{14}{2} = x$$
$$\{7\}$$

Check:
$$
\begin{array}{c|c}
\tfrac{1}{2} + 3 = ^-5 + x + \tfrac{3}{2} & \\
3\tfrac{1}{2} & ^-5 + 7 + \tfrac{3}{2} \\
& 2 + \tfrac{3}{2} \\
& 3\tfrac{1}{2}
\end{array}
$$

You will recall that you have found truth sets of open sentences such as $-x = 7$.

■ **P-6** What is the truth number for

$$-x = 7?$$

Remember that "taking the opposite" of each side gives an equivalent sentence. The sentence $-x = 7$ and the sentence $-(-x) = -7$ are equivalent. But the last sentence is the same as $x = {}^-7$, whose truth set is $\{{}^-7\}$.

Example 3: Find the truth set of

$$5 + (-x) + 2 = 5.$$

■ **P-7** What is the common name of the left side?

Using the common name of the left side, you get the equivalent sentence

$$7 + (-x) = 5.$$

Adding $^-7$ to each side, you have

$$7 + (-x) + {}^-7 = 5 + {}^-7,$$
$$-x = {}^-2.$$

■ **P-8** What is the truth set of the sentence

$$-x = {}^-2?$$

Check: $5 + (-x) + 2 = 5$
$ 5 + ({}^-2) + 2 \,\big|$
$ 5 \,\big|$

ORAL EXERCISES 9.8

Give the common name for each side of the open sentence in Written Exercises 9.8.

WRITTEN EXERCISES 9.8

A Find the truth set of each open sentence. Show the steps and check.

1. $2 + x + 5 = 2 + {}^-10$
2. ${}^-3 + x + 8 = 7 + 9$
3. $x + {}^-8 + 12 = {}^-3 + 7$
4. $x + 5 + {}^-13 = {}^-9 + {}^-6$
5. ${}^-13 + x + 19 = {}^-21 + {}^-16$
6. $21 + x + {}^-9 = {}^-14 + {}^-7$
7. $12 + {}^-19 = {}^-13 + x + 7$
8. ${}^-18 + 15 = 19 + x + {}^-23$

9. $5.2 + x + {}^-8.7 = {}^-9.3 + 5.8$

10. $12.5 + {}^-8.6 = 3.9 + x + {}^-4.5$

11. $\frac{1}{4} + x + {}^-(\frac{7}{4}) = \frac{5}{2}$ **12.** $\frac{5}{8} = \frac{3}{8} + x + {}^-(\frac{11}{8})$

13. $-x + 5 + {}^-2 = {}^-7$ **14.** $-x + {}^-8 + 12 = {}^-9$

15. ${}^-10 + {}^-12 = 5 + (-x) + {}^-6$

16. $16 + {}^-5 = {}^-2 + x + 7$ **17.** $13.2 + {}^-5.8 = 7.2 + (-x)$

18. $5.6 + {}^-8.9 = {}^-13.7 + (-x) + 9.6$

19. ${}^-2 + x + 5 = {}^-3 + x$ **20.** $x + {}^-8 = 2 + x + 5$

B   Find the truth set of each of the following sentences.

21. $x + {}^-8 + {}^-7 = 20 + x + {}^-35$

22. ${}^-5 + x + {}^-11 = x + {}^-3 + {}^-13$

23. $2x + 3 = 11$ **24.** $2x + {}^-5 = 13$

25. $\frac{1}{2}x + {}^-5 = 1$ **26.** $\frac{1}{3}x + 8 = 17$

9.9   The Opposite of the Sum of Two Numbers

You have learned that two nonzero numbers that are opposites are coordinates of points the same distance from 0 on the number line. Also, you have learned that 0 is its own opposite. You see then that each real number has exactly one opposite.

Next you will find a name for the opposite of the sum of two real numbers. Let the sum of any two real numbers be represented by the phrase $a + b$.

■ **P-1**   How do you know that such a sum is always a real number?

Since $(a + b)$ is a real number, it has an opposite. Represent its opposite by $-(a + b)$.

■ **P-2**   Why is the following sentence true?

$$(a + b) + \big(-(a + b)\big) = 0$$

Since a and b are real numbers, they have opposites, $-a$ and $-b$. Consider the following phrase.

$$(a + b) + \big((-a) + (-b)\big)$$

By using the commutative and associative properties of addition you can get the following phrase.

$$\big(a + (-a)\big) + \big(b + (-b)\big)$$

■ **P-3** What is the common name for $(a + (-a))$?

■ **P-4** What is the common name for $(b + (-b))$?

■ **P-5** What is the common name for $(a + b) + ((-a) + (-b))$?

By the Addition Property of Opposites, you know that the sum of a number and its opposite is 0.

$$x + (-x) = 0$$

You can see that for any true sentence, such as $x + y = 0$, the number represented by y must be the opposite of x.

Go back to the result of **P-5**.

$$(a + b) + ((-a) + (-b)) = 0$$

You can see that $((-a) + (-b))$ must be the opposite of $a + b$. Therefore, the following sentence is true for all real numbers a and b.

$$-(a + b) = (-a) + (-b)$$

In words, this says that the following is true.

> The opposite of the sum of two real numbers equals the sum of their opposites.

You will have occasion to use this result many times in your study of algebra.

■ **P-6** Express the following phrase, using the above generalization.

$$-(^-5 + 8) = \underline{\ ?\ }$$

ORAL EXERCISES 9.9

1. Does each real number have an opposite?
2. How many opposites does each real number have?
3. What property tells you the sentence $23 + (-23) = 0$ is true?
4. What property tells you the sentence $^-19 + -(^-19) = 0$ is true?
5. What property tells you that $r + s$ is a real number if r and s are real numbers?
6. Complete this statement: "The opposite of the sum of two real numbers equals $\underline{\ ?\ }$."

Express the following phrases, using the rule in Exercise 6. Do not give common names.

7. $-(5 + 9)$ **8.** $-(10 + {}^-3)$

9. $-({}^-5 + {}^-8)$ **10.** $-({}^-9 + 4)$

11. $-(5 + {}^-1)$ **12.** $-(\frac{1}{2} + \frac{1}{3})$

Give an equivalent sentence involving x for each of the following sentences.

13. $-x = -(5 + {}^-3)$ **14.** $-x = -({}^-7 + {}^-2)$

15. $5 = 3 + (-x)$ **16.** ${}^-2 = -(5 + (-x))$

17. $-x = {}^-7 + 5$ **18.** $-x = {}^-10 + {}^-19$

19. ${}^-1 = {}^-7 + (-x)$ **20.** $12 = {}^-5 + (-x)$

WRITTEN EXERCISES 9.9

A   Use $-(a + b) = (-a) + (-b)$ to write each phrase in another way.

1. $-({}^-5 + 7)$ **2.** $-(8 + {}^-3)$

3. ${}^-5 + 9$ **4.** $10 + {}^-13$

5. $-(x + 8)$ **6.** $-(10 + y)$

7. $-(12 + (-x))$ **8.** $-({}^-15 + r)$

9. $y + (-x)$ **10.** $-t + s$

11. $-({}^-9 + (-m))$ **12.** $-(-n + 13)$

13. $-(y + (-x))$ **14.** $-(-r + s)$

15. $(-m) + (-n)$ **16.** $-p + (-q)$

Find the truth set of each of the following. First get a sentence involving x.

Example:
$$
\begin{aligned}
{}^-5 &= {}^-3 + (-x) \\
-({}^-5) &= -({}^-3 + (-x)) \\
5 &= 3 + x \\
5 + {}^-3 &= 3 + x + {}^-3 \\
2 &= x \\
\{2\}
\end{aligned}
$$

Check: $-5 = {}^-3 + (-x)$
$\qquad\quad\ \Big|\ {}^-3 + (-2)$
$\qquad\quad\ \Big|\ {}^-5$

17. ${}^-2 = 5 + (-x)$ **18.** $5 = {}^-3 + (-y)$

19. $10 = {}^-7 + (-n)$ **20.** ${}^-4 = -m + 7$

21. $-x + 12 = 15$ **22.** ${}^-9 + (-x) = {}^-12$

CHAPTER SUMMARY

Important Terms

1. **Equivalent open sentences** are sentences that have the same truth set.

2. An **equation** is an open sentence in which the verb is represented by the symbol $=$.

3. The **sides** of an equation are the two phrases separated by the symbol $=$.

Important Ideas

1. The sum of two positive real numbers is the same as their sum as numbers of arithmetic.

2. The sum of two negative real numbers is the opposite of the sum of their absolute values.

3. To find the sum of a positive and a negative number,
   (a) find the difference between the absolute values if the positive number has the greater absolute value or if the absolute values are equal;
   (b) find the opposite of the difference between the absolute values if the negative number has the greater absolute value.

4. *Addition Property of Zero:* For any real number a, it is true that
$$a + 0 = a.$$

5. *Addition Property of Opposites:* For any real number a, it is true that
$$a + (-a) = 0.$$

6. The set of real numbers is closed under addition.

7. *Commutative Property of Addition:* For any real numbers, a and b, it is true that
$$a + b = b + a.$$

8. *Associative Property of Addition:* For any real numbers a, b, and c, it is true that
$$(a + b) + c = a + (b + c).$$

9. *Addition Property of Equality:* If any real number is added to both sides of an open equation, then the new equation is equivalent to the first.

10. For all real numbers a and b, it is true that
$$-(a + b) = (-a) + (-b).$$

CHAPTER REVIEW

Find the common name for each of the following sums.

1. $^-25 + 52$
2. $37 + {}^-63$
3. $^-33 + {}^-42$
4. $^-12 + 17 + {}^-36$
5. $9 + {}^-12 + 8 + {}^-5$
6. $^-7 + 9 + {}^-3 + 1 + {}^-5$
7. $^-(\frac{3}{16}) + \frac{5}{16} + \frac{1}{8}$
8. $\frac{3}{8} + {}^-(\frac{5}{8}) + \frac{1}{4}$

Give the number property of real numbers that is illustrated by each true sentence.

9. $(x + {}^-2) + 5 = x + ({}^-2 + 5)$
10. $5 + (x + {}^-7) = 5 + ({}^-7 + x)$
11. $({}^-17 + y) + x = x + ({}^-17 + y)$
12. $x + (15 + {}^-15) = x + 0$

Give the common name for each of the following.

13. $^-12 + {}^-3 + y + 15$
14. $x + 91 + {}^-83$
15. $4.3 + x + {}^-9.1$
16. $^-17.9 + y + {}^-5.1 + 2.7$

If a and b represent any real numbers, indicate by *Yes* and *No* whether each of the following pairs of sentences is equivalent. Let the domain be {real numbers}.

17. $x + a = b;\ \ x + a + 5 = b + 5$
18. $x = b;\ \ x + a = b + (-a)$
19. $x = b;\ \ x + (-a) = b + (-a)$
20. $x + b = a;\ \ 5 + x + b + 7 = a + 12$

Find the truth set of each of the following. Show steps and check.

21. $x + {}^-23 = 51$
22. $^-17 = 76 + y$
23. $^-8 + x + {}^-2 = 57 + {}^-8$
24. $2 + (-x) = {}^-17$
25. $-(-x + {}^-5) = 9$
26. $17.8 + {}^-5.6 = 2.7 + x + {}^-5.9$
27. $\frac{1}{4} + x + \frac{1}{2} = x + {}^-(\frac{5}{6})$
28. $^-3 + x + {}^-11 = 20 + x + {}^-6$

Translate each of the following into an open sentence. First choose a variable and tell what it represents.

29. The sum of the opposite of a number and 5 is the opposite of 50.
30. One day, a man loses $500 on one business transaction and makes a profit of $950 on another. How much does he gain or lose?
31. If the thermometer reads 15° below zero, how much will it have to rise to read 35° above zero?
32. When 5 and an unknown number are averaged, the result is the opposite of 2. What is the unknown number?

Translate each of the following to an open phrase using the variable that is suggested.

1. The number of meters in x centimeters

2. The number of months in y years

3. The number of cents in q quarters

4. The interest on d dollars at 6% for 1 year

5. The number of grams of salt in y grams of a 15% solution

6. The discount on an article listed at $500 at a rate of d%

Translate each of the following problems into an open sentence. First choose a variable and tell what it represents.

7. The width of a rectangle is 5 inches less than the length. Find the length if the perimeter is 38 inches.

8. The sum of two numbers is 7. Five times the lesser number decreased by $\frac{1}{2}$ equals the greater number. What is the lesser number?

9. The sum of the opposite of a number and its square is 8. What is the number?

10. Two trains leave cities that are 3150 miles apart and meet at a point between them in 30 hours. If one train averages 5 mph faster than the other, what is the average speed of the slower train?

11. The number of square inches in a board is less than 500. How many square feet are there in the board?

12. The value of a certain number of quarters and three more dimes is less than $5.10. How many dimes are there?

Tell whether each of the following sentences is *True* or *False*.

13. {rational numbers} is a subset of {real numbers}.

14. The number 15 is an element of {rational numbers}.

15. {integers} is a subset of {numbers of arithmetic}.

16. {real numbers} is a subset of {irrational numbers}.

17. The number $^-\pi$ is an element of {numbers of arithmetic}.

18. The number $|\,^-2\,|$ is an element of {real numbers}.

19. The number 0 is an element of {real numbers}.

20. The number $^-(\frac{1}{2})$ is an element of {real numbers}.

Express each of the following as the quotient of two integers.

21. $3\frac{1}{4}$ **22.** 0   **23.** 1.56 **24.** $0.6666\cdots$

Use > and < to form two true sentences with each pair of numbers.

25. ⁻13; 5   **26.** ⁻56; ⁻48

27. ⁻($\frac{1}{3}$); ⁻0.9   **28.** 3.5; ⁻5.3

Make a graph of the truth set for each sentence, using {integers} as the domain.

29. $x < $ ⁻2   **30.** $x \leq $ ⁻1.8   **31.** $x \geq $ ⁻5   **32.** $x < 5$

Make a graph of the truth set for each sentence, using {real numbers} as the domain.

33. $x < $ ⁻2   **34.** $x \leq $ ⁻1.8   **35.** $x \geq $ ⁻5   **36.** $x < 5$

Give the common name for each of the following.

37. $-(⁻7)$ **38.** $-(-r)$ **39.** $-(-(⁻9))$ **40.** $-(9 + ⁻8)$

41. $|⁻(\frac{1}{2})|$ **42.** $|0|$ **43.** $|-(⁻6)|$ **44.** $|⁻9| - |-(⁻6)|$

From each of the following sentences, form a true sentence involving the opposites of the given numbers.

45. ⁻2 < 7   **46.** ⁻10 < ⁻3

47. 3 > ⁻8   **48.** 12 < 15

Graph the truth sets of each of the following sentences. Let the domain be {real numbers}.

49. $-x \leq 5$ **50.** ⁻7 $\leq -x$ **51.** $-x > 1\frac{1}{2}$

52. $-x \leq 3$ and $-x > $ ⁻4   **53.** $|x| < 2\frac{1}{3}$ **54.** $|x| \geq 2\frac{1}{2}$

Make use of the commutative and associative properties to find the following sums easily.

55. $⁻(\frac{3}{4}) + 7 + ⁻3 + ⁻(\frac{1}{4}) + ⁻2$

56. $\frac{3}{8} + ⁻(\frac{5}{8}) + \frac{1}{8} + \frac{7}{8} + \frac{1}{4}$

57. $|⁻6| + ⁻3 + -|⁻2| + |\frac{1}{5}|$

58. $5.2 + ⁻9.3 + 1.8 + ⁻4.7$

Find the truth set of each sentence. Show steps and check.

59. $|⁻5| + x + ⁻3 = 7 + |⁻8|$

60. $12 + |⁻9| = y + 3 + |-(⁻3)|$

61. $-(⁻5 + (-x)) = |⁻16|$

62. $-x + 12 + ⁻8 = 13 + |⁻3|$

63. ⁻3 $+ (x + 5) = (⁻3 + 5) + x$

64. $x + (-x) + 5 = x + (-x)$

In the United Nations Headquarters in New York, a Foucault pendulum swings from side to side in uniform time. The time T that it takes for a pendulum to swing from one side to the other and back again is expressed by the formula $T = 2\pi q$, where q is the square root of the quotient of the length of the cord holding the pendulum and the force of gravity. This formula involves the product of real numbers, a topic that you will study in this chapter.

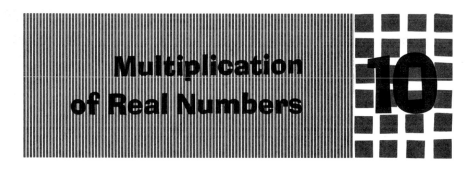

10.1 Product of a Positive Number and a Negative Number

You saw in the last chapter that all the properties of numbers of arithmetic are also the properties of the real numbers.

■ **P-1** Can you think of a property of the set of real numbers that does not apply to the set of numbers of arithmetic?

Again, in working with products of real numbers, your goal will be to allow the properties of multiplication of numbers of arithmetic to apply. Certainly, then, the product of two positive real numbers is the same as their product when they are considered to be numbers of arithmetic.

■ **P-2** Do you remember the Multiplication Property of Zero for numbers of arithmetic? State this property.

You may allow the Multiplication Property of Zero to apply to real numbers also.

■ **P-3** What is the common name for the following products?

$$(5)0; \quad (^-5)0; \quad 0 \cdot 0$$

The **Multiplication Property of Zero** for real numbers is stated as follows.

> If a is any real number, then the following are true.
>
> $a \cdot 0 = 0$ and $0 \cdot a = 0$

Patterns of products can help you decide what the rule should be for multiplying a positive number and a negative number. Consider the following.

$$5(6) = 30$$
$$5(5) = 25$$
$$5(4) = 20$$
$$5(3) = 15$$
$$5(2) = 10$$
$$5(1) = 5$$
$$5(0) = 0$$

If this pattern of products is continued, what would you expect for the following?

■ P-4 $5(^-1) = \underline{\ ?\ }$

■ P-5 $5(^-2) = \underline{\ ?\ }$

■ P-6 $5(^-3) = \underline{\ ?\ }$

Another example may be used to show the same idea.

$$4(5) = 20$$
$$4(4) = 16$$
$$4(3) = 12$$
$$4(2) = 8$$
$$4(1) = 4$$
$$4(0) = 0$$

■ P-7   Using the above pattern, what do you think the following products should be?

$$4(^-1) = \underline{\ ?\ }$$
$$4(^-2) = \underline{\ ?\ }$$
$$4(^-3) = \underline{\ ?\ }$$
$$4(^-4) = \underline{\ ?\ }$$
$$4(^-5) = \underline{\ ?\ }$$

These results suggest that the product of a positive number and a negative number is negative. The rule can be stated as follows.

> The product of a positive real number and a negative real number is the opposite of the product of their absolute values.

■ **P-8** If you want the Commutative Property of Multiplication to be true for real numbers, what should the following products be?

$$^-1(4) = \underline{\ ?\ }$$
$$^-2(4) = \underline{\ ?\ }$$
$$^-3(4) = \underline{\ ?\ }$$
$$^-4(4) = \underline{\ ?\ }$$
$$^-5(4) = \underline{\ ?\ }$$

■ **P-9** Complete the sequence of products in the following, using the pattern that is suggested.

$$6(2\tfrac{1}{2}) = 15$$
$$6(2) = 12$$
$$6(1\tfrac{1}{2}) = 9$$
$$6(1) = 6$$
$$6(\tfrac{1}{2}) = 3$$
$$6(0) = 0$$
$$6(^-\tfrac{1}{2}) = \underline{\ ?\ }$$
$$6(^-1) = \underline{\ ?\ }$$
$$6(^-1\tfrac{1}{2}) = \underline{\ ?\ }$$

The steps for multiplying a positive real number and a negative real number can be stated as follows.

1. Find the product of their absolute values.
2. Take the opposite of this product.

Consider $(^-12)(8)$.

■ **P-10** What is $|\ ^-12\ |$?

■ **P-11** What is $|\ 8\ |$?

■ **P-12** What is the common name for $12 \cdot 8$?

■ **P-13** What is the common name for the opposite of 96?

Thus, you see that

$$(^-12)(8) = ^-96.$$

You will probably have no trouble in multiplying the absolute values because these are numbers of arithmetic. However, remember that the product of a positive number and a negative number is negative.

ORAL EXERCISES 10.1

Give a common name for each of the following. The domain of the variable in any of these problems is {real numbers}.

1. $0(5)$ **2.** $(^-12)0$ **3.** $^-(\frac{1}{2}) \cdot 0$

4. $0(^-13)$ **5.** $0(\frac{1}{3})$ **6.** $0 \cdot x$

7. $(-y + y)(^-7)$ **8.** $^-1(r + (-r))$ **9.** $0(3 + ^-3)$

10. $0(3) + 0(^-3)$

Give the common name for each of the following products.

11. $7(8)$ **12.** $^-7(8)$ **13.** $8(^-7)$

14. $7(^-8)$ **15.** $^-8(7)$ **16.** $\frac{1}{2}(^-10)$

17. $^-(\frac{1}{3})(12)$ **18.** $\frac{1}{3}(^-12)$ **19.** $\frac{1}{2}(\frac{1}{3})$

20. $^-(\frac{1}{2})(\frac{1}{3})$

WRITTEN EXERCISES 10.1

A Find the truth set of each of the following. Let {real numbers} be the domain.

1. $^-17(n) = 0$ **2.** $y(^-9) = 0$ **3.** $r(0) = 0$

4. $0(a) = 0$ **5.** $^-3(0) = x$ **6.** $0(^-11) = n$

7. $2(x) = ^-6$ **8.** $5(y) = ^-15$ **9.** $^-7(x) = ^-28$

10. $^-10(r) = ^-70$ **11.** $\frac{1}{2}x = ^-9$ **12.** $\frac{1}{3}y = ^-12$

Find common names for the following products.

13. $22(^-3)$ **14.** $18(^-2)$ **15.** $^-7(4)$

16. $^-9(3)$ **17.** $\frac{1}{2}(^-26)$ **18.** $\frac{1}{2}(^-32)$

19. $(^-27)\frac{1}{3}$ **20.** $(^-18)\frac{1}{3}$ **21.** $^-(\frac{1}{2})(7)$

22. $^-(\frac{1}{2})(13)$ **23.** $^-(\frac{1}{4})(12)$ **24.** $^-(\frac{1}{3})(\frac{1}{5})$

25. $^-(\frac{2}{3}) \cdot (\frac{3}{4})$ **26.** $\frac{3}{8} \cdot ^-(\frac{4}{3})$ **27.** $| ^-3 | \cdot ^-15$

28. $^-13 \cdot | ^-2 |$ **29.** $-(| ^-7 | \cdot | 3 |)$ **30.** $-(| 4 | \cdot | ^-2 |)$

C Find the common name for each of the following.

31. $^-2(17 + ^-3)$ **32.** $^-5(^-8 + 12)$ **33.** $^-7(2 \cdot 4)$

34. $^-8(3 \cdot 2)$ **35.** $(^-7 \cdot 2)4$ **36.** $(^-8 \cdot 3)2$

37. $10(^-3 \cdot 5)$ **38.** $6(5 \cdot ^-2)$ **39.** $(10 \cdot ^-3)5$

40. $(6 \cdot 5) \cdot ^-2$

Indicate whether each of the following is *True* or *False*.

41. $9(^-5 + ^-7) = 9(^-5) + 9(^-7)$

42. $12(^-8 + 10) = 12(^-8) + 12(10)$

43. $(^-13 + ^-8)7 = ^-13(7) + ^-8(7)$

44. $(^-27 + ^-13)\frac{1}{2} = (^-27)\frac{1}{2} + (^-13)\frac{1}{2}$

10.2 Product of Two Negative Numbers

Again, patterns of products can help you to see what the rule should be for multiplying two negative numbers.

$$(^-5)4 = {}^-20$$
$$(^-5)3 = {}^-15$$
$$(^-5)2 = {}^-10$$
$$(^-5)1 = {}^-5$$
$$(^-5)0 = 0$$

■ **P-1** What are the next three terms of the sequence of products above?

$${}^-20, {}^-15, {}^-10, {}^-5, 0, \underline{\ ?\ }, \underline{\ ?\ }, \underline{\ ?\ }, \cdots$$

■ **P-2** If the pattern of products is continued, what should the following products be?

$$(^-5)(^-1) = \underline{\ ?\ }$$
$$(^-5)(^-2) = \underline{\ ?\ }$$
$$(^-5)(^-3) = \underline{\ ?\ }$$

Now try another example:

$$(^-4)3 = {}^-12$$
$$(^-4)2 = {}^-8$$
$$(^-4)1 = {}^-4$$
$$(^-4)0 = 0$$

■ **P-3** Continuing the pattern, what do you think are the following products?

$$(^-4)(^-1) = \underline{\ ?\ }$$
$$(^-4)(^-2) = \underline{\ ?\ }$$
$$(^-4)(^-3) = \underline{\ ?\ }$$

■ **P-4** What kind of number is the product of two negative numbers?

Getting a positive number as a product of two negative numbers is usually surprising to students. Perhaps another argument will convince you that this is the desired result. The example on the following page starts with the true sentence $0 = (^-5) \cdot 0$. You form this sentence by applying the Multiplication Property of Zero. While you study this example, remember that the same number properties that are true for numbers of arithmetic are also true for the real numbers. Any rules that define products of real numbers should be in agreement with the other properties and rules.

By the Multiplication Property of Zero ⟶ $0 = (^-5) \cdot 0$
Using $3 + {}^-3$ as a name for 0 ⟶ $0 = {}^-5(3 + {}^-3)$
By the Distributive Property (which is
   to be applied to real numbers) ⟶ $0 = (^-5) \cdot 3 + (^-5)(^-3)$
Because $^-15$ is the common name for $(^-5)3$ ⟶ $0 = {}^-15 + (^-5)(^-3)$

If $^-15$ plus some number equals 0, then that number must be the opposite of $^-15$, or 15. You can see that this example makes use of the following properties to "prove" that $(^-5)(^-3) = 15$.

| 1 | Multiplication Property of Zero
| 2 | Addition Property of Opposites
| 3 | Distributive Property

You could use this method for finding the product of any two negative real numbers.

The product of two negative numbers is a positive number. The rule can be stated as follows.

> **The product of two negative real numbers is the product of their absolute values.**

■ **P-5** What is the common name for $|\,^-7\,|$? for $|\,^-5\,|$?

■ **P-6** What is the common name for $|\,^-7\,| \cdot |\,^-5\,|$? for $(^-7)(^-5)$?

You have now covered all possible products of real numbers. You have seen that any two real numbers have a product and that their product is always a real number. This means that the **Closure Property of Multiplication** applies to the set of real numbers.

The rules for finding the product of any two real numbers are summarized as follows.

| 1 | The product of two positive real numbers is the same as their product as numbers of arithmetic.

| 2 | The product of a positive real number and a negative real number is the opposite of the product of their absolute values.

| 3 | The product of two negative real numbers is the product of their absolute values.

| 4 | The product of 0 and any real number is 0.

ORAL EXERCISES 10.2

Give the common name for each of the following.
1. $(^-2)(^-3)$ 2. $(^-1)(^-5)$ 3. $(^-5)(^-1)$ 4. $(^-2)(^-7)$
5. $(3)(5)$ 6. $(^-3)(5)$ 7. $(3)(^-5)$ 8. $(^-3)(^-5)$
9. $(^-7)(0)$ 10. $^-(\frac{1}{2}) \cdot {}^-(\frac{1}{2})$ 11. $\frac{1}{2}(\frac{1}{2})$ 12. $^-(\frac{1}{2})(\frac{1}{2})$
13. $(^-3) \cdot {}^-(\frac{1}{3})$ 14. $^-(\frac{1}{5})(^-5)$ 15. $^-(\frac{1}{5}) \cdot 5$ 16. $(^-2)(^-2)(^-2)$
17. $(^-2)(^-2)(2)$ 18. $2 \cdot 2 \cdot 2$ 19. $(^-2) \cdot 2 \cdot 2$ 20. $(^-1)(^-1)(^-1)(^-1)$

WRITTEN EXERCISES 10.2

A Write the common name for each of the following products.
1. $(^-7)(^-8)$ 2. $(^-9)(^-6)$ 3. $(^-13)(^-9)$
4. $(^-16)(^-7)$ 5. $^-(\frac{1}{2}) \cdot {}^-(\frac{1}{7})$ 6. $^-(\frac{1}{3}) \cdot {}^-(\frac{1}{5})$
7. $(^-3.2)(^-7)$ 8. $(^-5.4)(^-9)$ 9. $(^-9)11$
10. $(^-7)12$ 11. $5(^-22)$ 12. $6(^-25)$
13. $0(^-12)$ 14. $(^-15)0$ 15. $(^-0.5)(^-0.3)$
16. $(^-0.8)(^-0.4)$ 17. $(^-5)(^-4)(^-3)$ 18. $(^-2)(^-6)(^-5)$
19. $^-(\frac{1}{2}) \cdot {}^-(\frac{2}{3}) \cdot \frac{6}{5}$ 20. $^-(\frac{1}{3}) \cdot \frac{3}{4} \cdot {}^-(\frac{2}{7})$ 21. $(^-19)(^-11)$
22. $(^-13)(^-24)$ 23. $|\,^-19\,| \cdot |\,^-11\,|$ 24. $|\,^-13\,| \cdot |\,^-24\,|$

Find the truth set of each sentence. Let $\{\text{real numbers}\}$ be the domain.
25. $^-5x = 35$ 26. $^-6y = 54$
27. $^-5x = ^-35$ 28. $^-6y = ^-54$
29. $1 = ^-(\frac{1}{2})n$ 30. $^-(\frac{1}{3})r = 1$

Indicate by *Yes* or *No* whether each of the following sets is closed under multiplication.
31. $\{\text{real numbers}\}$ 32. $\{\text{integers}\}$
33. $\{\text{nonnegative real numbers}\}$ 34. $\{\text{negative real numbers}\}$
35. $\{\text{negative integers}\}$ 36. $\{\text{nonpositive integers}\}$

B Find the common name for each of the following.
37. $^-7(^-8 + 2)$ 38. $^-12(5 + ^-8)$
39. $^-10(^-7 \cdot 4)$ 40. $^-8(9 \cdot ^-5)$
41. $(^-10 \cdot ^-7)4$ 42. $(^-8 \cdot 9) \cdot ^-5$
43. $(^-12 + ^-3) \cdot ^-6$ 44. $(^-15 + 8) \cdot ^-7$
45. $(^-12)(^-6) + (^-3)(^-6)$ 46. $(^-15) \cdot (^-7) + (8)(^-7)$

C Find the truth set of each sentence. Let $\{\text{real numbers}\}$ be the domain.
47. $|\,t\,| \cdot |\,^-5\,| = 90$ 48. $|\,^-10\,| \cdot |\,m\,| = 120$
49. $|\,x\,| \cdot |\,3\,| = 3x$ 50. $|\,y\,| \cdot |\,5\,| = (^-y) \cdot 5$

10.3 Properties of Multiplication

It is desirable that the properties of the numbers of arithmetic apply also to the real numbers. The rules for addition and multiplication of positive and negative numbers were made with this aim in mind. You have had an opportunity to test some of these properties in assignment exercises.

You have already seen the Multiplication Property of Zero for real numbers and have noted that the Closure Property of Multiplication applies to the set of real numbers. Here is the **Multiplication Property of One** as it applies to real numbers:

> **For any real number a, it is true that**
>
> $$1(a) = a.$$

■ **P-1** What is the common name for each of the following products?

$$1(^-5); \quad 1(0); \quad ^-(\tfrac{1}{2}) \cdot 1$$

Of course, you can think of this property simply as "the product of any real number and 1 is the same real number."

The rules for multiplication suggest that the **Commutative Property of Multiplication** is true for all real numbers. This is stated as follows.

> **If a and b are any real numbers, then it is true that**
>
> $$ab = ba.$$

Here are some examples illustrating the Commutative Property of Multiplication for real numbers:

$$(^-8)(7) = (7)(^-8)$$
$$^-(\tfrac{1}{2}) \cdot {}^-(\tfrac{1}{3}) = {}^-(\tfrac{1}{3}) \cdot {}^-(\tfrac{1}{2})$$
$$(2 \cdot 7)(3 \cdot 2) = (3 \cdot 2)(2 \cdot 7)$$
$$(1)(^-56) = (^-56)(1)$$
$$(0)(^-12) = (^-12)(0)$$

■ **P-2** Does the following sentence illustrate the Commutative Property of Multiplication?

$$^-5(^-7 \cdot {}^-3) = {}^-5({}^-3 \cdot {}^-7)$$

Another important property that is true for the set of real numbers is the **Associative Property of Multiplication.** For the real numbers, this property is stated as follows.

> **If a, b, and c are any real numbers, then it is true that**
>
> **$(ab)c = a(bc)$.**

■ **P-3** Test this property by finding the common name for each side of the following sentences.

$$(^-5 \cdot 2)3 = {}^-5(2 \cdot 3)$$
$$\left(^-(\tfrac{1}{2}) \cdot 0\right) \cdot 3 = {}^-(\tfrac{1}{2})(0 \cdot 3)$$
$$(^-4 \cdot {}^-3)5 = {}^-4(^-3 \cdot 5)$$
$$(1 \cdot {}^-5.2) \cdot (^-1) = 1\left(^-5.2 \cdot (^-1)\right)$$
$$(^-2 \cdot {}^-3) \cdot (^-5) = {}^-2(^-3 \cdot {}^-5)$$

ORAL EXERCISES 10.3

Find the truth set of each of the following open sentences. Let the domain be {real numbers}.

1. $^-5x = {}^-5$
2. $^-(\tfrac{1}{2})y = {}^-(\tfrac{1}{2})$
3. $^-3r = 0$
4. $5m = 0$
5. $1x = {}^-100$
6. $1y = 50$
7. $1n = {}^-(\tfrac{2}{3})$
8. $1 \cdot t = t$
9. $1s = 1$
10. $1 \cdot a = 0$
11. $^-2r = 5(^-2)$
12. $x \cdot (^-7) = {}^-7 \cdot {}^-8$
13. $^-3(y \cdot 7) = {}^-3(7 \cdot {}^-8)$
14. $^-10(5 \cdot {}^-9) = (5 \cdot {}^-9)x$
15. $^-89(r \cdot {}^-75) = (^-89 \cdot {}^-56) \cdot {}^-75$
16. $(5.2 \cdot {}^-6.8) \cdot {}^-9.3 = n(^-6.8 \cdot {}^-9.3)$

Identify the property or properties that are used in each of the following.

17. $^-2(5 \cdot x) = (5 \cdot x) \cdot {}^-2$
18. $(^-3 \cdot a) \cdot 18 = {}^-3(a \cdot 18)$
19. $^-9(8x) = x(8 \cdot {}^-9)$
20. $1(^-5y) = y(^-5)$

WRITTEN EXERCISES 10.3

A Show that each of the following sentences is true by finding the common name for each side.

Example: $(^-2 \cdot {}^-5) \cdot {}^-3 = {}^-2(^-5 \cdot {}^-3)$

$$\begin{array}{c|c} 10 \cdot {}^-3 & {}^-2(15) \\ {}^-30 & {}^-30 \end{array}$$

1. $(^-7 \cdot {}^-3) \cdot 5 = {}^-7(^-3 \cdot 5)$
2. $(8 \cdot {}^-2) \cdot {}^-5 = 8 \cdot (^-2 \cdot {}^-5)$
3. $\frac{1}{2}(^-3 \cdot {}^-12) = (\frac{1}{2} \cdot {}^-3) \cdot {}^-12$
4. $(^-9 \cdot {}^-5) \cdot \frac{1}{3} = {}^-9(^-5 \cdot \frac{1}{3})$
5. $(^-10 \cdot {}^-8) \cdot {}^-5 = {}^-10(^-8 \cdot {}^-5)$
6. $^-12(^-6 \cdot {}^-2) = (^-12 \cdot {}^-6) \cdot {}^-2$
7. $7(^-3 \cdot 8) = {}^-3(8 \cdot 7)$
8. $(^-5 \cdot {}^-9) \cdot 3 = {}^-5(3 \cdot {}^-9)$

Use properties of this section to get a common name for each of the following by the easiest method.

9. $\frac{1}{3}(5 \cdot 6)$
10. $(10 \cdot {}^-9)\frac{1}{5}$
11. $(^-12 \cdot {}^-13) \cdot {}^-(\frac{3}{4})$
12. $^-(\frac{2}{3})(^-5 \cdot {}^-18)$
13. $(^-98 \cdot 56) \cdot 0$
14. $(^-78 \cdot {}^-91) \cdot 0$
15. $(^-5.5 \cdot 9)(^-2)$
16. $^-5(^-8.2 \cdot 3)$

Indicate whether each sentence illustrates the *Commutative* or the *Associative* Property of Multiplication or *Both*.

17. $^-3(^-7 \cdot 4) = (^-7 \cdot 4) \cdot {}^-3$
18. $(8 \cdot {}^-5) \cdot {}^-7 = (^-5 \cdot 8) \cdot {}^-7$
19. $(3.7 \cdot {}^-1.6) \cdot {}^-4.9 = 3.7(^-4.9 \cdot {}^-1.6)$
20. $8.3 \cdot (^-3.8 \cdot {}^-5.7) = {}^-5.7(^-3.8 \cdot 8.3)$
21. $\frac{1}{2}(^-5 \cdot {}^-(\frac{1}{3})) = (\frac{1}{2} \cdot {}^-5) \cdot {}^-(\frac{1}{3})$
22. $^-9(^-3 \cdot {}^-(\frac{3}{5})) = (^-(\frac{3}{5}) \cdot {}^-9) \cdot (^-3)$
23. $^-3(^-5 \cdot x) = (^-3 \cdot {}^-5)x$
24. $(^-10y) \cdot {}^-7 = {}^-10(y \cdot {}^-7)$

C Find the common name for each of the following phrases.

25. $(^-2)^2 + (^-5)$
26. $(^-3)^2 + (^-10)$
27. $(^-1)^2 + 2(^-3)$
28. $^-5(7) + (^-5)^2$
29. $^-(3^2)$
30. $^-(4^2)$
31. $(^-2)^3$
32. $(^-1)^3$
33. $5 \cdot (^-3)^2$
34. $3 \cdot (^-2)^3$
35. $(^-6)^2 + 8(^-5) + 17$
36. $^-3(8) + (^-7)^2 + (^-15)$

10.4 Distributive Property

You will recall that you used the Distributive Property with the numbers of arithmetic. As indicated for the other number properties, the Distributive Property also applies to the real numbers. (You will recall as well that this property was used with real numbers in Section 10.2 to show that the product of two negative real numbers is a positive real number.) Here is a statement of the **Distributive Property** for real numbers:

If a, b, and c are any real numbers, then it is true that

$$a(b + c) = ab + ac.$$

Remember that the Distributive Property involves both the operation of addition and the operation of multiplication. It is used to write sums as products or products as sums.

■ **P-1** Is the phrase $a(b + c)$ a sum or product?

■ **P-2** Is $ab + ac$ a sum or product?

You should also remember another common form of the Distributive Property:

If a, b, and c are any real numbers, then it is true that

$$(b + c)a = ba + ca.$$

■ **P-3** What number property is used in obtaining this last result from the first statement of the Distributive Property?

In Chapter 3, you learned to find the common name for a product such as $2(3x)$. You used the Associative Property to get the phrase $(2 \cdot 3)x$. Then, using 6 as the common name for $(2 \cdot 3)$, you obtained $6x$ as the result.

■ **P-4** What is the common name for $2(^-3x)$?

Using the Associative Property
of Multiplication ⟶ $2(^-3x) = (2 \cdot {}^-3)x$
Using $^-6$ as a name for $(2 \cdot {}^-3)$ ⟶ $ = {}^-6x$

■ **P-5** What is the common name for $(^-2x)(^-3x)$?

Here are the steps:

Using the Commutative and Associative
Properties of Multiplication ⟶ $(^-2x)(^-3x) = (^-2 \cdot ^-3)(x \cdot x)$
Using common names ⟶ $= 6x^2$

When you find common names for products like this, it will not be necessary to show each step. However, you should know that the properties of real numbers are a basis for your work.

■ **P-6** What is the common name for $(^-3x)(2y)(^-1x)$?

Now see how you can use this information in working with the Distributive Property.

Example 1: Write the following product as a sum in simplest form.

$$^-3(5 + 7x)$$

Using the Distributive Property ⟶ $^-3(5 + 7x) = ^-3(5) + ^-3(7x)$
Using the Associative Property
of Multiplication ⟶ $= ^-3(5) + (^-3 \cdot 7)x$
Using common names ⟶ $= ^-15 + ^-21x$

Again this shows how the result is obtained by the use of the number properties. You will soon learn to do it in one step.

■ **P-7** Express $(^-5x + 7) \cdot ^-5$ as a sum in simplest form.

Example 2: Express the following as a sum in simplest form.

$$^-3x(^-8x + y)$$

Using the Distributive
Property ⟶ $^-3x(^-8x + y) = (^-3x)(^-8x) + (^-3x)y$
Using the Associative and
Commutative Properties ⟶ $= (^-3 \cdot ^-8)(x \cdot x) + (^-3x)y$
Using common names ⟶ $= 24x^2 + ^-3xy$

You also use the Distributive Property to express sums as products. For example, $^-2x + ^-2y$ can be expressed as $^-2(x + y)$.

■ **P-8** How can you express $^-5a + ^-5b$ as a product?

Using the second form of the Distributive Property, you can express $^-5ax + ^-3x$ as the product $(^-5a + ^-3)x$.

ORAL EXERCISES 10.4

Give the common name for each of these products.

1. $^-5(8x)$ 2. $^-7(^-9y)$

3. $10(^-3w)$ 4. $(12r)(^-7x)$

5. $(2x)(^-7x)$ 6. $(^-3t)(^-7t)$

7. $(^-2ay)(3y)$ 8. $^-(\frac{1}{3})(3n)$

9. $\frac{1}{5}(^-5x)$ 10. $(^-3xy)(^-10xy)$

Express each of the following products as a sum in simplest form.

11. $^-2(x+5)$ 12. $(a+3) \cdot (^-6)$

13. $^-1(n+^-3)$ 14. $^-3(x+^-8)$

15. $(2x+3) \cdot (^-5)$ 16. $^-5(^-3x+1)$

Express each of the following sums as a product in simplest form.

17. $^-3y+^-3x$ 18. $a(^-5)+b(^-5)$

19. $5ax+(^-3x)$ 20. $(^-12ny)+(^-12nx)$

WRITTEN EXERCISES 10.4

A   Express each of the following products as a sum in simplest form.

1. $^-2(8a+^-5)$ 2. $^-3(10x+^-6)$

3. $^-5(^-3r+^-7)$ 4. $^-4(^-7n+^-9)$

5. $(5+3x)(^-7)$ 6. $(5a+^-3)(^-5)$

7. $\frac{1}{4}(12x+^-4)$ 8. $\frac{1}{3}(^-15y+6)$

9. $(6+^-9x)\frac{2}{3}$ 10. $(15y+10)\frac{3}{5}$

11. $x(^-5+2x)$ 12. $y(3+^-2y)$

13. $(^-3a+^-2)2a$ 14. $(5r+^-3) \cdot 3r$

15. $^-3n(2n+^-5)$ 16. $^-5t(^-3t+1)$

17. $\frac{1}{2}a(4a+^-2)$ 18. $\frac{1}{3}x(^-21x+^-15)$

19. $^-5a(4x+^-3y)$ 20. $3m(^-2n+^-12)$

Express each of the following sums as a product.

21. $(^-7x)+(^-7y)$ 22. $^-15a+^-15b$

23. $5m+^-5n$ 24. $8r+^-8s$

25. $t(^-8)+s(^-8)$ 26. $p(^-11)+q(^-11)$

27. $5ax+(^-6ay)$ 28. $10ab+(^-5a)$

29. $^-3xm+3my$ 30. $8rt+(^-8tw)$

10.5 Special Properties

See if you can find a pattern to these examples:

$$(^-1)(2) = {}^-2$$
$$(^-1)(^-5) = 5$$
$$(^-1)(100) = {}^-100$$
$$(^-1)(^-1000) = 1000$$
$$(^-1)(0) = 0$$

■ **P-1** What is the result when a real number is multiplied by $^-1$?

You can prove that $^-1$ times any real number gives a result that is the opposite of that number. In other words, you can show that the sentence $(^-1)a = -a$ is true for any real number a. Remember that the sum of a number and its opposite is 0.

■ **P-2** Why must you show that the sentence $a + (^-1)a = 0$ is true?

Using the Multiplication Property
of One ⟶ $a + (^-1)a = 1 \cdot a + (^-1)a$
Using the Distributive Property ⟶ $= (1 + {}^-1)a$
Using 0 as the common name for $1 + (^-1)$ ⟶ $= (0)a$
Using the Multiplication Property of Zero ⟶ $= 0$

Therefore, $a + (^-1)a = 0$ is true for any real number a. Thus, $(^-1)a$ is the opposite of a, and

$\boxed{1}$ $(^-1)a = -a$ is true for any real number a.

If a and b are real numbers, you know that $a + b$ is a real number by the Closure Property of Addition. Thus,

$$^-1(a + b) = -(a + b)$$

is true for all real numbers a and b. You can see that this follows from the result just proved. In the last chapter, you showed that

$$-(a + b) = (-a) + (-b).$$

Thus, you see that

$\boxed{2}$ $^-1(a + b) = (-a) + (-b)$ is true for all real numbers a and b.

Another important property is this:

$\boxed{3}$ For any real numbers a and b, $(-a)(b) = -(ab)$.

Let $a = {}^-5$ and $b = 7$.

■ **P-3** What value does the phrase $-a$ have?

■ **P-4** What is the value of $(-a)(b)$?

■ **P-5** What is the value of $-(ab)$?

You can show that $\boxed{3}$ is true for all real numbers as follows.

By property $\boxed{1}$ ──────────────────────→ $(-a)(b) = (^-1 \cdot a)b$
By the Associative Property of Multiplication ──────→ $= {}^-1(ab)$
By property $\boxed{1}$ ──────────────────────→ $= -(ab)$

Since $(-a)(b) = -(ab)$ for all real numbers a and b, you can use $-ab$ as the common name for these phrases.

The last special property to be shown here is this:

$\boxed{4}$ For any real numbers a and b, $(-a)(-b) = ab$.

Let $a = 3$ and $b = 12$.

■ **P-6** What is the value of $-a$? of $-b$?

■ **P-7** What is the value of $(-a)(-b)$?

■ **P-8** What is the value of ab?

Let $a = {}^-10$ and $b = {}^-5$.

■ **P-9** What is the value of $-a$? of $-b$?

■ **P-10** What is the value of $(-a)(-b)$? of ab?

You can show $\boxed{4}$ to be true for all real numbers as follows.

Using property $\boxed{1}$ ──────────────→ $(-a)(-b) = (^-1 \cdot a)(^-1 \cdot b)$
Using the Commutative and Associative
   Properties of Multiplication ──────────→ $= (^-1 \cdot {}^-1)(a \cdot b)$
Using the rule for the product of
   two negative numbers ──────────────→ $= (1)(ab)$
Using the Multiplication Property of One ──────→ $= ab$

Thus, $(-a)(-b) = ab$ is true for all real numbers a and b.

Here is a summary of the special properties that have been developed in this section:

$\boxed{1}$ $(^-1)a = -a$ is true for any real number a.
$\boxed{2}$ $^-1(a + b) = (-a) + (-b)$ is true for all real numbers a and b.
$\boxed{3}$ $(-a)(b) = -(ab)$ is true for all real numbers a and b.
$\boxed{4}$ $(-a)(-b) = ab$ is true for all real numbers a and b.

ORAL EXERCISES 10.5

Give another name for each of the following phrases, using property $\boxed{1}$ or $\boxed{2}$ of this section.

1. $^-1 \cdot x$
2. $r(^-1)$
3. $^-1(x + 2)$
4. $(^-1)5$
5. $(^-1)(^-5)$
6. $^-1(x + y)$
7. $(a + b)(^-1)$
8. $^-1(n + {}^-5)$
9. $(-x + 5)(^-1)$
10. $^-1(-a + {}^-3)$

Give another name for each of the following phrases, using property $\boxed{3}$ or $\boxed{4}$ of this section.

11. $(-r)s$
12. $m(-n)$
13. $(-p)(-q)$
14. $-(a + b) \cdot -(m + n)$
15. $5(-x)$
16. $(^-10)(-a)$
17. $-y(3)$
18. $(-3x)y$
19. $(-3x)(-y)$
20. $(-a)(b)(-c)$
21. $(-x)(-x)$
22. $(-x)x$

WRITTEN EXERCISES 10.5

A Find the value of each phrase if $a = {}^-2$, $b = {}^-1$, and $c = 3$.

1. $-a$
2. $-c$
3. $(-a)(b)$
4. $(-a)(c)$
5. $(-b)(-c)$
6. $(-a)(-b)$
7. $-(a + b)$
8. $^-1(a + b)$
9. $^-1 \cdot a$
10. $^-1 \cdot b$
11. a^2
12. b^2
13. $(-a)^2$
14. $(-b)^2$
15. $2a^2$
16. $3b^2$
17. $-a^2$
18. $-b^2$
19. $^-1 \cdot a^2$
20. $^-1 \cdot b^2$

Find a phrase that is the opposite of each of the following without just placing the opposite sign, $-$, in front of the given phrase.

21. $-x$
22. $^-5$
23. $-x + 2$
24. $5 + (-y)$
25. $(-a) + (-b)$
26. $m + (-n)$
27. ^-3y
28. ^-5a
29. $(-x)y$
30. $a(-b)$
31. $-(-m + n)$
32. $-(x + (-y))$
33. $a^2 + 5$
34. $^-3x^2 + (^-2)$

Give the common name for each of the following phrases.

35. $(-r)s$
36. $m(-n)$
37. $^-1(-y)x$
38. $(-xy)(^-1)$
39. $(-r)(^-3s)$
40. $(^-5a)(-b)$
41. $(-a)(^-2n)(-y)$
42. $^-3x(-a)(-b)$

Use the Distributive Property to write the following products as sums in simplest form.

43. $-x(y + {}^-2)$
44. $-y(-a + 5)$
45. $^-2a(-b + 5)$
46. $(10 + (-r))(^-3t)$
47. $(-m + n)(^-2a)$
48. $(p + {}-q)(^-5n)$
49. $-x(2x + {}^-3)$
50. $-y(^-3y + 7)$

10.6 Adding Like Terms

In a previous chapter, you used the Distributive Property to find the common name for a phrase like $2x + 3x$. First you wrote it as the product $(2 + 3)x$ and then as $5x$.

A phrase such as $2x + 3x$ is called a **binomial,** and $2x$ and $3x$ are called **terms.** Actually, in any phrase involving addition, its terms are the symbols separated by the addition sign, $+$.

In the phrase $2x^2 + 3y + (^-5)$, the terms are $2x^2$, $3y$, and $^-5$.

■ **P-1** What are the terms of the phrase $10 + (-a) + (^-5b^2)$?

In the phrase $2x + 3x$, the terms $2x$ and $3x$ are called **like terms.**

> **Like terms are made up of exactly the same variable or variables and the same powers of these variables.**

Thus, $^-2x^2$ and $3x^2$ are like terms, and $5a^2x$ and $^-3a^2x$ are like terms.

■ **P-2** Are $6rs^2$ and $3s^2$ like terms? Explain.

■ **P-3** Are $3x^3$ and $2x^2$ like terms? Explain.

When you found $5x$ as the common name for $2x + 3x$, you were actually adding two real numbers represented by like terms. Their sum is the real number represented by the phrase $5x$. This process is often called **addition of like terms.**

Look at some more examples:

Example 1: Find the common name for $7x + (^-3x)$.

By the Distributive Property $\longrightarrow 7x + {}^-3x = (7 + {}^-3)x$
Using 4 as the name for $(7 + {}^-3)$ $\longrightarrow \qquad = 4x$

Example 2: Find the common name for $3x + (-x)$.

By one of the special properties $\longrightarrow 3x + (-x) = 3x + (-1)x$
By the Distributive Property $\longrightarrow \qquad = (3 + {}^-1)x$
Since 2 is a name for $(3 + {}^-1)$ $\longrightarrow \qquad = 2x$

■ **P-4** What is the common name for the phrase $^-10y^2 + 3y^2$? for the phrase $5ab + (-ab)$?

You can sometimes simplify phrases by adding the terms that are like terms.

Example 3: Simplify $2x + 3y + {}^-5x + 8y$.

Using the Commutative and Associative Properties
 of Addition ⟶ $2x + 3y + {}^-5x + 8y = (2x + {}^-5x) + (3y + 8y)$
Using the Distributive Property ⟶ $= (2 + {}^-5)x + (3 + 8)y$
Using common names ⟶ $= {}^-3x + 11y$

The phrase ${}^-3x + 11y$ is a simpler name for the given phrase.

▪ **P-5** Is it possible to get a simpler name for ${}^-3x + 11y$?

▪ **P-6** What is a simpler name for $5a^2 + {}^-2b + {}^-3b + (-a^2)$?

The Distributive Property allows you to get a simpler name for the sum of like terms. If the terms are unlike, then it cannot be applied. However, it is often desirable to express sums as products.

Example 4: Express $2x + {}^-2y$ as a product.

By one of the special properties ⟶ $2x + -2y = 2x + 2(-y)$
By the Distributive Property ⟶ $= 2(x + -y)$

It is not true that $2(x + -y)$ is a simpler name than $2x + {}^-2y$. One is a product and the other is a sum.

▪ **P-7** How would you express the phrase ${}^-3a + 3b$ as a product?

Example 5: Express $ay + b(-y)$ as a product.

By one of the special properties ⟶ $ay + b(-y) = ay + -by$
By the Distributive Property⟶ $= (a + -b)y$

▪ **P-8** How would you express the phrase $x^2 + (-x)$ as a product?

Here are the steps:

$$x^2 + (-x) = x \cdot x + {}^-1(x)$$
$$= (x + {}^-1)x$$

ORAL EXERCISES 10.6

Tell whether or not the terms in each binomial are like terms.
 1. $x + 2$ **2.** $2x^2 + x$ **3.** $3x + {}^-7x$ **4.** $a + b$
 5. $ax + ay$ **6.** $5x^2y + x^2y$ **7.** $2ab^2y + {}^-3yb^2a$ **8.** $5c + (-c)$

Add like terms to simplify each of the following phrases.

9. $2x + {}^-5x$ 10. $x + {}^-3x$ 11. ${}^-7a^2 + {}^-3a^2$

12. $5y + (-y)$ 13. ${}^-3ab + 2ab$ 14. $-xy + {}^-3xy$

15. $x + 2 + 3x$ 16. $2a^2 + 3x + a^2 + ({}^-8x)$

Use the Distributive Property to express these sums as products.

17. $2x + (-xy)$ 18. $y^2 + (-y)$ 19. $ax + (-ay)$ 20. $0.5x + {}^-0.5y$

WRITTEN EXERCISES 10.6

A   Simplify each phrase by adding like terms.

1. $3m + {}^-8m$ 2. ${}^-12t + 8t$ 3. ${}^-15x + {}^-12x$

4. ${}^-5y + {}^-8y$ 5. $7ab + {}^-2ab$ 6. ${}^-9pq + 3pq$

7. $y + {}^-8y$ 8. ${}^-10n + n$ 9. $3xy + (-xy)$

10. $-ab + 7ab$ 11. ${}^-5a^2b + {}^-3a^2b$ 12. ${}^-11x^2y + {}^-5x^2y$

13. $2x + {}^-7 + 5x$ 14. $5a + 12 + {}^-17a$

15. ${}^-3r + (-r) + 2 + {}^-3$ 16. $15 + (-x) + {}^-3x + {}^-13$

17. $3a^2b + 2ab^2 + {}^-5a^2b$ 18. ${}^-7x^2y^2 + 2xy + 3x^2y^2$

19. $2x + (-x) + {}^-5 + 15x + {}^-3$

20. $7y + (-y) + {}^-17 + {}^-3y + 15$

Use the Distributive Property to write each sum as a product.

21. $3x + 3y$ 22. $7a + 7b$ 23. $ay + by$ 24. $rx + sx$

25. $12m + ({}^-12n)$ 26. ${}^-5x + 5y$ 27. $a^2 + (-a)$

28. $-x^2 + x$ 29. $2x + {}^-4y$ 30. ${}^-3a + 6b$

10.7   Product of Two Binomials

You learned to express a product such as $(x + 2)(x + 3)$ as a sum in a previous chapter. Here are the steps again to refresh your memory:

Using the Distributive

Property ⎯⎯⎯⎯⎯→ $(x + 2)(x + 3) = (x + 2)x + (x + 2)3$

Using the Distributive Property ⎯⎯⎯⎯→ $= x \cdot x + 2 \cdot x + x \cdot 3 + 2 \cdot 3$

Using common names ⎯⎯⎯⎯→ $= x^2 + 2x + 3x + 6$

Adding like terms ⎯⎯⎯⎯→ $= x^2 + 5x + 6$

Now look at an example that involves some negative numbers:

$$(x + {}^-2)(x + {}^-3) = (x + {}^-2)x + (x + {}^-2)({}^-3)$$
$$= x \cdot x + {}^-2x + x({}^-3) + ({}^-2)({}^-3)$$
$$= x^2 + {}^-2x + {}^-3x + 6$$
$$= x^2 + {}^-5x + 6$$

P-1 Can you explain each step in the last example on the previous page?

Here is another example:

$$(x + 5)(x + {}^-3) = (x + 5)x + (x + 5) \cdot {}^-3$$
$$= x \cdot x + 5x + x({}^-3) + 5({}^-3)$$

P-2 What is this sum expressed in simplest form?

P-3 What property tells you that $2x$ is the common name for $5x + ({}^-3x)$?

See if you can complete the steps in the following problem of changing a product of binomials to a sum.

P-4 $(2x + 3)(3x + {}^-2) = (2x + 3)(\underline{?}) + (\underline{?})(\underline{?})$
$$= (2x)(3x) + 3(3x) + 2x({}^-2) + 3({}^-2)$$

P-5 $= \underline{?} + \underline{?} + \underline{?} + \underline{?}$

P-6 $= \underline{?} + \underline{?} + \underline{?}$

The phrase $(x + y)^2$ represents the square of the binomial $(x + y)$. Of course, you know that it means $(x + y)(x + y)$. Recall that the domain of both x and y is {real numbers}.

Now use this last form to see if you can find a pattern for writing the square of a binomial as a sum.

$$(x + y)(x + y) = (x + y)x + (x + y)y$$
$$= x \cdot x + y \cdot x + x \cdot y + y \cdot y$$
$$= x^2 + 2xy + y^2$$

Compare this result with the binomial $(x + y)$ that was squared. The phrase x^2 is the square of x. The second term, $2xy$, is twice the product of x and y, the terms of the binomial. The term y^2 is the square of the second term y.

Consider the product $(x + -y)(x + -y)$. This can also be written in the form $(x + -y)^2$.

$$(x + -y)(x + -y) = (x + -y) \cdot x + (x + -y)(-y)$$
$$= x \cdot x + (-y) \cdot x + x(-y) + (-y)(-y)$$
$$= x^2 + (-xy) + (-xy) + y^2$$
$$= x^2 + {}^-1(xy) + {}^-1(xy) + y^2$$
$$= x^2 + {}^-2(xy) + y^2$$

P-7 Can this last phrase also be written as $x^2 + 2(-xy) + y^2$?

The last two examples suggest the following rule for squaring a binomial.

> The square of a binomial is equal to the square of the first term plus twice the product of the two terms plus the square of the second term.

■ **P-8** How can you write $(2x + 3)^2$ as a sum, using this rule?

An error that some students make is to forget the result just shown. They write $(x + y)^2$ as $x^2 + y^2$.

■ **P-9** Can you show that the sentence $(x + y)^2 = x^2 + y^2$ is false if $x = 2$ and $y = 3$?

ORAL EXERCISES 10.7

Express the square of each binomial as a sum, using the rule just given.

1. $(x + 1)^2$ 2. $(x + 2)^2$ 3. $(x + {}^-1)^2$ 4. $(x + 3)^2$
5. $(a + 5)^2$ 6. $(a + {}^-3)^2$ 7. $(a + 10)^2$ 8. $(x + 8)^2$
9. $(x + {}^-5)^2$ 10. $(a + 12)^2$

State the first step in expressing each product as a sum.

11. $(x + {}^-2)(x + 3)$ 12. $(x + 1)(x + 2)$
13. $(x + 3)(x + 1)$ 14. $(x + {}^-1)(x + {}^-3)$
15. $(x + 1)(x + 5)$ 16. $(x + {}^-5)(x + 1)$
17. $(x + {}^-1)(x + {}^-5)$ 18. $(x + 5)(x + {}^-1)$
19. $(a + 3)(a + 10)$ 20. $(a + {}^-3)(a + {}^-10)$

WRITTEN EXERCISES 10.7

A   Express each product as a sum in simplest form. Show steps.

1. $(x + 1)(x + 2)$ 2. $(x + 1)(x + 3)$
3. $(x + {}^-1)(x + {}^-2)$ 4. $(x + {}^-1)(x + {}^-3)$
5. $(x + {}^-1)(x + 2)$ 6. $(x + {}^-1)(x + 3)$
7. $(x + 1)(x + {}^-2)$ 8. $(x + 1)(x + {}^-3)$
9. $(x + 2)(x + 5)$ 10. $(x + 3)(x + 4)$
11. $(x + {}^-2)(x + {}^-5)$ 12. $(x + {}^-3)(x + {}^-4)$
13. $(x + {}^-2)(x + 5)$ 14. $(x + {}^-3)(x + 4)$
15. $(x + 2)(x + {}^-5)$ 16. $(x + 3)(x + {}^-4)$
17. $(2x + 5)(x + 2)$ 18. $(2x + {}^-5)(x + {}^-2)$
19. $(2x + 5)(x + {}^-2)$ 20. $(2x + {}^-5)(x + 2)$

CHAPTER SUMMARY

Important Ideas

1. *Multiplication Property of Zero:* If a is any real number, then it is true that
$$a \cdot 0 = 0 \quad \text{and} \quad 0 \cdot a = 0.$$

2. *Closure Property of Multiplication:* The product of any two real numbers is a real number.

3. *Commutative Property of Multiplication:* If a and b are any real numbers, then it is true that
$$ab = ba.$$

4. *Associative Property of Multiplication:* If a, b, and c are any real numbers, then it is true that
$$(ab)c = a(bc).$$

5. *Distributive Property:* If a, b, and c are any real numbers, then it is true that
$$a(b + c) = ab + ac.$$

6. *Rules for Finding the Product of Any Two Real Numbers:*

   1 The product of two positive real numbers is the same as their product as numbers of arithmetic.

   2 The product of a positive real number and a negative real number is the opposite of the product of their absolute values.

   3 The product of two negative real numbers is the product of their absolute values.

   4 The product of 0 and any real number is 0.

7. *Special Properties:*

   1 $(^-1)a = -a$

   2 $^-1(a + b) = (-a) + (-b)$

   3 $(-a)b = -(ab)$

   4 $(-a)(-b) = ab$

8. Only like terms can be added. The term $5x$ is the common name for $2x + 3x$. The phrase $2x + 3y$ has no simpler name.

9. The square of a binomial expressed as a sum has three terms. Thus, $(x + y)^2$ is equal to $x^2 + 2xy + y^2$.

10. The square of a binomial is equal to the square of the first term plus twice the product of the two terms plus the square of the second term.

CHAPTER REVIEW

Give the common name for each of the following products.

1. $(^-12)(5)$ 2. $(^-12)(^-5)$ 3. $(12)(^-5)$
4. $0(^-150)$ 5. $^-(\frac{1}{3})15$ 6. $^-12(\frac{3}{4})$
7. $(^-10)\frac{1}{2}$ 8. $(^-10) \cdot {}^-(\frac{1}{2})$ 9. $(^-2.7)(^-3.4)$
10. $5(^-5.6)$ 11. $(^-1.7)(^-1.7)$ 12. $(^-2)(^-3)(^-5)$
13. $(^-2)(3)(5)$ 14. $(^-2)(^-3)(5)$ 15. $(^-2)(3)(^-5)$
16. $(^-1)(^-1)(^-1)$ 17. $(^-1)(^-1)(^-1)(^-1)$ 18. $(^-1)(^-1)$
19. $(^-1)(^-1)(^-1)(^-1)(^-1)$ 20. $(^-1)(^-1)(^-1)(^-1)(^-1)(0)$

Use the Distributive Property to write each product as a sum in simplest form.

21. $^-3(x + 5)$ 22. $^-7(2x + {}^-3)$ 23. $5(x + {}^-7)$
24. $8(^-5x + {}^-3)$ 25. $2x(x + {}^-3)$ 26. $3x(-x + 5)$
27. $-x(^-3x + 7)$ 28. $-x(5x + {}^-10)$ 29. $^-3x(2x + {}^-5)$
30. $^-5x(^-3x + 2)$

Express each of the following sums as a product.

31. $2x + 2y$ 32. $^-5a + {}^-5b$ 33. $-ax + bx$
34. $^-5x + 5y$ 35. $3ab + {}^-3ab$ 36. $r^2 + -r$

Find the value of each phrase if $x = {}^-2$ and $y = 5$.

37. $-x$ 38. $-y$ 39. $-xy$
40. $x(-y)$ 41. $-x^2$ 42. $-(x^2)$
43. $(-x)^2$ 44. xy^2 45. yx^2
46. $-|x|$ 47. $|x|$ 48. $|xy|$

Add like terms to get a common name for each of the following phrases.

49. $10a + {}^-2a$ 50. $-r + 5r$
51. $x^2 + 5 + 3x^2$ 52. $^-10x + {}^-12x$
53. $3a + {}^-25a$ 54. $10a + b + {}^-3a + {}^-5b$
55. $2x^2 + 5x + {}^-3x + 7$ 56. $3ax + 2x + {}^-10ax + {}^-9x$

Write the square of each of the following binomials as a sum.

57. $(x + 9)^2$ 58. $(x + {}^-7)^2$
59. $(2x + 5)^2$ 60. $(3x + {}^-2)^2$

Write each product as a sum in simplest form.

61. $(x + 10)(x + 7)$ 62. $(x + 4)(x + 6)$
63. $(x + {}^-5)(x + {}^-7)$ 64. $(2x + 1)(x + {}^-3)$

MULTIPLICATION OF REAL NUMBERS   341

A thunderhead cloud, 50 miles wide and 55,000 feet high, looms over southwest Oklahoma. It could soon become a thundercloud and sweep the land in a great storm. How can the weatherman foretell the changes in atmospheric conditions, such as changes in temperature, moisture, and winds? Mathematics plays an important part in meteorology, the science that relates to weather.

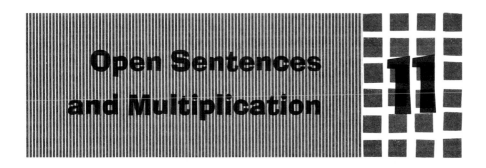

Open Sentences and Multiplication

11.1 Multiplicative Inverse

In working with the numbers of arithmetic, you learned what the reciprocal of a number is. Two numbers of arithmetic are said to be reciprocals of each other if their product is 1. Now you will extend this idea to the set of real numbers.

■ **P-1** What is the common name for each of the following products?

$$(\tfrac{2}{3})(\tfrac{3}{2}); \quad {}^-(\tfrac{1}{2}) \cdot ({}^-2); \quad {}^-(\tfrac{3}{4}) \cdot {}^-(\tfrac{4}{3}); \quad ({}^-100) \cdot {}^-(\tfrac{1}{100})$$

Since the product of each pair of numbers is 1, you might call the numbers reciprocals. There is another name, however, that is also used by mathematicians to describe these numbers.

> If the product of two real numbers is 1, they are said to be **multiplicative inverses** of each other.

■ **P-2** Is it possible for a positive number and a negative number to be multiplicative inverses of each other? Why or why not?

■ **P-3** Is there any real number that is its own multiplicative inverse?

■ **P-4** What is the truth set of the sentence $0 \cdot x = 1$ if the domain is {real numbers}?

■ **P-5** Does 0 have a multiplicative inverse?

> Every real number except 0 has exactly one multiplicative inverse.

Your knowledge of finding a name for the reciprocal of a number will help you in finding multiplicative inverses.

■ **P-6** What is the multiplicative inverse of each of the following numbers?

$$10; \quad {}^-(\tfrac{1}{4}); \quad \tfrac{2}{5}; \quad {}^-(\tfrac{5}{8}); \quad {}^-1$$

ORAL EXERCISES 11.1

Using {real numbers} as the domain, find the truth set of each of the following sentences.

1. $5x = 1$ **2.** ${}^-3y = 1$ **3.** $\tfrac{1}{3}a = 1$ **4.** ${}^-(\tfrac{1}{8})x = 1$
5. $\tfrac{4}{3}n = 1$ **6.** $1\tfrac{2}{3}x = 1$ **7.** $0 \cdot x = 1$ **8.** $t \cdot 0 = 1$
9. ${}^-(\tfrac{5}{13}) \cdot {}^-(\tfrac{13}{5}) = n$ **10.** $5x = {}^-7 \cdot {}^-(\tfrac{1}{7})$

11. What is meant by the *multiplicative inverse* of a real number?
12. What real number does not have a multiplicative inverse?
13. How many multiplicative inverses does each real number have?
14. Are ${}^-(\tfrac{1}{2})$ and ${}^-0.5$ two different multiplicative inverses of ${}^-2$?
15. Name two numbers each of which is its own multiplicative inverse. (HINT: One is positive and the other is negative.)
16. Why can a positive number and a negative number *not* be multiplicative inverses of each other?

WRITTEN EXERCISES 11.1

A Give the common name for the multiplicative inverse of each of the following numbers.

1. 12 **2.** 15 **3.** ${}^-7$ **4.** ${}^-8$ **5.** $\tfrac{1}{8}$
6. $\tfrac{1}{4}$ **7.** ${}^-(\tfrac{1}{9})$ **8.** ${}^-(\tfrac{1}{12})$ **9.** $\tfrac{5}{6}$ **10.** $\tfrac{3}{8}$
11. ${}^-(\tfrac{7}{12})$ **12.** ${}^-(\tfrac{15}{16})$ **13.** ${}^-3.2$ **14.** ${}^-5.6$ **15.** ${}^-2\tfrac{5}{8}$
16. ${}^-3\tfrac{3}{4}$ **17.** ${}^-(\tfrac{12}{4})$ **18.** ${}^-(\tfrac{15}{3})$ **19.** ${}^-(\tfrac{15}{15})$ **20.** $\tfrac{17}{17}$

Find the truth set of each open sentence. Let {real numbers} be the domain.

21. $\tfrac{3}{5}x = 1$ **22.** $\tfrac{12}{11}y = 1$ **23.** $({}^-5)({}^-2x) = 1$
24. $({}^-7)(2a) = 1$ **25.** $(-x)(5) = 1$ **26.** $({}^-3)({}^-y) = 1$
27. $|x| \cdot |{}^-3| = 1$ **28.** $|\tfrac{1}{2}| \cdot |-y| = 1$ **29.** $|3x| = 1$
30. $|\tfrac{1}{3}y| = 1$

B Indicate what real number you would multiply each phrase by to get x as the result.

31. $\tfrac{1}{3}x$ **32.** ${}^-5x$ **33.** $7x$ **34.** ${}^-(\tfrac{1}{4})x$
35. $\tfrac{3}{8}x$ **36.** $\tfrac{8}{5}x$ **37.** ${}^-9.7x$ **38.** ${}^-2\tfrac{4}{5}x$

11.2 Multiplication Property of Equality

In Chapter 9, you learned what is meant by *equivalent open sentences*. They are sentences that have the same truth set. You learned to use the Addition Property of Equality to find the truth sets of the open sentences called *equations*.

For example, $x + 3 = 10$ and $x + 3 + {}^-3 = 10 + {}^-3$ are equivalent sentences. However, the second sentence leads to the simpler form $x = 7$, and you can readily see that the truth set is $\{7\}$.

In working with open sentences in this chapter, you will use {real numbers} as the domain.

■ **P-1** What is the truth number of the sentence $2x = 6$?

■ **P-2** What is the truth number of $5(2x) = 5(6)$?

■ **P-3** Are the following sentences equivalent?

$$2x = 6 \quad \text{and} \quad 5(2x) = 5(6)$$

■ **P-4** What is the truth number of the sentence $3x = 12$?

■ **P-5** How can you simplify the sentence $\frac{1}{3}(3x) = \frac{1}{3}(12)$? What is its truth number?

■ **P-6** Are the following sentences equivalent?

$$3x = 12 \quad \text{and} \quad \tfrac{1}{3}(3x) = \tfrac{1}{3}(12)$$

Now consider another example.

■ **P-7** What is the truth number of the sentence $\frac{2}{3}x = 6$?

■ **P-8** What is a simpler form for the sentence $\frac{3}{2}(\frac{2}{3}x) = \frac{3}{2}(6)$? What is its truth number?

■ **P-9** Are the following sentences equivalent?

$$\tfrac{2}{3}x = 6 \quad \text{and} \quad \tfrac{3}{2}(\tfrac{2}{3}x) = \tfrac{3}{2}(6)$$

These examples suggest that there is a **Multiplication Property of Equality** much like the one for addition. It is stated as follows.

> If both sides of an open equation are multiplied by the same nonzero real number, then the new equation is equivalent to the first.

Example 1: Find the truth set of the following sentence.

$$\tfrac{3}{5}x = 18$$

By the Multiplication Property of Equality,

$$\tfrac{3}{5}x = 18 \quad \text{is equivalent to} \quad \tfrac{5}{3}(\tfrac{3}{5}x) = \tfrac{5}{3}(18).$$

By the Associative Property of Multiplication,

$$\tfrac{5}{3}(\tfrac{3}{5}x) = \tfrac{5}{3}(18) \quad \text{is equivalent to} \quad (\tfrac{5}{3} \cdot \tfrac{3}{5})x = \tfrac{5}{3}(18).$$

By using common names for each side, you see that

$$(\tfrac{5}{3} \cdot \tfrac{3}{5})x = \tfrac{5}{3}(18) \quad \text{is equivalent to} \quad x = 30.$$

It is evident that $\tfrac{3}{5}x = 18$ has the truth set $\{30\}$.
Here are the steps:

$$\tfrac{3}{5}x = 18$$
$$\tfrac{5}{3}(\tfrac{3}{5}x) = \tfrac{5}{3}(18)$$
$$(\tfrac{5}{3} \cdot \tfrac{3}{5})x = \tfrac{5}{3}(\tfrac{18}{1})$$
$$1 \cdot x = \frac{5 \cdot 18}{3}$$
$$x = 30$$
$$\{30\}$$

Check: $\tfrac{3}{5}x = 18$
$\tfrac{3}{5} \cdot 30$
18

■ **P-10** Why was $\tfrac{5}{3}$ chosen as the number by which to multiply each side?

■ **P-11** How are $\tfrac{5}{3}$ and $\tfrac{3}{5}$ related?

Example 2: Find the truth set of the following sentence.

$$^{-}4x = 30$$

■ **P-12** By what number would you multiply each side of this sentence to get x alone on one side?

■ **P-13** What equation do you get that is equivalent to the equation $^{-}4x = 30$?

Here are the steps.

$$^-4x = 30$$
$$^-(\tfrac{1}{4})(^-4x) = ^-(\tfrac{1}{4})(30)$$
$$1 \cdot x = \frac{^-(30)}{4}$$
$$x = ^-7\tfrac{1}{2}$$
$$\{^-7\tfrac{1}{2}\}$$

Check: $\quad ^-4x = 30$

$\quad ^-4(^-7\tfrac{1}{2})$

$\quad 30$

In Chapter 5, you found that the truth number of the sentence $ax = b$ is the product of b and the reciprocal of a, where a and b are numbers of arithmetic, $a \neq 0$. You can now extend this method to include real values of a and b.

> **The truth number of the sentence $ax = b$ where a and b represent any real numbers, $a \neq 0$, is the product of b and the multiplicative inverse of a.**

■ **P-14** Why must $a \neq 0$ be true?

ORAL EXERCISES 11.2

Tell what number you would multiply each side by in each sentence of Written Exercises 11.2 as the first step in finding its truth set.

WRITTEN EXERCISES 11.2

A Find the truth set of each of the following sentences by using the Multiplication Property of Equality. Show steps and check.

1. $2x = 42$ **2.** $3x = 39$ **3.** $^-5x = ^-60$

4. $^-4x = ^-56$ **5.** $\tfrac{1}{3}x = ^-5$ **6.** $\tfrac{1}{4}x = ^-7$

7. $13 = ^-(\tfrac{1}{2})x$ **8.** $17 = ^-(\tfrac{1}{5})x$ **9.** $\tfrac{2}{3}x = ^-12$

10. $\tfrac{3}{5}x = ^-21$ **11.** $^-(\tfrac{5}{6})x = ^-15$ **12.** $^-(\tfrac{7}{8})x = ^-14$

13. $^-18 = 5x$ **14.** $^-23 = 4x$ **15.** $^-(\tfrac{1}{2})x = ^-(\tfrac{1}{4})$

16. $^-(\tfrac{1}{3})x = ^-(\tfrac{1}{8})$ **17.** $^-3x = \tfrac{3}{5}$ **18.** $^-5x = \tfrac{5}{13}$

19. $^-(\tfrac{3}{4})x = \tfrac{3}{8}$ **20.** $^-(\tfrac{4}{7})x = \tfrac{8}{21}$

11.3 Truth Sets of Open Sentences

One of your aims in the study of algebra is to gain some skill in finding truth sets of open sentences. Already you have learned methods of solving some simple equations. Now you are going to find the truth sets of some equations that require both the Addition and Multiplication Properties of Equality.

Example 1: Find the truth set of the following equation.

$$2x + 3 = 21$$

Using the Addition Property of Equality $\longrightarrow 2x + 3 + {}^-3 = 21 + {}^-3$
Using common names $\longrightarrow 2x = 18$
Using the Multiplication Property of
Equality $\longrightarrow \frac{1}{2}(2x) = \frac{1}{2}(18)$
Using common names $\longrightarrow x = 9$

The truth set of the sentence $x = 9$ is $\{9\}$. Since all the sentences written above are equivalent to $2x + 3 = 21$, the truth set of the sentence $2x + 3 = 21$ is also $\{9\}$.

You should always check to make sure that you have made no error.

Check:
$$2x + 3 = 21$$
$$2(9) + 3$$
$$18 + 3$$
$$21$$

■ **P-1** Which property of equality was used first, the Addition Property or the Multiplication Property?

Notice that your goal is to obtain a sentence with the variable by itself on one side. You do this in steps, applying the Addition Property of Equality first.

Example 2: Find the truth set of the following sentence.

$${}^-3 + 5x = {}^-33$$

Supply the reason for each step.

■ **P-2** $\qquad {}^-3 + 5x + 3 = {}^-33 + 3 \qquad \underline{\;?\;}$

■ **P-3** $\qquad\qquad\quad 5x = {}^-30 \qquad \underline{\;?\;}$

■ **P-4** $\qquad\qquad \frac{1}{5}(5x) = \frac{1}{5}({}^-30) \qquad \underline{\;?\;}$

■ **P-5** What open sentence do you get with x alone on one side?

■ **P-6** What is the truth set of $-3 + 5x = -33$?

Check:
$$-3 + 5x = -33$$
$$-3 + 5(-6)$$
$$-3 + -30$$
$$-33$$

Example 3: Find the truth set of the following sentence.
$$-26 = 5 + -6x$$

■ **P-7** What real number should be added to both sides as the first step?

You should get this equivalent sentence:
$$-26 + -5 = 5 + -6x + -5$$

■ **P-8** What is a simpler form of the sentence above?

■ **P-9** By what real number do you multiply each side?

Here are the remaining steps:

$$-31 = -6x$$ $$\qquad Check: -26 = 5 + -6x$$
$$-(\tfrac{1}{6})(-31) = -(\tfrac{1}{6})(-6x) \qquad 5 + -6(\tfrac{31}{6})$$
$$\tfrac{31}{6} = x \qquad\qquad 5 + -(6 \cdot \tfrac{31}{6})$$
$$\{\tfrac{31}{6}\} \qquad\qquad 5 + -31$$
$$\qquad\qquad -26$$

ORAL EXERCISES 11.3

Tell what the first step would be in finding the truth set of each sentence in the Written Exercises 11.3.

WRITTEN EXERCISES 11.3

A Find the truth set of each sentence. Show steps and check.

1. $2x + -1 = 15$ 2. $2x + -3 = 21$ 3. $3x + 5 = -8$
4. $3x + 2 = -19$ 5. $-2x + 3 = 17$ 6. $-3x + 1 = 19$
7. $1 = \frac{1}{2}x + -5$ 8. $1 = \frac{1}{2}x + 7$ 9. $-13 = 8 + 3x$
10. $-15 = 9 + 2x$ 11. $5 + 3x = 15$ 12. $3 + 4x = 17$
13. $5 = 5 + 3x$ 14. $-10 = -10 + 10x$ 15. $-2 + -5x = -13$
16. $-3 + -4x = -16$ 17. $\frac{1}{3}x + -5 = 7$ 18. $\frac{1}{4}x + -7 = 5$
19. $\frac{2}{3}x + 3 = -5$ 20. $\frac{3}{4}x + 5 = -10$

11.4 More Open Sentences

You have seen that, in finding the truth set of an open sentence, your aim has been to obtain a much simpler equivalent sentence. In fact, you usually try to get a simpler sentence that has the variable all by itself on one side. The truth set of such a sentence is easily found.

Often, you can simplify the phrases that make up each side of an equation by adding like terms or real numbers. When this is possible, it is usually best to do this as the first step.

Example 1: Find the truth set of the following sentence.

$$5x + 3 + (-x) = 14 + {}^-17$$

■ **P-1** What is a common name for the left side?

■ **P-2** What is a common name for the right side?

You can see that you obtain the following sentence, which is equivalent to the first.

$$4x + 3 = {}^-3$$

■ **P-3** What is the next step in finding the truth set?

Here are the remaining steps:

$$4x + 3 + {}^-3 = {}^-3 + {}^-3$$
$$4x = {}^-6$$
$$\tfrac{1}{4}(4x) = \tfrac{1}{4}({}^-6)$$
$$x = {}^-(\tfrac{3}{2})$$
$$\{{}^-(\tfrac{3}{2})\}$$

Check:
$$5x + 3 + (-x) = 14 + {}^-17$$
$$5 \cdot {}^-(\tfrac{3}{2}) + 3 + (-{}^-(\tfrac{3}{2})) \quad | \quad {}^-3$$
$${}^-(\tfrac{15}{2}) + 3 + \tfrac{3}{2}$$
$$3 + {}^-6$$
$${}^-3$$

Example 2: Find the truth set of the following sentence.

$$2(3x + {}^-5) + {}^-8x = {}^-6 + 12$$

■ **P-4** Can you simplify the left side by adding the like terms $3x$ and ${}^-8x$?

First apply the Distributive Property to express $2(3x + {}^-5)$ as a sum.

$$6x + {}^-10 + {}^-8x = {}^-6 + 12$$
$$ {}^-2x + {}^-10 = 6$$
$$ {}^-2x + {}^-10 + 10 = 6 + 10$$
$$ {}^-2x = 16$$
$$ {}^-(\tfrac{1}{2}) \cdot {}^-2x = {}^-(\tfrac{1}{2}) \cdot 16$$
$$x = {}^-8$$
$$\{{}^-8\}$$

Check:
$$2(3x + {}^-5) + {}^-8x = {}^-6 + 12$$

$2(3 \cdot {}^-8 + {}^-5) + {}^-8({}^-8)$	6
$2({}^-24 + {}^-5) + 64$	
$2({}^-29) + 64$	
${}^-58 + 64$	
6	

Notice that, in checking, you always use the original equation. This makes it possible to check all the steps for error.

Example 3: Find the truth set of the following sentence.
$$x(3x + {}^-5) + 2x + {}^-3x^2 = {}^-27$$

■ **P-5** What is the first step in finding the truth set of this sentence?

Again applying the Distributive Property, you get the following sentence.
$$3x^2 + {}^-5x + 2x + {}^-3x^2 = {}^-27$$

■ **P-6** What is the common name for $3x^2 + {}^-3x^2$?

■ **P-7** What is the common name for the left side of the above sentence?

You should get the following equation, which is equivalent to the given equation.
$$ {}^-3x = {}^-27$$

Using the Multiplication Property of Equality, you find the equivalent sentence
$$x = 9.$$

Check to see if $\{9\}$ is the truth set of the given equation.

Check:
$$x(3x + {}^-5) + 2x + {}^-3x^2 = {}^-27$$
$$9(3 \cdot 9 + {}^-5) + 2 \cdot 9 + {}^-3 \cdot 9^2$$
$$9(27 + {}^-5) + 18 + {}^-3(81)$$
$$9(22) + 18 + {}^-243$$
$$198 + 18 + {}^-243$$
$$-27$$

Keep in mind that usually the best step to take first is to find a common name for the phrase on each side.

ORAL EXERCISES 11.4

In each of Written Exercises 11.4, give a common name of the phrase on each side.

WRITTEN EXERCISES 11.4

A Find the truth set of each of the following sentences. Show steps and check.

1. $2x + 5 + 3x = 10$
2. $x + 2 + 4x = {}^-8$
3. $5x + {}^-2 + {}^-3x = {}^-8$
4. $7x + {}^-5 + {}^-4x = 13$
5. $-x + {}^-3 + {}^-2x = 9$
6. ${}^-4 + {}^-2x + {}^-5x = 24$
7. $4x + {}^-5 + {}^-7 = {}^-36$
8. ${}^-8 + 3x + {}^-2 = {}^-40$
9. $x + {}^-5 + {}^-2x + (-x) = 6$
10. $-x + {}^-3x + 2 + x = {}^-19$
11. ${}^-7x + 1 + 4x = {}^-7 + {}^-4$
12. $8x + {}^-1 + {}^-11x = 9 + {}^-1$
13. ${}^-11 = \frac{1}{2}x + {}^-2 + \frac{1}{2}x$
14. $12 = -x + \frac{1}{3}x + {}^-3 + x$
15. $5 + {}^-6 = x + 3 + {}^-2$
16. $11 + {}^-5 = {}^-3x + {}^-2 + x$
17. $14 + {}^-12 = x + {}^-4x + 1$
18. $5x + {}^-1 + {}^-2x = 9 + {}^-8$
19. $\frac{3}{4}x + 5 + {}^-(\frac{1}{4})x = {}^-2$
20. $\frac{5}{8}x + {}^-(\frac{3}{8})x + {}^-3 = {}^-7$
21. ${}^-3(x + {}^-2) + 5x = 11$
22. ${}^-2(3x + {}^-1) + 2x = {}^-8$

C Find the truth set of each of the following sentences.

23. $(x + 2)(x + 3) + {}^-3 + (-x^2) = {}^-22$
24. $x(x + 3) + (-x)(x + {}^-2) = {}^-5$
25. $2x(-x + 5) + {}^-3 + 2x^2 = 7$
26. ${}^-3x^2 + {}^-5 + (x + 1)(3x + 1) = 0$
27. $4x + (2 - x)(1 + x) + (x - 3)(2 + x) = 0$
28. $(2x - 4)(3 - 4x) + (1 + 8x)(x - 3) + 16 = 0$

11.5 Open Sentences with the Variable on Both Sides

You are learning to solve more and more difficult open equations. As you have seen, the problem of finding truth sets often involves many steps. While there is a general plan for solving equations, most of the thinking rests with you. Although each sentence has exactly one truth set, there are many different correct ways of finding it.

Here are the general steps in finding truth sets of open equations:

1 Write a common name of each side by expressing products as sums, adding like terms, and adding real numbers.

2 Get a sentence that is equivalent to the given sentence having the variable by itself on one side. You may have to use the Addition and Multiplication Properties of Equality more than once in order to do this.

3 Write down the truth set of the simple sentence that you get. This is also the truth set of the given sentence.

4 Check your truth set with the original sentence to catch any errors.

You are now going to consider some open sentences in which the variable appears on both sides.

Example 1: Find the truth set of the following sentence.

$$3x + 5 = 2x + 8$$

Since {real numbers} is the domain, ^-2x represents a real number for any replacement of x. Therefore, you can add ^-2x to each side by the Addition Property of Equality. This gives the following equivalent sentence.

$$3x + 5 + {}^-2x = 2x + 8 + {}^-2x$$

■ **P-1** What is a common name for the left side? for the right side?

You may continue as follows.

$$
\begin{array}{ll}
x + 5 = 8 & \text{\textit{Check:}} \quad 3x + 5 = 2x + 8 \\
x + 5 + {}^-5 = 8 + {}^-5 & \qquad\quad 3 \cdot 3 + 5 \mid 2 \cdot 3 + 8 \\
x = 3 & \qquad\qquad 9 + 5 \mid 6 + 8 \\
\{3\} & \qquad\qquad\quad 14 \mid 14
\end{array}
$$

■ **P-2** Why did you add ^-2x to both sides?

Example 2: Find the truth set of the following sentence.
$$^-2x + {}^-3 = x + 3$$

■ **P-3** What phrase would you add to both sides to eliminate ^-2x on the left side?

This gives the following equivalent sentence.
$$^-2x + {}^-3 + 2x = x + 3 + 2x$$

■ **P-4** What is a common name for the left side? for the right side?

$$^-3 = 3x + 3$$
$$^-3 + {}^-3 = 3x + 3 + {}^-3$$
$$^-6 = 3x$$
$$\tfrac{1}{3}(^-6) = \tfrac{1}{3}(3x)$$
$$^-2 = x$$
$$\{^-2\}$$

Check: $\quad ^-2x + {}^-3 = x + 3$

$-2(^-2) + {}^-3$	$^-2 + 3$
$4 + {}^-3$	1
1	

From these two examples, you can see that the first task is to eliminate the variable on one side. You can do this by adding to both sides the opposite of the term that you wish to eliminate from one side.

Example 3: Find the truth set of the following sentence.
$$3x + {}^-1 = {}^-2x + 4$$

■ **P-5** What equation do you get by adding the opposite of ^-2x to both sides?

$$3x + {}^-1 + 2x = {}^-2x + 4 + 2x$$
$$5x + {}^-1 = 4$$
$$5x + {}^-1 + 1 = 4 + 1$$
$$5x = 5$$
$$\tfrac{1}{5}(5x) = \tfrac{1}{5}(5)$$
$$x = 1$$
$$\{1\}$$

Check: $\quad 3x + {}^-1 = {}^-2x + 4$

$3 \cdot 1 + {}^-1$	$^-2(1) + 4$
$3 + {}^-1$	$^-2 + 4$
2	2

Suppose, in Example 3, you had decided to eliminate the variable from the left side. Your work would look like this:

$$3x + {}^-1 = {}^-2x + 4$$
$$3x + {}^-1 + {}^-3x = {}^-2x + 4 + {}^-3x$$
$${}^-1 = {}^-5x + 4$$
$${}^-1 + {}^-4 = {}^-5x + 4 + {}^-4$$
$${}^-5 = {}^-5x$$
$${}^-(\tfrac{1}{5})({}^-5) = {}^-(\tfrac{1}{5})({}^-5x)$$
$$1 = x$$
$$\{1\}$$

You can see that the result is the same.

In this section, you have applied the Addition Property of Equality to adding open phrases to both sides of an equation. This is permissible whenever the open phrase names a real number.

ORAL EXERCISES 11.5

For each of Written Exercises 11.5, indicate three different things you could do as the first step in finding the truth set.

WRITTEN EXERCISES 11.5

A Find the truth set of each of the following sentences. Show steps and check.

1. $2x + 3 = x + 5$
2. $3x + 5 = 2x + 7$
3. $x + 1 = 3x + 5$
4. $x + {}^-2 = 4x + 1$
5. $^-2x + {}^-3 = x + 6$
6. $^-4x + {}^-5 = x + 10$
7. $^-5x + {}^-1 = {}^-3x + {}^-9$
8. $2x + {}^-6 = {}^-5x + 7$
9. $x + {}^-5 = -x + 2$
10. $-x + {}^-3 = x + {}^-2$
11. $2x + {}^-5 = {}^-4x + 13$
12. $3x + {}^-6 = {}^-2x + 24$
13. $x + 5 + {}^-2x = 2x + 3$
14. $2x + {}^-3 + x = x + {}^-5$
15. $^-5 + x + {}^-2 = {}^-2x + 1 + (-x)$
16. $-x + 5 + 3x = {}^-10 + x + 8$

C Find the truth set of each sentence. Show steps and check.

17. $^-2(x + 3) + x = 3x + {}^-2$
18. $3(x + {}^-5) + {}^-2x = 2x + {}^-10$
19. $x(x + 3) + {}^-2 = x^2 + 1$
20. $x(2x + {}^-1) + 10 = 2x^2 + {}^-3$

11.6 Products and Zero

Consider the following sentence.

$$(x + 2)(x + {}^-3) = 0$$

■ **P-1** What value does the phrase $(x + 2)$ have when x is replaced by 3?

■ **P-2** What value does the phrase $(x + {}^-3)$ have when x is replaced by 3?

■ **P-3** Is 3 a truth number of the sentence $(x + 2)(x + {}^-3) = 0$?

■ **P-4** What number put in place of x will give $(x + 2)$ the value 0? What value does it give $(x + {}^-3)$?

■ **P-5** Is ${}^-2$ a truth number of the sentence $(x + 2)(x + {}^-3) = 0$?

You can see that 3 and ${}^-2$ are truth numbers of the sentence $(x + 2)(x + {}^-3) = 0$. The Multiplication Property of Zero is used to show this.

$$(3 + 2)(3 + {}^-3) = 5 \cdot 0$$
$$= 0$$
$$({}^-2 + 2)({}^-2 + {}^-3) = 0 \cdot {}^-5$$
$$= 0$$

Now you are going to see how you can find the truth sets of other sentences like the above example. First, you must find out something about two real numbers whose product is zero.

Let a and b represent real numbers with a not equal to 0. Suppose $a \cdot b = 0$ is true. Since $a \neq 0$ is true, then $\dfrac{1}{a}$ is the multiplicative inverse of a.

By the Multiplication Property of Equality $\longrightarrow$ $\dfrac{1}{a}(ab) = \dfrac{1}{a}(0)$

By the Associative Property of Multiplication $\longrightarrow$ $\left(\dfrac{1}{a} \cdot a\right)b = \dfrac{1}{a}(0)$

Using the common names $\longrightarrow$ $\begin{cases} 1 \cdot b = 0 \\ \quad b = 0 \end{cases}$

Therefore, if $a \cdot b = 0$ is true and $a \neq 0$ is true, then $b = 0$ is also true.

Now suppose that $a \cdot b = 0$ is true and that $b \neq 0$ is true. Let $\frac{1}{b}$ represent the multiplicative inverse of b. Then you have the following.

$$(ab) \cdot \frac{1}{b} = 0 \cdot \frac{1}{b}$$

$$a\left(b \cdot \frac{1}{b}\right) = 0 \cdot \frac{1}{b}$$

$$a \cdot 1 = 0$$

$$a = 0$$

Therefore, if $ab = 0$ is true and $b \neq 0$ is true, then $a = 0$ is also true. Of course it is obvious that $ab = 0$ is a true sentence if both a and b are zero.

You can now make the following statement.

If $ab = 0$ is true and a and b are real numbers, then it is true that

$$a = 0 \quad \text{or} \quad b = 0.$$

Now you can apply this result to find truth sets of special open sentences.

■ **P-6** What is the truth set of

$$5x = 0?$$

■ **P-7** What is the truth set of

$$n(^-3) = 0?$$

■ **P-8** What is the truth set of

$$^-5(x + ^-1) = 0?$$

■ **P-9** Can you find the truth set of

$$(x + ^-5)(x + 1) = 0?$$

The phrases $(x + ^-5)$ and $(x + 1)$ represent real numbers whose product is 0. You seek the truth numbers of the compound sentence

$$x + ^-5 = 0 \quad \text{or} \quad x + 1 = 0.$$

You will recall that a truth number of an *or* sentence makes at least one of the two clauses true.

■ **P-10** What is the truth number of the left clause of the compound sentence $x + {}^-5 = 0$ *or* $x + 1 = 0$?

■ **P-11** What is the truth number of the right clause?

■ **P-12** What is the truth set of $(x + {}^-5)(x + 1) = 0$?

Here is another example that shows the steps:

Example: Find the truth set of the following sentence.

$$(2x + 1)(x + {}^-3) = 0$$

$$
\begin{array}{ccc}
2x + 1 = 0 & or & x + {}^-3 = 0 \\
2x + 1 + {}^-1 = 0 + {}^-1 & & x + {}^-3 + 3 = 0 + 3 \\
2x = {}^-1 & & x = 3 \\
\tfrac{1}{2}(2x) = \tfrac{1}{2}({}^-1) & & \\
x = {}^-(\tfrac{1}{2}) & &
\end{array}
$$

$$\{{}^-(\tfrac{1}{2}), 3\}$$

Suppose the product of two real numbers is 5. That is, suppose

$$a \cdot b = 5,$$

where a and b are real numbers.

■ **P-13** Must a or b equal 5? Explain.

ORAL EXERCISES 11.6

Find the truth set of each of the following sentences.

1. ${}^-3 \cdot x = 0$
2. $n \cdot (\tfrac{1}{3}) = 0$
3. $100y = 0$
4. $\tfrac{3}{5}x = 0$
5. $3(x + 1) = 0$
6. ${}^-2(y + {}^-3) = 0$
7. $(a + \tfrac{1}{2}) \cdot 5 = 0$
8. $(b + \tfrac{1}{3}) \cdot ({}^-5) = 0$
9. $(x + {}^-1)(x + {}^-2) = 0$
10. $(x + 3)(x + 3) = 0$
11. $\tfrac{1}{2}(x + {}^-2) = {}^-5 + 5$
12. $(x + 7) \cdot \tfrac{1}{3} = -x + x$

13. If $a = 0$, what can you say about $a \cdot b$ if b is a real number?
14. If $b = 0$, what can you say about $a \cdot b$ if a is a real number?
15. If $a \cdot b = 0$ and a and b are real numbers, what can you say about a or b?
16. Complete this statement: "If the product of two real numbers is zero, then ? ."

WRITTEN EXERCISES 11.6

A Find the truth set of each sentence. First write an *or* sentence and find its truth set.

1. $(x + 1)(x + 2) = 0$

2. $(x + 3)(x + 5) = 0$

3. $(x + {}^-2)(x + 5) = 0$

4. $(x + {}^-1)(x + 6) = 0$

5. $(x + {}^-3)(x + {}^-2) = 0$

6. $(x + {}^-5)(x + {}^-3) = 0$

7. $(n + 5)(n + {}^-5) = 0$

8. $(a + 10)(a + {}^-10) = 0$

9. $(y + \frac{1}{2})(y + {}^-3) = 0$

10. $(r + {}^-5)(r + \frac{1}{3}) = 0$

11. $(x + 3.5)(x + {}^-1.7) = 0$

12. $(x + {}^-8.2)(x + {}^-5.3) = 0$

13. $5(n + {}^-3) = 0$

14. ${}^-3(x + {}^-12) = 0$

15. ${}^-10(2x + 3) = 0$

16. $6(3x + {}^-2) = 0$

17. $n(n + {}^-1) = 0$

18. $x(x + 3) = 0$

19. $(2x + 6)(x + {}^-5) = 0$

20. $(3x + {}^-9)(x + 3) = 0$

11.7 Solving Word Problems

In Chapter 7, you learned how to translate word sentences to open sentences. At that time, you were not expected to find the truth sets of the sentences. Now you should be able to apply your skill at finding truth sets to solving word problems.

To start with, you will use one of the problems of Chapter 7 as an example.

Example 1: The total score in a football game is 52 points. The winning team scores 6 more points than the losing team. How many did the winning team score?

Let p equal the number of points by the losing team. Then $p + 6$ equals the number of points by the winning team. Therefore,

$$p + (p + 6) = 52$$

is the open sentence that describes the problem.

Now you can find its truth number.

$$p + (p + 6) = 52$$
$$2p + 6 = 52$$
$$2p + 6 + {}^-6 = 52 + {}^-6$$
$$2p = 46$$
$$\tfrac{1}{2}(2p) = \tfrac{1}{2}(46)$$
$$p = 23$$

The truth number for the sentence $p + (p + 6) = 52$ is 23, but this is the number of points scored by the losing team. The winning team scored $(p + 6)$, or 29, points. Finding the truth number of the open sentence has enabled you to solve the problem.

You should check a word problem by seeing that the answer satisfies the conditions of the problem.

■ **P-1** Is the total score 52 points in Example 1 above?

■ **P-2** Did the winning team score 6 more points than the losing team?

Now consider another problem that you have seen before in Chapter 7.

Example 2: The length of a rectangle is 3 centimeters greater than the width. The perimeter is 50 centimeters. What are the length and width in centimeters?

Let x equal the number of centimeters in the width. Then $x + 3$ equals the number of centimeters in the length. Hence, recalling that the perimeter is the sum of twice the length and twice the width, you see that

$$50 = 2(x + 3) + 2x$$

is the open sentence that describes the perimeter of this rectangle.

Now you proceed to the truth number as follows.

$$50 = 2(x + 3) + 2x$$
$$50 = 2x + 6 + 2x$$
$$50 = 4x + 6$$
$$50 + {}^-6 = 4x + 6 + {}^-6$$
$$44 = 4x$$
$$\tfrac{1}{4}(44) = \tfrac{1}{4}(4x)$$
$$11 = x$$

The width is 11 centimeters and the length is $(11 + 3)$, or 14, centimeters.

■ **P-3** Is the length of the rectangle in Example 2 three centimeters more than its width?

■ **P-4** Is its perimeter 50 centimeters?

ORAL EXERCISES 11.7

In the word problems of Written Exercises 11.7, tell how to represent each unknown by a variable or an open phrase.

WRITTEN EXERCISES 11.7

A For each of the word problems in Exercises 1–8, (a) represent each unknown in the problem by a variable or an open phrase, (b) give an open sentence that describes the problem, (c) find the truth set of the sentence, (d) find the answer or answers to the problem, and (e) make sure that your answers satisfy the conditions of the problem.

1. The sum of two numbers is 5, and one is 9 times as great as the other. What are the numbers?

2. One number is 3 less than the other, and their sum is 10. What are the numbers?

3. The length of a rectangle is 2 feet more than the width, and the perimeter is 44 feet. What is the length of the rectangle?

4. The width of a rectangle is 3 centimeters less than the length, and the perimeter is 106 centimeters. What is the width of the rectangle?

5. One number is 10 less than another number and their sum is ⁻6. What are the numbers?

6. One number is 12 more than another number, and their sum is ⁻18. What are the two numbers?

7. Charles has 3 more nickels than dimes. If he has $1.95 in dimes and nickels, how many dimes does he have?

8. Mary Ann gets $2.29 in change. The change is made up of quarters and pennies. If she gets 5 more quarters than pennies, how many quarters does she get?

C 9. Suppose that you are given this problem: "The sum of a whole number and its successor is 48. Find the number." Can this problem be solved? If it can be solved, show how. If it cannot, explain why.

10. Suppose you are given this problem: "The length of a rectangle is 7 feet more than the width. If the sum of the length and width is 3 feet, find the width." Show what happens when you try to solve this problem.

CHAPTER SUMMARY

Important Ideas

1. Two real numbers whose product is 1 are multiplicative inverses of each other.
2. Every real number except 0 has exactly one multiplicative inverse.
3. *Multiplication Property of Equality:* If both sides of an open equation are multiplied by the same nonzero real number, the new equation is equivalent to the first.
4. The truth number of the sentence $ax = b$, where a and b represent real numbers, $a \neq 0$, is the product of b and the multiplicative inverse of a.
5. The following are important points to keep in mind in finding truth sets of equations.

   $\boxed{1}$ Try to simplify each side first.

   $\boxed{2}$ Apply number properties and the properties of equality to get an equivalent equation having the variable on one side by itself.

   $\boxed{3}$ Find the truth set of this equation and check this truth set with the given equation.

6. If $a \cdot b = 0$ is true and a and b are real numbers, then it is true that
$$a = 0 \quad or \quad b = 0.$$

7. Word problems can often be solved by finding the truth set of an open sentence that is a translation of the problem.

CHAPTER REVIEW

Give the common name for the multiplicative inverse of each of the following.

1. 22   **2.** $^-50$ **3.** $^-(\frac{1}{10})$ **4.** $^-(\frac{8}{9})$ **5.** $|\,^-(\frac{3}{4})\,|$ **6.** $3\frac{5}{8}$

Find the truth set of each of the following sentences. Show steps and check.

7. $12x + 3 = {}^-21$

8. $13 = \frac{2}{5}x + {}^-3$

9. $13a + 5 + {}^-8a = {}^-30$

10. $^-(1\frac{3}{4})y + 3 + {}^-(\frac{1}{4})y = {}^-14$

11. $r + 2r + {}^-3 + {}^-3r = -r + 7$

12. $(t + {}^-3) \cdot ({}^-7) + {}^-18 = 0$

13. $x = 3x + {}^-5$

14. $4y + {}^-3 = 2y + {}^-3$

15. $12x + {}^{-}3 = 7x + {}^{-}38$ **16.** $3a + {}^{-}3 + {}^{-}9a = a + 25$

17. $|{}^{-}2| + \frac{1}{2}x = \frac{1}{4}x + -|{}^{-}5|$

18. $2(3x + {}^{-}5) + x + 8 + {}^{-}5x = 0$

19. ${}^{-}3(2x + 3) + {}^{-}7 = -x + 2 + {}^{-}5x$

20. $3y + {}^{-}5 + 2y + (-y) = {}^{-}6 + {}^{-}2y + 1$

Find the truth set of each of the following special open sentences.

21. $x \cdot ({}^{-}3) = 0$ **22.** $7(x + {}^{-}5) = 0$

23. $(x + 15)(x + {}^{-}8) = 0$ **24.** $(x + {}^{-}5)^2 = 0$

25. $(x + \frac{2}{3})(x + \frac{3}{8}) = 0$ **26.** $(x + 1.9)(x + {}^{-}5.8) = 0$

27. $(3x + 1)(2x + 3) = 0$ **28.** $x(x + 2) = 0$

Translate each of the following word problems into an open sentence. Find its truth set and solve the problem.

29. The sum of two numbers is 2, and one of them is 9 times the other. What are the two numbers?

30. On a football team the center weighs 40 pounds more than the quarterback, and the sum of their weights is 370 pounds. How much does each weigh?

31. The length of the base of a triangle is 2 inches longer than the shortest side. The longest side is 5 inches longer than the shortest side. How long is the shortest side if the perimeter is 34 inches?

32. Dick starts for the lake on his bicycle going at a speed of 15 mph. Pete leaves 2 hours later on his scooter going 35 mph. How long will it take Pete to catch up with Dick?

Cosmic rays are formed from atomic particles that are given great energy in the stars and in the sun. From outer space, they penetrate deeply into the earth's atmosphere and strike the atoms and molecules of air with great force, causing them to split into smaller particles. This photograph, obtained from within a satellite, shows the particle paths of cosmic rays far above the earth's atmosphere. Scientists study these particle paths and, through the application of mathematics, try to learn the secrets of these mysterious rays.

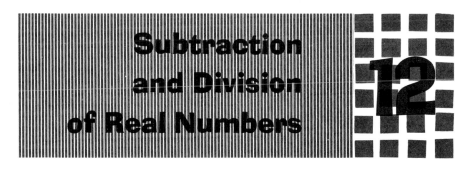

Subtraction and Division of Real Numbers

12.1 Meaning of Subtraction

You used subtraction with the numbers of arithmetic, but you found that it was always necessary to subtract a number from one that was greater or equal to it. You could not subtract a number from one that was smaller.

You now need to define the operation of subtraction for real numbers. It would be nice for you to be able to subtract any real number from any other real number. Also, the results ought to agree with those for the numbers of arithmetic.

■ **P-1** What is the common name for $8 - 5$?

■ **P-2** What is the common name for $8 + (^-5)$?

You can see that this sentence is true:

$$8 - 5 = 8 + (^-5).$$

You will recall that you have been using $^-5$ as the common name for "the opposite of 5"; that is, -5 equals $^-5$. It does not really matter which of these names you use. As you can see, one is no more complicated to write than the other. In most books, -5 is used rather than $^-5$. The important thing is for you to understand that they are names for the same number.

The example just given for positive real numbers suggests the way you can define subtraction for any two real numbers.

> If a and b are any real numbers, then it is true that
>
> $$a - b = a + (-b);$$
>
> that is, to subtract b from a, add the opposite of b to a.

You can see that you can express every subtraction problem as an addition problem by using the one rule that $a - b = a + (-b)$. This means that you do not have to learn a completely new set of rules for subtracting various kinds of real numbers.

You will recall that a phrase involving subtraction is usually called a **difference.** Often, open phrases are expressed using subtraction. It is important that you learn to find common names for such phrases.

The following table shows some differences between real numbers expressed as sums.

Difference		Sum
$5 - 8$	$=$	$5 + (^-8)$
$8 - (^-5)$	$=$	$8 + 5$
$5 - (^-8)$	$=$	$5 + 8$
$(^-8) - (^-5)$	$=$	$(^-8) + 5$
$(^-5) - (^-8)$	$=$	$(^-5) + 8$
$0 - 5$	$=$	$0 + (^-5)$
$0 - (^-8)$	$=$	$0 + 8$
$(^-10) - (^-10)$	$=$	$(^-10) + (10)$

■ **P-3** What is the common name for each of the differences in the above table?

■ **P-4** How can you express each of the following as a sum?

$$1 - 10; \quad (^-7) - (3); \quad (^-2) - (^-8); \quad x - y; \quad x - (-y)$$

You have been using the dash, −, in three ways. Here is a summary of each use of the dash so that there will not be confusion:

1	In a phrase of the form $a - b$, the dash, −, stands between two numerals and indicates subtraction. The phrase $a - b$ is read "a minus b."
2	In a phrase of the form $a + (-b)$, the dash, −, indicates "the opposite of." The phrase $a + (-b)$ is read "a plus the opposite of b."
3	When you have used the dash, −, in the raised position as in $^-5$, it is part of the name for a negative number. The phrase $a + (^-5)$ is read "a plus negative 5." The phrase $a - (^-5)$ is read "a minus negative 5."

In phrases of the form $a - (-b)$, parentheses are needed only for the purpose of clarity. The parentheses clearly show that the first dash means subtraction since it is between two numerals. The second dash means "the opposite of."

Read each of the following as a phrase involving addition of an opposite.

1. $12 - 3$ **2.** $3 - 12$ **3.** $3 - (^-12)$

4. $3 - (-12)$ **5.** $12 - (^-3)$ **6.** $(^-3) - (^-12)$

7. $(^-12) - (^-3)$ **8.** $0 - 10$ **9.** $0 - (^-10)$

10. $x - 15$ **11.** $x - (^-15)$ **12.** $15 - x$

13. $15 - (-x)$ **14.** $x - y$ **15.** $y - x$

16. $x - (-y)$ **17.** $3x - x$ **18.** $x - 3x$

19. $3 - (x + 2)$ **20.** $5 - (^-3 + 7)$

WRITTEN EXERCISES 12.1

A   First write each of the following differences as a sum; then find the common name.

Example: $3 - 10 = 3 + (^-10)$
$$= {}^-7$$

1. $15 - 7$ **2.** $13 - 6$ **3.** $7 - 15$

4. $6 - 13$ **5.** $15 - (^-7)$ **6.** $13 - (^-6)$

7. $^-15 - 7$ **8.** $^-13 - 6$ **9.** $(^-15) - (^-7)$

10. $(^-13) - (^-6)$ **11.** $7 - (^-15)$ **12.** $6 - (^-13)$

13. $(^-7) - (^-15)$ **14.** $(^-6) - (^-13)$ **15.** $0 - 13$

16. $0 - 15$ **17.** $0 - (^-13)$ **18.** $0 - (^-15)$

19. $33 - 33$ **20.** $99 - 99$ **21.** $33 - (^-33)$

22. $99 - (^-99)$ **23.** $(^-33) - 33$ **24.** $(^-99) - 99$

Write a phrase for each of the following in two ways. First use subtraction; then use addition.

25. Subtract $^-11$ from 13.

26. Subtract $^-25$ from 18.

27. What is $^-17$ less 5?

28. What is $^-5$ less 12?

29. Find a number that is 3 less than 1.

30. Find a number that is 8 less than 5.

31. How much greater is $^-2$ than $^-10$?

32. How much greater is $^-3$ than $^-15$?

33. Find "negative five minus eighteen."

34. Find "negative sixteen minus the opposite of seven."

B **35.** What is the common name for $5 - 2$?

36. What is the common name for $2 - 5$?

37. Is the operation of subtraction a commutative operation?

38. Is $5 + (^-2) = ^-2 + 5$ a true sentence? What property is illustrated?

39. What is the common name for $3 - (10 - 6)$?

40. What is the common name for $(3 - 10) - 6$?

41. Is the operation of subtraction an associative operation?

42. What property is illustrated by the following true sentence?

$$(3 + {}^-10) + {}^-6 = 3 + ({}^-10 + {}^-6)$$

12.2 Subtraction in Open Phrases

Consider the difference $5x - 2x$.

P-1 How can you express this difference as a sum?

P-2 What is a common name for $5x + (^-2x)$?

You can see that finding a common name for such a phrase involves first expressing the difference as a sum. Then you can apply your knowledge of adding like terms to get a common name.

Here are some more examples:

Writing the differences as sums ⟶ $8a - 7 - 5a = 8a + (^-7) + (^-5a)$
Adding like terms ⟶ $= 3a + {}^-7$
By the meaning of subtraction ⟶ $= 3a - 7$

The sentence $3a + {}^-7 = 3a - 7$ is true for all real numbers that are used to replace the variable a. The open phrases $3a + {}^-7$ and $3a - 7$ are **equivalent.**

> Two open phrases are **equivalent** if they have the same value when the variables are replaced by the same numbers from the domain.

The phrase $3a - 7$ is considered a simpler name than $3a + {}^-7$ because it uses fewer symbols. Thus, $3a - 7$ is the common name for $8a - 7 - 5a$.

Example 1: Find the common name for the phrase
$$7 + x - 10 - 5x.$$

Writing the differences
   as sums $\longrightarrow$ $7 + x - 10 - 5x = 7 + x + (^-10) + (^-5x)$

Using the Commutative and
   Associative Properties of Addition $\longrightarrow = (x + {}^-5x) + (7 + {}^-10)$

Using common names $\longrightarrow = {}^-4x + {}^-3$

By the meaning of subtraction $\longrightarrow = {}^-4x - 3$

Thus, $^-4x - 3$ is the common name for $7 + x - 10 - 5x$.

■ **P-3** How would you express the phrase $5 - x - 2$ as a sum?

■ **P-4** What is its common name?

$$\begin{aligned} 5 - x - 2 &= 5 + (-x) + {}^-2 \\ &= (5 + {}^-2) + (-x) \\ &= 3 + (-x) \\ &= 3 - x \end{aligned}$$

However, you might have chosen to do it this way:

$$\begin{aligned} 5 - x - 2 &= 5 + (-x) + {}^-2 \\ &= (-x) + (5 + {}^-2) \\ &= -x + 3 \end{aligned}$$

The phrases $3 - x$ and $-x + 3$ can both be considered common names for $5 - x - 2$. The Commutative Property of Addition tells you that $3 - x$ and $-x + 3$ are equivalent.

Some problems that you worked in the last section suggested, however, that subtraction is *not* a commutative operation.

$$8 - 5 \neq 5 - 8$$

Also, subtraction is not an associative operation. You can show this with the following true sentence.

$$(8 - 5) - 1 \neq 8 - (5 - 1)$$

■ **P-5** What is the common name for $(8 - 5) - 1$?

■ **P-6** What is the common name for $8 - (5 - 1)$?

The set of real numbers is closed under subtraction. This is true because subtraction can always be expressed as addition, and you know there is a closure property of addition of real numbers.

The **Closure Property of Subtraction** of Real Numbers tells you that the difference of any two real numbers is a real number.

Another type of problem in finding a common name for a phrase involves the property about the opposite of a sum.

■ **P-7** What is another name for $-(a + b)$?

Example 2: Find the common name for the phrase

$$2x - 3 - (3x + 7).$$

Writing differences
as sums$\longrightarrow 2x - 3 - (3x + 7) = 2x + {}^-3 + -(3x + 7)$

Opposite of a sum equals
the sum of the opposites $\longrightarrow = 2x + {}^-3 + ({}^-3x) + ({}^-7)$

Using Commutative
and Associative Properties$\longrightarrow = (2x + {}^-3x) + ({}^-3 + {}^-7)$

Adding like terms $\longrightarrow = {}^-1x + {}^-10$

Using a common name $\longrightarrow = -x - 10$

ORAL EXERCISES 12.2

Give a common name for each of the following.

1. $x - ({}^-2)$
2. $x + ({}^-3)$
3. $5x - 2x$
4. $3x - 2x$
5. $4x - 9x$
6. $5x - x$
7. $6x - 5x$
8. $5 + x - 3$
9. $3 + x - 10$
10. $x - 5 - 3x$
11. $12 - 3x - 9$
12. $5 - x - 6$
13. $5 + (x - 3)$
14. $5 - (3 - x)$
15. $5 - (x - 3)$
16. $5 - (x + 3)$
17. $2x + 6 - x - 5$
18. $x - 5 - 3x - 7$
19. $-x - 1 - 2x - 3$
20. $x^2 - 5 - x^2 - 2$

WRITTEN EXERCISES 12.2

A Find a common name for each of the following. First express the differences as sums.

1. $5x - ({}^-7)$
2. $8a - ({}^-12)$
3. $13y - 9y$
4. $20x - 13x$
5. $4a - a$
6. $8a - a$
7. $x - 5x$
8. $y - 10y$
9. $4x - 5x$
10. $11a - 12a$
11. $3x - 5 - 2x$
12. $5x - 7 - 4x$

13. $^-8x + 3 - 2x$

14. $^-3x + 7 - 12x$

15. $2a - 3 - 5a - 8$

16. $5t - 1 - 9t - 5$

17. $5 - (x + 3)$

18. $12 - (y + 7)$

19. $3x - (10 - x)$

20. $4y - (15 - y)$

21. $(x + 2) - (3x - 5)$

22. $5x - (8x - x)$

23. $(y - 1) - (4y + 5)$

24. $3a - (5a - 9a)$

Find the truth set of each of the following. First change differences to sums.

25. $x - 3 = {^-7}$

26. $y - 10 = {^-9}$

27. $3x - 5 = 10$

28. $2x - 7 = 13$

29. $x - 2 - 2x = 7$

30. $3y - 5 - 4y = {^-2}$

31. $2x - 3 = x - 5$

32. $3x - 1 = 2x - 7$

12.3 Special Properties of Subtraction

In the preceding section, you learned to simplify open phrases involving subtraction. One such phrase is $3x - (x - 5)$. This was simplified as follows.

$$
\begin{aligned}
3x - (x - 5) &= 3x + -(x + {^-5}) \\
&= 3x + (-x) + -({^-5}) \\
&= 3x + (-x) + 5 \\
&= 2x + 5
\end{aligned}
$$

Since this kind of phrase is so common in algebra, it may be considered as an example of a special property.

> For any real numbers a, b, and c, it is true that
>
> $$a - (b + c) = a - b - c.$$
>
> You will recall that $a - b - c$ means $(a - b) - c$.

Here is how it can be proved:

Writing the difference
as a sum ⟶ $a - (b + c) = a + -(b + c)$

Since the opposite of a sum
is the sum of the opposites ⟶ $= a + (-b) + (-c)$

Using a common name ⟶ $= a - b - c$

To show that $a - (b + c)$ does not mean $a - b + c$, let $a = 3$, $b = 2$, and $c = 1$.

■ **P-1** What is the value of $a - (b + c)$?

■ **P-2** What is the value of $a - b + c$?

■ **P-3** What is a phrase without parentheses that is equivalent to $a - (b - c)$?

Here is how the answer to **P-3** can be shown:

■ **P-4** $a - (b - c) = a + -(b + -c)$ Why?

■ **P-5** $\qquad\qquad = a + (-b + c)$ Why?

■ **P-6** $\qquad\qquad = (a + -b) + c$ Why?

■ **P-7** $\qquad\qquad = (a - b) + c$ Why?

$\qquad\qquad = a - b + c$

■ **P-8** Using the special properties just shown, what do you think is a common name for each of the following phrases?

$$3x - (2y + 5); \quad 2a - (^-3 - 5b)$$

You will soon be able to apply these properties in order to simplify a phrase in one step. You can also use these properties for a phrase like the following.

$$a - (b + c - d - e)$$

Without showing a proof, you have this result:

$$a - (b + c - d - e) = a - b - c + d + e$$

■ **P-9** What phrase without parentheses is equivalent to

$$(a - b) - (c + d - e)?$$

You have seen that the commutative and associative properties do not apply to subtraction. Now look at a distributive property that relates multiplication and subtraction.

■ **P-10** Are the following sentences true?

$$3(9 - 4) = 3 \cdot 9 - 3 \cdot 4$$
$$^-5(2 - 5) = (^-5)2 - (^-5) \cdot 5$$

These suggest the **Distributive Property of Multiplication over Subtraction.**

> If a, b, and c are any real numbers, then it is true that
>
> $a(b - c) = ab - ac.$

This property can be shown as follows.

Writing the difference as a sum ─────────▶ $a(b - c) = a(b + -c)$
Using the Distributive Property of
  Multiplication over Addition ─────────▶ $= ab + a(-c)$
Using one of the special properties ─────────▶ $= ab + -(ac)$
Writing the sum as a difference ─────────▶ $= ab - ac$

■ **P-11** What phrase expresses the following product as a difference?

$$3a(2a - 5)$$

The Distributive Properties may also apply to more general sums and differences. The following examples show their use.

$$2(x^2 + 3x + 5) = 2x^2 + 6x + 10$$
$$3(x^2 - 5x - 10) = 3x^2 - 15x - 30$$
$$2a(-x + y - 5) = -2ax + 2ay - 10a$$

■ **P-12** What phrase involving sums and differences expresses the following product?

$$3x(x - y + 6)$$

ORAL EXERCISES 12.3

Express each of the following phrases without parentheses in simplest form.

1. $x - (y + 2)$ 2. $5 - (x - y)$ 3. $^-3 - (-x + y)$
4. $^-1 - (y - x)$ 5. $y - (^-3 + x)$ 6. $x - (5 - y)$
7. $(a + b) - (2a - b)$ 8. $(x - y) - (x + y)$

Express the following products as differences.

9. $2(x - y)$ 10. $3(x - 2)$ 11. $5(2x - 3)$
12. $(a - 3)3$ 13. $(r - 2)r$ 14. $(x - 5)2x$
15. $\frac{1}{2}(2a - 6)$ 16. $\frac{1}{3}(3x - 3)$ 17. $3(-x - 1)$
18. $2(-3x - \frac{1}{2})$ 19. $2(x - y - 3)$ 20. $3(x + y - 5)$

A Simplify each of the following phrases.

1. $5 - (x - 2)$ **2.** $8 - (y - 3)$

3. $a - (3a - 1)$ **4.** $2x - (5x - 2)$

5. $^-3 - (2y + 5)$ **6.** $^-6 - (6t + 9)$

7. $3x - (2 - x)$ **8.** $5a - (8 - 2a)$

9. $5t - (7 - 5t)$ **10.** $10n - (^-3 - 10n)$

11. $6m - (-m + 5)$ **12.** $8p - (-p + 1)$

13. $(x + 2) - (3x - 2)$ **14.** $(y - 3) - (^-3 + 3y)$

15. $(2 - 3x) - (^-3x + 2)$ **16.** $(2a - 5) - (^-5 + 2a)$

17. $3 - (5x + 2 - 3x)$ **18.** $10 - (^-7 - 1 + 2a)$

19. $(a^2 + 2) - (3a^2 - 5a - 2)$ **20.** $(x^2 + 3x - 5) - (2x^2 - 5x)$

Use the Distributive Property to express the following products as phrases involving sums and differences.

21. $2(x - 3)$ **22.** $3(x - 5)$ **23.** $7(2x - 6)$

24. $8(3y - 7)$ **25.** $x(2x - 5)$ **26.** $y(5y - 3)$

27. $2a(3a - 7)$ **28.** $3n(5n - 4)$ **29.** $^-3(x - 7)$

30. $^-2(r - 9)$ **31.** $^-2(^-3x + 5)$ **32.** $^-9(^-5a + 3)$

33. $^-1(x - 10)$ **34.** $^-1(2y - 5)$

35. $2(x - 2y + 5)$ **36.** $3(a - 5b - 3)$

37. $^-3(5a + 3b - 5)$ **38.** $^-5(2x - 3y - 5)$

39. $\frac{1}{2}(^-6x - 4y + 10)$ **40.** $\frac{1}{4}(^-8a - 4b - 12)$

12.4 Distances and Subtraction

Consider the two points whose coordinates are 2 and 7 on the number line.

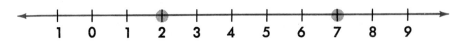

■ P-1 What is the distance between these two points expressed as a number of units?

■ P-2 Does the phrase $7 - 2$ represent this distance?

■ P-3 Does the phrase $2 - 7$ represent this distance? Explain.

■ P-4 Does the phrase $|2 - 7|$ represent this distance?

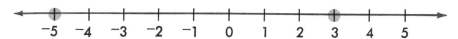

P-5 What is the distance between these two points?

P-6 Does the phrase $| 3 - (^-5) |$ represent this distance?

P-7 Does the phrase $| (^-5) - 3 |$ represent this distance?

Now consider one more case in which both points have coordinates that are negative.

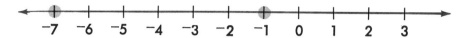

P-8 What is the distance between these two points?

P-9 Does the phrase $| (^-1) - (^-7) |$ represent this distance?

P-10 Does the phrase $| (^-7) - (^-1) |$ represent this distance?

Since distance is really a measure of length, it is expressed by a positive real number. You know that the difference of two real numbers is not always a positive number. Since the absolute value of any real number is nonnegative, this suggests a way to express the distance between two points.

Suppose you have two points whose coordinates are x and y on the number line. The distance between these two points is given either by the phrase $| x - y |$ or by the phrase $| y - x |$.

> **The distance between two points is the absolute value of the difference of their coordinates.**

You may also refer to the distance between the coordinates, or numbers, instead of the distance between the points.

P-11 What are two phrases using absolute value that represent the distance between $^-2$ and $^-10$ on the number line?

P-12 What is a common name for the distance in **P-11**?

You can use the distance between numbers to help find truth sets of special sentences. Consider the open sentence

$$|x - 3| = 4.$$

Think of the phrase $|x - 3|$ as representing the distance between x and 3.

■ **P-13** What must this distance be to make the sentence true?

You want to find values for x such that the distance between each value and 3 is 4.

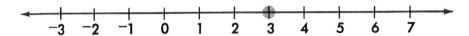

■ **P-14** Name two numbers that are each four units from 3.

■ **P-15** Are there any other numbers that are four units from 3?

■ **P-16** What is the truth set of the sentence $|x - 3| = 4$?

The truth set of a sentence such as the following can also be found by this method.

$$|x + 1| < 3$$

■ **P-17** How can $x + 1$ be expressed as a difference?

Expressing $x + 1$ as a difference allows you to write the sentence

$$|x - (^-1)| < 3.$$

You can think of this sentence as follows: "The distance between x and $^-1$ is less than 3."

Do you see that the graph of the truth set of this sentence is the one shown below in which the distance between any point of the graph and the point with coordinate $^-1$ is less than three units?

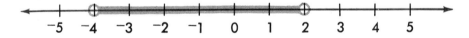

ORAL EXERCISES 12.4

Find the common name for each of the following.

1. $|5 - 3|$ 2. $|3 - 5|$ 3. $|(^-5) - 3|$ 4. $|5 - (^-3)|$
5. $|(^-5) - (^-3)|$ 6. $|(^-3) - (^-5)|$ 7. $|0 - 8|$
8. $|(^-7) - 0|$ 9. $|(^-10) - 10|$ 10. $|10 - (^-10)|$

What is the distance between these numbers on the number line?

11. 7 and 9   **12.** ⁻1 and 4   **13.** ⁻5 and ⁻2   **14.** 0 and 7   **15.** 0 and ⁻6

Tell whether or not the truth set of each open sentence has the graph that is shown.

16. $|x - 2| = 2$

17. $|x + 2| = 3$

18. $|x - 1| < 2$

19. $|x - 2| > 3$

20. $|x - 0| \leq 1$

WRITTEN EXERCISES 12.4

A Find the distance between each of the following pairs of numbers. First express the distance as the absolute value of the difference of the pair of numbers in two ways. Then find the common name.

1. 9 and 14   **2.** 4 and 11   **3.** ⁻3 and 7   **4.** ⁻4 and 9
5. ⁻8 and ⁻2   **6.** ⁻13 and ⁻9   **7.** 0 and 8   **8.** 0 and 16
9. 0 and ⁻12   **10.** 0 and ⁻13   **11.** $3\frac{1}{2}$ and ⁻$(5\frac{1}{2})$
12. $2\frac{1}{2}$ and ⁻$(8\frac{1}{2})$ **13.** $\frac{3}{4}$ and ⁻$(\frac{1}{2})$ **14.** $1\frac{1}{2}$ and ⁻$(2\frac{1}{4})$
15. ⁻6.3 and ⁻3.7   **16.** ⁻5.9 and ⁻4.6

Express each of the following sums as a difference.

Example: $5 + 2 = 5 - (⁻2)$
17. $8 + 5$ **18.** $3 + 12$ **19.** $⁻7 + 2$ **20.** $⁻11 + 5$
21. $x + 7$ **22.** $x + 3$ **23.** $a + b$ **24.** $x + y$

Graph the truth set of each open sentence. Let {real numbers} be the domain.

25. $|x - 1| = 5$ **26.** $|x - 2| = 4$ **27.** $|x + 3| = 1$
28. $|x + 2| = 3$ **29.** $|x - \frac{1}{2}| = 2$ **30.** $|x - 1\frac{1}{2}| = 3$
31. $|x - 2| < 3$ **32.** $|x - 3| < 2$ **33.** $|x + 1| \geq 2$
34. $|x + 2| \geq 3$

35. What is the truth set of $|x - 2| < ⁻3$?
36. What is the truth set of $|x| \geq 0$?

12.5 Meaning of Division

You are familiar with division of numbers of arithmetic. You also know that division is related to multiplication. In considering what number is represented by the quotient $8 \div 4$, you can think of it as "the number whose product with 4 equals 8."

The definition of division of real numbers should be made so that the results agree with those for the numbers of arithmetic. Also, any two numbers should have a real number as a quotient, except that it is not possible to allow 0 as a divisor. In this section, $\frac{a}{b}$ will generally be used instead of $a \div b$ to represent the "quotient of a divided by b."

Before considering the meaning of division, you should review two simple but important properties that you are familiar with in arithmetic.

> **1** If a is any real number, then $\frac{a}{1} = a$ is true.

> **2** If a is any real number except 0, then $\frac{a}{a} = 1$ is true.

As in the preceding chapter, let the multiplicative inverse of b be represented by $\frac{1}{b}$.

■ **P-1** Why must b not equal zero?

At this point you should show that this is a reasonable choice as a name for the multiplicative inverse. You want to show that, for any real number except 0, it is true that

$$b \cdot \frac{1}{b} = 1.$$

By property **1** above ⟶ $b \cdot \frac{1}{b} = \frac{b}{1} \cdot \frac{1}{b}$

If the rule for the product of two numbers in fraction form is to apply to fractions showing real numbers as numerators ⟶ $= \frac{b \cdot 1}{1 \cdot b}$

Using the Multiplication Property of One ⟶ $= \frac{b}{b}$

Using property **2** above ⟶ $= 1$

Thus, $\frac{1}{b}$ is a reasonable name for the multiplicative inverse of b.

P-2 What is the multiplicative inverse of $-x$?

Here is the definition of division for real numbers:

> For any real numbers a and b, $b \neq 0$, it is true that
> $$\frac{a}{b} = a \cdot \frac{1}{b}.$$

The above definition states that "a divided by b" equals "a times the multiplicative inverse of b."

P-3 How can you express the following quotients as products?

$$\frac{3}{5}; \qquad \frac{-2}{7}; \qquad \frac{x}{-y}; \qquad \frac{a}{a}$$

Here is another important fact that you must remember:

> If a is any real number, $\frac{a}{0}$ does not represent a number.

The reason that $\frac{a}{0}$ does not represent a number is clear from the meaning of division. If $\frac{a}{0}$ were to represent a number, then it would be the "product of a and the multiplicative inverse of 0." But 0 does not have a multiplicative inverse, as was stated before!

P-4 What is the truth set of the following sentence?

$$0 \cdot n = 1$$

P-5 What value does the phrase $0 \cdot n$ have for any real number replacing n?

ORAL EXERCISES 12.5

Give the common name for each of the following.

1. $\dfrac{16}{1}$ 2. $\dfrac{13}{13}$ 3. $\dfrac{-7}{1}$ 4. $\dfrac{-3}{-3}$ 5. $\dfrac{-(\frac{1}{2})}{1}$

6. $\dfrac{\frac{2}{3}}{\frac{2}{3}}$ 7. $\dfrac{x}{1}$ 8. $\dfrac{x}{x}$ 9. $\dfrac{-5.6}{-5.6}$ 10. $\dfrac{0}{1}$

Express each of the following quotients as a product.

11. $\dfrac{2}{3}$ **12.** $\dfrac{^-5}{7}$ **13.** $\dfrac{3}{^-5}$ **14.** $\dfrac{^-5}{^-8}$ **15.** $\dfrac{2}{n}; n \neq 0$

16. $\dfrac{x}{y}; y \neq 0$ **17.** $\dfrac{1}{8}$ **18.** $\dfrac{3}{\frac{2}{3}}$ **19.** $\dfrac{\frac{1}{2}}{5}$ **20.** $\dfrac{3}{^-(\frac{2}{3})}$

WRITTEN EXERCISES 12.5

A Give a common name for each of the following. Indicate any restrictions on the variables to avoid zero divisors.

Example: $\dfrac{x-1}{x-1}$ *Answer:* $1; x \neq 1$

1. $\dfrac{5}{5}$ **2.** $\dfrac{10}{10}$ **3.** $\dfrac{^-12}{^-12}$ **4.** $\dfrac{^-13}{^-13}$

5. $\dfrac{a}{1}$ **6.** $\dfrac{y}{1}$ **7.** $\dfrac{n}{n}$ **8.** $\dfrac{m}{m}$

9. $\dfrac{x+5}{1}$ **10.** $\dfrac{y+3}{1}$ **11.** $\dfrac{x+1}{x+1}$ **12.** $\dfrac{a+3}{a+3}$

13. $\dfrac{y-5}{y-5}$ **14.** $\dfrac{t-10}{t-10}$ **15.** $\dfrac{^-(\frac{1}{3})}{^-(\frac{1}{3})}$ **16.** $\dfrac{^-(\frac{3}{4})}{^-(\frac{3}{4})}$

Express each of the following as a product, using the meaning of division. Assume that no divisor is zero.

17. $\frac{2}{5}$ **18.** $\frac{5}{8}$ **19.** $\frac{^-4}{7}$

20. $\dfrac{^-3}{10}$ **21.** $\dfrac{^-5}{^-12}$ **22.** $\dfrac{^-1}{^-7}$

23. $\dfrac{5}{^-7}$ **24.** $\dfrac{4}{^-9}$ **25.** $\dfrac{6}{y}$

26. $\dfrac{9}{a}$ **27.** $\dfrac{^-3}{x}$ **28.** $\dfrac{^-5}{y}$

29. $\dfrac{1}{\frac{2}{3}}$ **30.** $\dfrac{1}{\frac{5}{6}}$ **31.** $\dfrac{^-3}{\frac{1}{5}}$

32. $\dfrac{^-5}{\frac{1}{8}}$ **33.** $\dfrac{\frac{3}{5}}{\frac{7}{12}}$ **34.** $\dfrac{\frac{5}{6}}{\frac{3}{4}}$

35. $\dfrac{r}{s}$ **36.** $\dfrac{p}{q}$ **37.** $\dfrac{x}{x+2}$

38. $\dfrac{y}{y-3}$ **39.** $\dfrac{a-b}{a+b}$ **40.** $\dfrac{x+y}{x-y}$

12.6   Special Properties of Division

Consider the quotient $\frac{a}{b}$, where a and b are any real numbers except that b is not equal to 0.

By the meaning of division $\longrightarrow$ $\dfrac{-a}{b} = (-a) \cdot \dfrac{1}{b}$

Because $^-1 \cdot x = -x$ for any number x $\longrightarrow$ $= (^-1 \cdot a) \cdot \dfrac{1}{b}$

By the Associative Property of Multiplication $\longrightarrow$ $= {}^-1\left(a \cdot \dfrac{1}{b}\right)$

By the meaning of division $\longrightarrow$ $= {}^-1\left(\dfrac{a}{b}\right)$

Because $^-1 \cdot x = -x$ for any number x $\longrightarrow$ $= -\dfrac{a}{b}$

Thus, $\dfrac{-a}{b}$ and $-\dfrac{a}{b}$ are equivalent phrases.

■ **P-1**   What is another name for $\dfrac{-5}{12}$ using this result?

You can also show that $-\dfrac{1}{b}$ is the multiplicative inverse of $-b$.

Since $-1 \cdot x = -x$
for any number x $\longrightarrow$ $(-b)\left(-\dfrac{1}{b}\right) = (-1 \cdot b)\left(-1 \cdot \dfrac{1}{b}\right)$

Using the Commutative and Associative
Properties of Multiplication $\longrightarrow$ $= (-1)(-1)\left(b \cdot \dfrac{1}{b}\right)$

Using common names $\longrightarrow$ $\begin{cases} = 1 \cdot 1 \\ = 1 \end{cases}$

Thus, $-\dfrac{1}{b}$ is the multiplicative inverse of $-b$, but so is $\dfrac{1}{-b}$. Therefore, for any nonzero real number b,

$$-\frac{1}{b} = \frac{1}{-b}.$$

See if you can give the reasons for the steps of the example on the following page.

■ **P-2** $$\frac{a}{-b} = a\left(\frac{1}{-b}\right) \qquad \underline{?}$$

■ **P-3** $$= a\left(-\frac{1}{b}\right) \qquad \underline{?}$$

■ **P-4** $$= -a\left(\frac{1}{b}\right) \qquad \underline{?}$$

■ **P-5** $$= (-1 \cdot a)\left(\frac{1}{b}\right) \qquad \underline{?}$$

■ **P-6** $$= -1 \cdot \left(a \cdot \frac{1}{b}\right) \qquad \underline{?}$$

■ **P-7** $$= -1 \cdot \left(\frac{a}{b}\right) \qquad \underline{?}$$

■ **P-8** $$= -\frac{a}{b} \qquad \underline{?}$$

This shows that $\frac{a}{-b}$ is equal to $-\frac{a}{b}$ for all real numbers a and b, $b \neq 0$. The examples of this section have shown that $-\frac{a}{b}$, $\frac{-a}{b}$, and $\frac{a}{-b}$ are all equivalent phrases. Usually, $-\frac{a}{b}$ is considered to be the common name.

■ **P-9** What is the common name of $\frac{-7}{12}$?

■ **P-10** What is the common name of $\frac{7}{-12}$?

■ **P-11** What is the common name of $\frac{-7}{-12}$? of $\frac{-x}{-y}$?

A phrase such as $\frac{x-2}{2-x}$ can be given a simpler name. Recall that $-(x-2)$ equals $-x+2$, or $2-x$. Thus, you have the following.

$$\frac{x-2}{2-x} = \frac{x-2}{-(x-2)}$$

$$= -\frac{x-2}{x-2}$$

■ **P-12** What is the common name for $-\dfrac{x-2}{x-2}$?

■ **P-13** What value can x not have?

It will be helpful for you to note the following examples.

$$-(a - 1) = 1 - a$$
$$-(y - 10) = 10 - y$$
$$-(a - b) = b - a$$

ORAL EXERCISES 12.6

Using the results of this section, give two other names for each of the following.

1. $\dfrac{-3}{5}$ **2.** $\dfrac{7}{-12}$ **3.** $-\dfrac{8}{9}$ **4.** $\dfrac{-x}{5}$

5. $\dfrac{a}{-3}$ **6.** $-\dfrac{y}{2}$ **7.** $\dfrac{a-2}{-3}$ **8.** $-\dfrac{x-3}{5}$

9. $\dfrac{x}{-y}$; $y \neq 0$ **10.** $\dfrac{a-b}{-c}$; $c \neq 0$ **11.** $-\dfrac{x-y}{t}$; $t \neq 0$

Give another name for each of the following, using fewer opposite signs.

12. $-\dfrac{-3}{7}$ **13.** $-\dfrac{-2}{-11}$ **14.** $-\dfrac{1}{-13}$

15. $\dfrac{-9}{-13}$ **16.** $-\dfrac{x}{-y}$; $y \neq 0$ **17.** $-\dfrac{-x}{-y}$; $y \neq 0$

18. $\dfrac{-a}{-b}$; $b \neq 0$ **19.** $-\dfrac{x+2}{-5}$ **20.** $-\dfrac{-(x+y)}{a}$; $a \neq 0$

WRITTEN EXERCISES 12.6

A Using the fact that $-\dfrac{a}{b}$, $\dfrac{-a}{b}$, and $\dfrac{a}{-b}$ are equivalent phrases, write two other names for each of the following.

1. $\dfrac{-12}{17}$ **2.** $\dfrac{15}{-19}$ **3.** $-\dfrac{10}{19}$ **4.** $\dfrac{-3}{11}$

5. $\dfrac{8}{-11}$ **6.** $-\dfrac{1}{9}$ **7.** $\dfrac{-(a+2)}{3}$ **8.** $\dfrac{x+5}{-3}$

9. $-\dfrac{y+1}{7}$ **10.** $-\dfrac{a+3}{9}$ **11.** $\dfrac{-a}{t}$; $t \neq 0$

12. $-\dfrac{p}{q}$; $q \neq 0$ **13.** $\dfrac{a+b}{-r}$; $r \neq 0$ **14.** $\dfrac{-2}{a-b}$; $a \neq b$

Write a common name for each of the following, using fewer opposite signs or subtraction symbols.

15. $-\dfrac{-7}{-12}$

16. $-\dfrac{17}{-19}$

17. $\dfrac{-a}{-x}; x \neq 0$

18. $-\dfrac{-r}{-t}; t \neq 0$

19. $-\dfrac{a-b}{2}$

20. $-\dfrac{3}{x-2}; x \neq 2$

21. $-\dfrac{x-2}{x-3}; x \neq 3$

22. $-\dfrac{a-2}{-y}; y \neq 0$

Write a common name for each of the following.

23. $-\dfrac{x-3}{x-3}; x \neq 3$

24. $-\dfrac{a+5}{a+5}; a \neq {}^-5$

25. $\dfrac{a-2}{2-a}; a \neq 2$

26. $\dfrac{x-10}{10-x}; x \neq 10$

27. $-\dfrac{-(5-t)}{t-5}; t \neq 5$

28. $\dfrac{a-7}{-(7-a)}; a \neq 7$

B Write a common name for each of the following sums.

29. $\dfrac{2}{5} + \dfrac{-1}{5}$

30. $\dfrac{3}{7} - \dfrac{-2}{7}$

31. $\dfrac{5}{6} + \dfrac{4}{-6}$

32. $\dfrac{3}{x} - \dfrac{-2}{x}; x \neq 0$

33. $\dfrac{2}{a-b} - \dfrac{-1}{a-b}; a \neq b$

34. $\dfrac{5}{x-2} - \dfrac{-3}{2-x}; x \neq 2$

12.7   Products of Real Numbers in Fraction Form

Now consider how to find the product of two numbers named by fractions whose numerators and denominators are real numbers. Certainly, it is desirable that the method be the same as it is for the fractions that represent numbers of arithmetic.

You will show the following.

If a, b, c, and d are any real numbers with $b \neq 0$ and $d \neq 0$, then it is true that

$$\frac{a}{b} \cdot \frac{c}{d} = \frac{ac}{bd}.$$

■ **P-1** What is the common name for the product $\dfrac{-2}{3} \cdot \dfrac{5}{-7}$?

Before considering a "proof" of the rule that $\dfrac{a}{b} \cdot \dfrac{c}{d} = \dfrac{ac}{bd}$, you must show that the following is true for any real numbers b and d where $b \neq 0$ and $d \neq 0$.

$$\frac{1}{b} \cdot \frac{1}{d} = \frac{1}{bd}$$

By the Commutative and Associative
  Properties of Multiplication ⟶ $\left(\dfrac{1}{b} \cdot \dfrac{1}{d}\right)bd = \left(\dfrac{1}{b} \cdot b\right)\left(\dfrac{1}{d} \cdot d\right)$

Using common names ⟶ $\begin{cases} = 1 \cdot 1 \\ = 1 \end{cases}$

Thus, $\left(\dfrac{1}{b} \cdot \dfrac{1}{d}\right)$ is the multiplicative inverse of bd. Since $\dfrac{1}{bd}$ is also a name for the multiplicative inverse of bd, this means that $\left(\dfrac{1}{b} \cdot \dfrac{1}{d}\right)$ and $\dfrac{1}{bd}$ are equivalent.

■ **P-2** What is the product $\dfrac{1}{-5} \cdot \dfrac{1}{-2}$?

Now you can proceed to prove that $\dfrac{a}{b} \cdot \dfrac{c}{d} = \dfrac{ac}{bd}$.

■ **P-3** How can you express $\dfrac{a}{b}$ as a product?

■ **P-4** How can you express $\dfrac{c}{d}$ as a product?

$$\frac{a}{b} \cdot \frac{c}{d} = \left(a \cdot \frac{1}{b}\right)\left(c \cdot \frac{1}{d}\right)$$

■ **P-5** $\qquad\qquad = (ac)\left(\dfrac{1}{b} \cdot \dfrac{1}{d}\right)$ Why?

By the result just proved ⟶ $= (ac)\left(\dfrac{1}{bd}\right)$

By the meaning of division ⟶ $= \dfrac{ac}{bd}$

■ **P-6** What is the common name for the product $-\frac{1}{2}\cdot\frac{-6}{7}$?

■ **P-7** What is a common name for the product $\frac{2x}{3}\cdot\frac{-5}{y}$, $y \neq 0$?

ORAL EXERCISES 12.7

Find a single fraction that names each product, assuming no divisor is zero.

1. $\frac{2}{7}\cdot\frac{3}{11}$

2. $\frac{-1}{5}\cdot\frac{2}{-7}$

3. $\frac{a}{5}\cdot\frac{-3}{x}$

4. $\frac{2x}{5}\cdot\frac{-3}{10}$

5. $\frac{-2}{y}\cdot\frac{5}{-x}$

6. $-\frac{2}{3}\cdot\frac{-x}{y}$

7. $\frac{-3a}{2y}\cdot\frac{a}{-5y}$

8. $\frac{5x}{2a}\cdot\frac{-3y}{-7a}$

9. $\frac{2ac}{3d}\cdot\frac{-5b}{x}$

10. $\frac{-\frac{1}{3}}{\frac{5}{6}}\cdot\frac{6}{6}$

11. $\frac{2}{5}\cdot\frac{x-2}{x-3}$

12. $\frac{x+2}{5}\cdot\frac{x-3}{2}$

13. $\frac{-a}{-b}\cdot\frac{-x}{-y}$

14. $\left(-\frac{3}{4}\right)\cdot\left(-\frac{5}{-11}\right)$

15. $\left(\frac{-1}{5}\right)\left(\frac{1}{-2}\right)\left(-\frac{1}{3}\right)$

16. $\left(\frac{2}{3}\right)\left(\frac{-2}{3}\right)\left(\frac{2}{-3}\right)$

WRITTEN EXERCISES 12.7

A Give a common name for each of the following by writing each product as a single fraction. Assume that no divisor is zero.

1. $\frac{-1}{8}\cdot\frac{1}{7}$

2. $\frac{1}{3}\cdot\frac{1}{-8}$

3. $\frac{-2}{5}\cdot\frac{-3}{11}$

4. $\frac{5}{-8}\cdot\frac{3}{7}$

5. $\frac{a}{6}\cdot\frac{-3}{x}$

6. $\frac{-y}{5}\cdot\frac{2}{t}$

7. $\frac{-3x}{5}\cdot\frac{-2y}{7}$

8. $\frac{5a}{-3}\cdot\frac{-2b}{11}$

9. $\frac{2}{-y}\cdot\frac{3}{-5y}$

10. $\frac{-3x}{7}\cdot\frac{2x}{5}$

11. $\frac{-1}{5}\left(-\frac{2}{x}\right)$

12. $-\frac{3}{y}\cdot-\frac{2}{y}$

13. $\frac{2a}{3}\cdot\frac{-a}{-5}$

14. $\frac{-3x}{7}\cdot\frac{x}{-5}$

15. $\frac{2}{-3}\cdot\frac{x+2}{-5}$

16. $\frac{3}{y+1}\cdot\frac{-7}{5}$

17. $\frac{(x+1)}{-3}\cdot\frac{(x+2)}{y}$

18. $\frac{(a-2)}{7}\cdot\frac{(a+3)}{-10}$

19. $\frac{1}{x}\cdot\frac{1}{-y}\cdot\frac{-1}{y}$

20. $\frac{2}{a}\cdot\frac{-3}{b}\cdot\frac{-1}{a}$

12.8 Fractions as Common Names

You agreed in a previous section that a fraction of the form $-\dfrac{a}{b}$ would be the common name rather than $\dfrac{-a}{b}$ or $\dfrac{a}{-b}$.

■ **P-1** What is the common name for $\dfrac{3}{-x}$?

Again you may use the Multiplication Property of One to obtain common names for fractions that can be simplified.

For example, the common name for $\dfrac{-15}{20}$ can be found as follows.

Using factored form $\longrightarrow$ $\dfrac{-15}{20} = \dfrac{-(3)(5)}{2 \cdot 2 \cdot 5}$

Using the rule for the product of numbers
   in fraction form $\longrightarrow$ $= \dfrac{-3}{2 \cdot 2} \cdot \dfrac{5}{5}$

Since $\dfrac{a}{a} = 1$ for $a \neq 0$ $\longrightarrow$ $= \dfrac{-3}{2 \cdot 2} \cdot 1$

Using the Multiplication Property of One $\longrightarrow$ $= \dfrac{-3}{2 \cdot 2}$

Using the common name $\longrightarrow$ $= -\dfrac{3}{4}$

Give the reason for each step in finding the common name for the fraction

$$\frac{2x}{-3x}, \quad x \neq 0.$$

■ **P-2** $\dfrac{2x}{-3x} = \dfrac{2}{-3} \cdot \dfrac{x}{x}$ $\underline{?}$

■ **P-3** $= \dfrac{2}{-3} \cdot 1$ $\underline{?}$

■ **P-4** $= -\dfrac{2}{3}$ $\underline{?}$

■ **P-5** For the fraction $\dfrac{-3}{x-2}$, what restriction is there on the value of the variable?

Now consider finding a common name for $\dfrac{2x + 4}{6x + 2}$, $x \neq -\dfrac{1}{3}$.

■ **P-6** Why can x not equal $-\frac{1}{3}$?

By the Distributive Property $\longrightarrow$ $\dfrac{2x + 4}{6x + 2} = \dfrac{2(x + 2)}{2(3x + 1)}$

By the rule for the product of
two numbers in fraction form $\longrightarrow$ $= \dfrac{2}{2} \cdot \dfrac{x + 2}{3x + 1}$

Since 1 is the common name for $\frac{2}{2}$ $\longrightarrow$ $= 1 \cdot \dfrac{x + 2}{3x + 1}$

By the Multiplication Property of One $\longrightarrow$ $= \dfrac{x + 2}{3x + 1}$

Often, in finding the product of numbers in fraction form, you must simplify the fraction for the product. Consider $\dfrac{-3x}{y} \cdot \dfrac{2y}{-x}$, $y \neq 0$, $x \neq 0$.

■ **P-7** What fraction represents the above product?

$$\dfrac{-3x}{y} \cdot \dfrac{2y}{-x} = \dfrac{-6xy}{-xy}$$
$$= \dfrac{-6}{-1} \cdot \dfrac{xy}{xy}$$
$$= 6 \cdot 1$$
$$= 6$$

As a final example, find the common name for $\dfrac{x + 2}{-10} \cdot \dfrac{5x}{x + 2}$, $x \neq {}^-2$.

■ **P-8** $\qquad \dfrac{x + 2}{-10} \cdot \dfrac{5x}{x + 2} = \dfrac{(x + 2)5x}{-10(x + 2)}$ Why?

$$= -\dfrac{(x + 2)5x}{10(x + 2)}$$
$$= -\dfrac{(x + 2) \cdot 5x}{2 \cdot 5(x + 2)}$$
$$= -\dfrac{5(x + 2)}{5(x + 2)} \cdot \dfrac{x}{2}$$
$$= (-1) \cdot \dfrac{x}{2}$$
$$= -\dfrac{x}{2}$$

What name for 1 can you use to find a common name for each of the following?

1. $\dfrac{2 \cdot 3}{3 \cdot 5}$

2. $\dfrac{5(-2)}{2 \cdot 3}$

3. $\dfrac{2(-3)(5)}{3 \cdot 7 \cdot 5}$

4. $\dfrac{5x}{3x}; \ x \neq 0$

5. $\dfrac{-5x}{5y}; \ y \neq 0$

6. $\dfrac{2(-a)3}{3 \cdot a \cdot 5}; \ a \neq 0$

7. $\dfrac{2(x + 2)}{5(x + 2)}; \ x \neq {}^-2$

8. $\dfrac{-x(y + 1)}{(y + 3)x}; \ y \neq -3, \ x \neq 0$

9. $\dfrac{25a}{-35ab}; \ a \neq 0, \ b \neq 0$

10. $\dfrac{12a^2b}{16ab}; \ a \neq 0, \ b \neq 0$

Supply the missing numerals in each of the following. Assume that no divisor is zero.

11. $\dfrac{-15a}{10} = \dfrac{-3a}{2} \cdot \dfrac{?}{?}$

12. $\dfrac{2x^2y}{3xy^2} = \dfrac{2x}{3y} \cdot \dfrac{?}{?}$

13. $\dfrac{(-y) \cdot 18}{24y^2} = -\dfrac{y \cdot 2 \cdot ? \cdot ?}{2 \cdot 2 \cdot 2 \cdot ? \cdot y \cdot y} = -\dfrac{3}{2 \cdot 2 \cdot y} \cdot \dfrac{?}{?}$

14. $\dfrac{-3(x - 5)}{5(x - 5)} = -\dfrac{3}{5} \cdot \dfrac{?}{?}$

15. $\dfrac{2x + 4}{6y} = \dfrac{2(\ ?\ )}{2 \cdot 3 \cdot y} = \dfrac{x + 2}{3y} \cdot \dfrac{?}{?}$

16. $\dfrac{15ab^2}{-21ab} = -\dfrac{3 \cdot 5 \cdot a \cdot b \cdot b}{? \cdot 7 \cdot a \cdot b} = -\dfrac{5b}{7} \cdot \dfrac{?}{?}$

WRITTEN EXERCISES 12.8

A Supply the missing numerals. Assume that no divisor is zero.

1. $\dfrac{-4}{12} = -\dfrac{2 \cdot 2}{2 \cdot 2 \cdot 3} = -\dfrac{1}{3} \cdot \dfrac{?}{?} = \underline{\ ?\ }$

2. $\dfrac{6}{-15} = -\dfrac{2 \cdot 3}{3 \cdot 5} = -\dfrac{2}{5} \cdot \dfrac{?}{?} = \underline{\ ?\ }$

3. $\dfrac{6x}{8x} = \dfrac{2 \cdot 3 \cdot x}{2 \cdot 2 \cdot 2 \cdot x} = \dfrac{3}{2 \cdot 2} \cdot \dfrac{?}{?} = \underline{\ ?\ }$

4. $\dfrac{10y}{15y} = \dfrac{2 \cdot 5 \cdot y}{3 \cdot 5 \cdot y} = \dfrac{2}{3} \cdot \dfrac{?}{?} = \underline{\ ?\ }$

5. $\dfrac{3x + 6}{5x + 10} = \dfrac{3(\ ?\ )}{5(\ ?\ )} = \dfrac{3}{5} \cdot \dfrac{?}{?} = \underline{\ ?\ }$

6. $\dfrac{2x + 10}{3x + 15} = \dfrac{2(\ ?\ )}{3(\ ?\ )} = \dfrac{2}{3} \cdot \dfrac{?}{?} = \underline{\ ?\ }$

Use the Multiplication Property of One to simplify the following. Show steps. Assume that no divisor is zero.

7. $\dfrac{5x^2}{3xy}$ **8.** $\dfrac{7ab}{12b^2}$ **9.** $\dfrac{20a}{30a}$ **10.** $\dfrac{18y}{24y}$ **11.** $\dfrac{5x-15}{3x-9}$ **12.** $\dfrac{4y+8}{7y+14}$

Find the common name for each of the following products. Assume that no divisor is zero.

13. $\dfrac{-2}{3} \cdot \dfrac{9}{10}$ **14.** $\dfrac{3}{4} \cdot \dfrac{8}{-9}$ **15.** $\dfrac{2a}{3b} \cdot \dfrac{b}{4}$

16. $-\dfrac{x}{y} \cdot \dfrac{2y}{x^2}$ **17.** $\dfrac{3a}{-2b} \cdot \dfrac{-5a}{9b}$ **18.** $\dfrac{2x}{-5y} \cdot \dfrac{10x}{3y}$

19. $\dfrac{2(x+2)}{y} \cdot \dfrac{3xy}{x+2}$ **20.** $\dfrac{5}{(y-2)} \cdot \dfrac{3(y-2)}{10x}$

12.9 Sums and Differences of Numbers in Fraction Form

In adding two numbers of arithmetic that showed the same denominator, you placed the sum of the numerators over the common denominator. For example, you do this in the following.

$$\frac{5}{13} + \frac{6}{13} = \frac{5+6}{13} = \frac{11}{13}$$

You can now show that this rule applies to numbers in fraction form that show numerators and denominators that are real numbers. Consider

$$\frac{a}{c} + \frac{b}{c}, \quad c \neq 0.$$

By the meaning of division ⟶ $\dfrac{a}{c} + \dfrac{b}{c} = a \cdot \dfrac{1}{c} + b \cdot \dfrac{1}{c}$

By the Distributive Property ⟶ $= (a + b) \cdot \dfrac{1}{c}$

By the meaning of division ⟶ $= \dfrac{a+b}{c}$

Thus, the sum of two real numbers in fraction form that show a common denominator is the sum of the numerators divided by the common denominator.

P-1 What is a common name for the following sum?

$$\frac{2x}{y} + \frac{3x}{y}, \quad y \neq 0$$

P-2 What is a common name for the following sum?

$$\frac{3}{x-2} + \frac{-5}{x-2}, \quad x \neq 2$$

The difference of two real numbers in fraction form can be found in much the same way.

By the meaning of subtraction $\longrightarrow \quad \dfrac{a}{c} - \dfrac{b}{c} = \dfrac{a}{c} + \left(-\dfrac{b}{c}\right)$

Since $\dfrac{-b}{c}$ and $-\dfrac{b}{c}$ are equivalent $\longrightarrow \quad = \dfrac{a}{c} + \dfrac{-b}{c}$

By the rule for addition of numbers in
fraction form $\longrightarrow \quad = \dfrac{a + (-b)}{c}$

Using the common name for the numerator $\longrightarrow \quad = \dfrac{a - b}{c}$

In adding real numbers in fraction form that do not show a common denominator, you will find that the Multiplication Property of One is again important.

Example 1: Find a common name for $\dfrac{a}{2} + \dfrac{a}{3}$.

P-3 What is the least common multiple of 2 and 3?

The least common multiple of 2 and 3 suggests the names to use for 1, as in the following.

Using the Multiplication Property of One $\longrightarrow \quad \dfrac{a}{2} + \dfrac{a}{3} = \dfrac{a}{2} \cdot \dfrac{3}{3} + \dfrac{a}{3} \cdot \dfrac{2}{2}$

By the rule for the product of numbers in
fraction form $\longrightarrow \quad = \dfrac{3a}{6} + \dfrac{2a}{6}$

By the rule for the sum of numbers in
fraction form $\longrightarrow \quad = \dfrac{3a + 2a}{6}$

Adding like terms $\longrightarrow \quad = \dfrac{5a}{6}$

Example 2: Find a common name for $\dfrac{5x}{12} - \dfrac{x}{30}$.

■ **P-4** What is the prime factorization of 12?

■ **P-5** What is the prime factorization of 30?

■ **P-6** What is the least common multiple of 12 and 30?

Here are the steps:

$$\frac{5x}{12} - \frac{x}{30} = \frac{5x}{12} \cdot \frac{5}{5} - \frac{x}{30} \cdot \frac{2}{2}$$

$$= \frac{25x}{60} - \frac{2x}{60}$$

$$= \frac{25x - 2x}{60}$$

$$= \frac{23x}{60}$$

ORAL EXERCISES 12.9

Give a common name for each of the following.

1. $\dfrac{x}{9} + \dfrac{3x}{9}$ **2.** $\dfrac{3y}{7} + \dfrac{2y}{7}$ **3.** $\dfrac{a}{5} + \dfrac{a}{5}$ **4.** $\dfrac{3t}{4} - \dfrac{2t}{4}$

5. $\dfrac{x}{8} - \dfrac{x}{8}$ **6.** $\dfrac{5}{x} + \dfrac{2}{x}$ **7.** $\dfrac{3}{y} + \dfrac{1}{y}$ **8.** $\dfrac{9}{w} + \dfrac{1}{w}$

9. $\dfrac{5}{x+2} + \dfrac{2}{x+2}$ **10.** $\dfrac{3}{x-3} + \dfrac{7}{x-3}$ **11.** $\dfrac{a}{x} + \dfrac{b}{x}$

12. $\dfrac{x}{y} - \dfrac{t}{y}$ **13.** $\dfrac{3y}{x-2} + \dfrac{y}{x-2}$ **14.** $\dfrac{2a}{b} - \dfrac{a}{b}$

15. $\dfrac{x}{5} + \dfrac{x}{3}$ **16.** $\dfrac{y}{2} + \dfrac{y}{5}$

WRITTEN EXERCISES 12.9

A Rewrite each of the following and fill in the missing numerals.

1. $\dfrac{2x}{7} + \dfrac{x}{5} = \dfrac{2x}{7} \cdot \dfrac{5}{5} + \dfrac{x}{5} \cdot \dfrac{?}{?}$

$= \dfrac{10x}{35} + \dfrac{?}{?}$

$= \dfrac{?}{35}$

2. $\dfrac{y}{3} + \dfrac{2y}{11} = \dfrac{y}{3} \cdot \dfrac{?}{?} + \dfrac{2y}{11} \cdot \dfrac{3}{3}$

$= \dfrac{?}{?} + \dfrac{6y}{33}$

$= \dfrac{?}{33}$

3. $\dfrac{a}{10} + \dfrac{a}{12} = \dfrac{a}{10} \cdot \dfrac{6}{6} + \dfrac{a}{12} \cdot \dfrac{?}{?}$

$= \dfrac{6a}{60} + \dfrac{?}{?}$

$= \dfrac{?}{60}$

4. $\dfrac{x}{8} + \dfrac{x}{12} = \dfrac{x}{8} \cdot \dfrac{?}{?} + \dfrac{x}{12} \cdot \dfrac{2}{2}$

$= \dfrac{?}{?} + \dfrac{2x}{24}$

$= \dfrac{?}{24}$

Find a common name for each of the following. Show steps. Assume that no divisor is zero.

5. $\dfrac{2x}{3} + \dfrac{3x}{7}$

6. $\dfrac{3y}{11} + \dfrac{y}{3}$

7. $\dfrac{5a}{2} - \dfrac{a}{5}$

8. $\dfrac{3x}{3} - \dfrac{2x}{5}$

9. $\dfrac{y}{6} + \dfrac{2y}{8}$

10. $\dfrac{2t}{10} + \dfrac{t}{15}$

11. $\dfrac{x}{2} - \dfrac{x}{10}$

12. $\dfrac{y}{5} - \dfrac{y}{20}$

13. $\dfrac{a}{15} + \dfrac{2a}{21}$

14. $\dfrac{p}{14} + \dfrac{3p}{35}$

Find the common name for each of the following. Be sure to simplify each fraction if possible.

15. $\dfrac{2x}{9} + \dfrac{x}{9}$

16. $\dfrac{5y}{12} + \dfrac{y}{12}$

17. $\dfrac{8a}{10} - \dfrac{3a}{10}$

18. $\dfrac{12x}{15} - \dfrac{9x}{15}$

19. $\dfrac{y}{12} - \dfrac{3y}{12}$

20. $\dfrac{2t}{9} - \dfrac{5t}{9}$

12.10 Division of Real Numbers in Fraction Form

You have learned the meaning of the quotient of two real numbers. You can also apply this to the quotient of two real numbers in fraction form. The phrase $\dfrac{a}{b} \div \dfrac{c}{d}$ means "$\dfrac{a}{b}$ multiplied by the reciprocal of $\dfrac{c}{d}$."

$$\dfrac{a}{b} \div \dfrac{c}{d} = \dfrac{a}{b} \cdot \dfrac{d}{c}$$

Of course, $b \neq 0$, $d \neq 0$, and $c \neq 0$ must be true.

■ **P-1** What is the common name for the quotient $\frac{2}{3} \div \frac{5}{7}$?

In this section, you will be more concerned about simplifying quotients that are expressed in fraction form. These forms are sometimes called **complex fractions** when the numerator or the denominator is also in fraction form. For example, $\dfrac{\frac{2}{3}}{\frac{5}{7}}$ is a complex fraction.

Again you can use the Multiplication Property of One in simplifying complex fractions.

Example 1: Find a common name for the following complex fraction.

$$\dfrac{\frac{x}{3}}{\frac{2}{5}}$$

■ **P-2** What is the least common multiple of the two denominators, 3 and 5?

Use $\frac{15}{15}$ as a name for 1 and proceed as follows.

Using the rule for the product of numbers in fraction form $\longrightarrow$ $\dfrac{\frac{x}{3}}{\frac{2}{5}} \cdot \dfrac{15}{15} = \dfrac{\frac{x}{3} \cdot 15}{\frac{2}{5} \cdot 15}$

Since $a = \dfrac{a}{1}$ for all real numbers $\longrightarrow$ $= \dfrac{\frac{x}{3} \cdot \frac{15}{1}}{\frac{2}{5} \cdot \frac{15}{1}}$

By rule for product of numbers in fraction form $\longrightarrow$ $= \dfrac{\frac{15x}{3}}{\frac{30}{5}}$

Using common names $\longrightarrow$ $= \dfrac{5x}{6}$

This example suggests that you can simplify a complex fraction by multiplying by $\dfrac{m}{m}$, where m is a common multiple of the denominators. You can show this to be true for the following complex fraction, for which $b \neq 0$, $c \neq 0$, and $d \neq 0$ are true.

$$\dfrac{\frac{a}{b}}{\frac{c}{d}}$$

■ **P-4**   Is bd a multiple of both b and d for all real numbers b and d?

■ **P-5**
$$\frac{\dfrac{a}{b}}{\dfrac{c}{d}} = \frac{\dfrac{a}{b}}{\dfrac{c}{d}} \cdot \frac{bd}{bd} \qquad \text{Why?}$$

■ **P-6**
$$= \frac{\dfrac{a}{b} \cdot bd}{\dfrac{c}{d} \cdot bd} \qquad \text{Why?}$$

$$= \frac{ad}{cb}$$

Example 2: Find a common name for the following complex fraction, for which $a \neq 0$ is true.

$$\frac{\dfrac{3a}{10}}{\dfrac{a}{15}}$$

■ **P-7**   Why must you have the restriction $a \neq 0$?

■ **P-8**   What is the least common multiple of 10 and 15?

Using the Multiplication Property of One $\longrightarrow$
$$\frac{\dfrac{3a}{10}}{\dfrac{a}{15}} = \frac{\dfrac{3a}{10}}{\dfrac{a}{15}} \cdot \frac{30}{30}$$

Finding the product of fractions $\longrightarrow$
$$= \frac{\dfrac{3a}{10} \cdot 30}{\dfrac{a}{15} \cdot 30}$$

$$= \frac{3a \cdot 3}{a \cdot 2}$$

$$= \frac{9}{2} \cdot \frac{a}{a}$$

$$= \frac{9}{2}$$

Supply the missing numerals in the following.

1. $\dfrac{\frac{2}{3}}{\frac{5}{6}} = \dfrac{\frac{2}{3}}{\frac{5}{6}} \cdot \dfrac{6}{6} = \dfrac{?}{?}$

2. $\dfrac{\frac{3}{4}}{\frac{5}{6}} = \dfrac{\frac{3}{4}}{\frac{5}{6}} \cdot \dfrac{12}{12} = \dfrac{?}{?}$

3. $\dfrac{\frac{1}{3}}{\frac{5}{9}} = \dfrac{\frac{1}{3}}{\frac{5}{9}} \cdot 1 = \dfrac{\frac{1}{3}}{\frac{5}{9}} \cdot \dfrac{?}{?} = \dfrac{?}{?}$

4. $\dfrac{\frac{1}{5}}{\frac{13}{15}} = \dfrac{\frac{1}{5}}{\frac{13}{15}} \cdot 1 = \dfrac{\frac{1}{5}}{\frac{13}{15}} \cdot \dfrac{?}{?} = \dfrac{?}{?}$

5. $\dfrac{\frac{a}{4}}{\frac{2a}{10}} = \dfrac{\frac{a}{4}}{\frac{2a}{10}} \cdot \dfrac{?}{?} = \dfrac{5a}{4a} = \dfrac{?}{?}$

6. $\dfrac{\frac{x}{6}}{\frac{3x}{10}} = \dfrac{\frac{x}{6}}{\frac{3x}{10}} \cdot \dfrac{?}{?} = \dfrac{5x}{9x} = \dfrac{?}{?}$

Give a name for 1 that can be used in simplifying each quotient.

7. $\dfrac{\frac{a}{5}}{\frac{3}{10}}$ 　　 **8.** $\dfrac{\frac{x}{7}}{\frac{5}{21}}$ 　　 **9.** $\dfrac{\frac{y}{3}}{\frac{7}{10}}$ 　　 **10.** $\dfrac{\frac{t}{5}}{\frac{11}{12}}$ 　　 **11.** $\dfrac{\frac{x}{10}}{\frac{3x}{28}}$ 　　 **12.** $\dfrac{\frac{3y}{12}}{\frac{2y}{30}}$

First express each quotient as a fraction; then simplify it if possible.

13. $\dfrac{a}{5} \div \dfrac{2a}{3}$ 　　 **14.** $\dfrac{2x}{3} \div \dfrac{x}{9}$ 　　 **15.** $\dfrac{5}{2y} \div \dfrac{10}{y}$ 　　 **16.** $\dfrac{3}{4a} \div \dfrac{9}{a}$

WRITTEN EXERCISES 12.10

A　Express each quotient as a product; then give the common name.

1. $\dfrac{3}{5} \div \dfrac{7}{8}$ 　　 **2.** $\dfrac{4}{7} \div \dfrac{3}{5}$ 　　 **3.** $\dfrac{5}{6} \div \dfrac{7}{12}$ 　　 **4.** $\dfrac{3}{8} \div \dfrac{3}{4}$

5. $\dfrac{a}{3} \div \dfrac{2a}{9}$ 　　 **6.** $\dfrac{5}{x} \div \dfrac{10}{7x}$

7. $\dfrac{5}{x-2} \div \dfrac{3}{x-2}$ 　　 **8.** $\dfrac{a+3}{2} \div \dfrac{a+3}{5}$

Rewrite each of the following by filling in the missing numerals.

9. $\dfrac{\frac{2a}{9}}{\frac{a}{18}} = \dfrac{\frac{2a}{9}}{\frac{a}{18}} \cdot \dfrac{?}{?} = \dfrac{?}{?}$

10. $\dfrac{\frac{3y}{4}}{\frac{y}{8}} = \dfrac{\frac{3y}{4}}{\frac{y}{8}} \cdot \dfrac{?}{?} = \dfrac{?}{?}$

11. $\dfrac{\frac{x}{15}}{\frac{3x}{25}} = \dfrac{\frac{x}{15}}{\frac{3x}{25}} \cdot \dfrac{?}{?} = \dfrac{?}{?}$

12. $\dfrac{\frac{5t}{14}}{\frac{5t}{21}} = \dfrac{\frac{5t}{14}}{\frac{5t}{21}} \cdot \dfrac{?}{?} = \dfrac{?}{?}$

Simplify each of the following complex fractions.

13. $\dfrac{\frac{1}{5}}{\frac{3}{5}}$ 14. $\dfrac{\frac{1}{3}}{\frac{2}{3}}$ 15. $\dfrac{\frac{2}{7}}{\frac{5}{7}}$ 16. $\dfrac{\frac{3}{11}}{\frac{8}{11}}$ 17. $\dfrac{\frac{1}{8}}{\frac{1}{12}}$ 18. $\dfrac{\frac{1}{6}}{\frac{1}{15}}$

19. $\dfrac{\frac{x}{5}}{\frac{2x}{5}}$ 20. $\dfrac{\frac{a}{7}}{\frac{2a}{7}}$ 21. $\dfrac{\frac{3}{10}}{\frac{5}{14}}$ 22. $\dfrac{\frac{5}{12}}{\frac{7}{30}}$ 23. $\dfrac{\frac{5x}{18}}{\frac{2x}{15}}$ 24. $\dfrac{\frac{3y}{14}}{\frac{y}{35}}$

CHAPTER SUMMARY

Important Ideas

1. *Meaning of Subtraction:* If a and b are real numbers, then it is true that
$$a - b = a + (-b).$$

2. *Equivalent* open phrases have the same value when the variables are replaced by the same numbers from the domain.

3. *Closure Property of Subtraction:* The difference of any two real numbers is a real number.

4. *Distributive Property of Multiplication over Subtraction:* If a, b, and c are any real numbers, then it is true that
$$a(b - c) = ab - ac.$$

5. The distance between two points on a number line if their coordinates are x and y is given by either $|\,x - y\,|$ or $|\,y - x\,|$.

6. If a is any real number, then $\dfrac{a}{1} = a$.

7. If a is any real number except 0, then $\dfrac{a}{a} = 1$.

8. *Meaning of Division:* For any real numbers a and b, $b \neq 0$, it is true that
$$\frac{a}{b} = a \cdot \frac{1}{b}.$$

The phrase $\dfrac{1}{b}$ represents the multiplicative inverse of b.

9. If a is any real number, $\dfrac{a}{0}$ does not represent a number.

10. For all real numbers a and b, $b \neq 0$, the following are equivalent phrases.
$$-\frac{a}{b}; \quad \frac{-a}{b}; \quad \frac{a}{-b}$$

11. If a, b, c, and d are any real numbers with $b \neq 0$ and $d \neq 0$ true, then it is true that

$$\frac{a}{b} \cdot \frac{c}{d} = \frac{ac}{bd}.$$

12. If a, b, and c are any real numbers, $c \neq 0$, then it is true that

$$\frac{a}{c} + \frac{b}{c} = \frac{a+b}{c}.$$

13. A fraction in which either the numerator or the denominator or both numerator and denominator are fractions is called a **complex fraction.**

14. If a, b, c, and d are real numbers and $b \neq 0$, $c \neq 0$, $d \neq 0$ are true, then it is true that

$$\frac{\dfrac{a}{b}}{\dfrac{c}{d}} = \frac{a}{b} \cdot \frac{d}{c}.$$

CHAPTER REVIEW

Express each of the following as a sum.

1. $50 - 40$ **2.** $26 - 27$ **3.** $\frac{1}{4} - \frac{1}{2}$ **4.** $q - p$ **5.** $r - (-s)$

Write a numerical phrase for each of the following as an indicated difference.

6. Subtract $^-5$ from 8.   **7.** 13 less than $^-10$.

8. a subtracted from $\mid b \mid$.   **9.** $^-12$ less 17.

10. Amount by which 13 is greater than $^-2$.

Give a common name for each of the following.

11. $3y - (-2)$ **12.** $9x - 5x$ **13.** $-5a - 2a$

14. $\frac{1}{2}t - 5 - \frac{3}{2}t$ **15.** $(n - 3) - (2n + 1)$

Use the Distributive Property to express the following products as sums or as differences. Use common names.

16. $5(x - 3)$ **17.** $^-3(2x - 5)$ **18.** $\frac{1}{2}(2a - 8)$

19. $5(2y - 3x + 2)$ **20.** $\frac{1}{3}(3x - 6y + 12)$

Find the distance between two points whose coordinates are the given numbers. First express the distance with the absolute value symbol.

21. 17 and 23   **22.** $^-8$ and 2   **23.** $^-12$ and $^-27$

24. 0 and $^-15\frac{1}{2}$ **25.** $^-11\frac{1}{4}$ and $5\frac{1}{2}$

Find the truth set of each sentence. Let {real numbers} be the domain.

26. $|y - 1| = 2$ **27.** $|x - 3| = 1$ **28.** $|a + 1| = {}^-3$

29. $|t - 2| = 0$ **30.** $|r - 0| = 1$

Express each of the following as a product, using the meaning of division.

31. $\dfrac{13}{15}$ **32.** $\dfrac{-27}{5}$ **33.** $\dfrac{x}{-3}$ **34.** $\dfrac{m + n}{m - n}; m \neq n$ **35.** $\dfrac{a}{a + 2}; a \neq {}^-2$

Give a name for each of the following, using the least number of "opposite" symbols or "subtraction" symbols.

36. $\dfrac{10 - x}{-7}$ **37.** $-\dfrac{-a}{5}$ **38.** $-\dfrac{-3}{-x}, x \neq 0$

39. $\dfrac{-(a - b)}{6}$ **40.** $-\dfrac{-x}{-y}, y \neq 0$

Write each of the following products as a single fraction using the common name. Assume that no divisor is zero.

41. $\dfrac{-3}{7} \cdot \dfrac{-2}{-5}$ **42.** $\dfrac{2y}{3} \cdot \dfrac{3x}{-a}$ **43.** $\dfrac{-a}{-5} \cdot \dfrac{-7}{-x}$

44. $\dfrac{2}{x} \cdot \dfrac{-3}{-y} \cdot \dfrac{-5}{-t}$ **45.** $\dfrac{\frac{-2}{3}}{\frac{-1}{6}} \cdot \dfrac{6}{6}$

Use the Multiplication Property of One to simplify the following. Assume that no divisor is zero.

46. $\dfrac{3a}{5a}$ **47.** $\dfrac{8y^2}{10xy}$ **48.** $\dfrac{15m}{25mn}$ **49.** $\dfrac{2x + 4}{2a}$ **50.** $\dfrac{3x - 6}{2x - 4}$

Give a common name for each of the following. Assume that no divisor is zero.

51. $\dfrac{2x}{5} \cdot \dfrac{3}{x}$ **52.** $\dfrac{2}{a} \cdot \dfrac{3}{10}$ **53.** $\dfrac{5x}{3} \cdot \dfrac{9}{10x}$ **54.** $\dfrac{1}{a-2} \cdot \dfrac{2(a-2)}{5}$ **55.** $\dfrac{-5}{2a} \cdot \dfrac{-3a}{10}$

56. $\dfrac{2x}{5} + \dfrac{5x}{5}$ **57.** $\dfrac{x}{5} + \dfrac{y}{7}$ **58.** $\dfrac{3a}{8} + \dfrac{5a}{12}$ **59.** $\dfrac{t}{2} - \dfrac{3t}{10}$ **60.** $\dfrac{-3y}{20} - \dfrac{\cdot 2y}{15}$

Find the common name for each of the following. Assume that no divisor is zero.

61. $\dfrac{\frac{2}{3}}{\frac{7}{3}}$ **62.** $\dfrac{\frac{2}{5}}{\frac{3}{10}}$ **63.** $\dfrac{\frac{x}{9}}{\frac{y}{6}}$ **64.** $\dfrac{\frac{-2x}{3}}{\frac{a}{12}}$ **65.** $\dfrac{\frac{t}{12}}{\frac{3t}{18}}$

CUMULATIVE REVIEW (CHAPTERS 10–12)

Find common names for the following products.

1. $(-15)(-4)$

2. $5(-3)(-1)(-2)$

3. $\left(\dfrac{-2}{3}\right)(15)$

4. $(-3x)(5y)(-2)$

5. $(-5)(-7)$

Complete each sentence, using the property that is indicated.

6. $-2(3 \cdot x) = \underline{\ ?\ }$; Associative Property of Multiplication

7. $(-x)9 = \underline{\ ?\ }$; Commutative Property of Multiplication

8. $a(y + {}^-3) = \underline{\ ?\ }$; Commutative Property of Multiplication

9. $({}^-3 + y)x = \underline{\ ?\ }$; Distributive Property

10. $({}^-13 \cdot a)({}^-7) = \underline{\ ?\ }$; Associative Property of Multiplication

Express each product as a sum and each sum as a product. Use the Distributive Property, and express the result in simplest form.

11. $-5(5a - 3)$

12. $3m - 6n$

13. $(-3r + 5)(-3a)$

14. $-6x - 3xy$

15. $\frac{1}{5}t(15 - 5a)$

Write a phrase for the opposite of each of the following in simplest form.

16. $-w$

17. $m - n$

18. $r(-s)$

19. $-x - y$

20. $-x^2$

Simplify each of the following phrases by adding like terms.

21. $22q + 5 - 3q$

22. $-5x^2 + 3x - 8x^2$

23. $-3a - 7a - 5$

24. $8x - 5x - 11x + 7$

25. $5 - 31t - 7 + 29t$

Express each product as a sum in simplest form.

26. $(y + 6)(y + 7)$

27. $(n - 1)(n + 2)$

28. $(s - 3)(s - 5)$

29. $(d + 5)^2$

30. $(r - 4)^2$

Find the truth set of each sentence. Show steps and check.

31. $\frac{3}{5}a = 12$

32. $2r + 5 = 12$

33. $5s + 7 - 3s = 13$

34. $11w + 3 = 8w - 7$

35. $3n - 2 - 8n = n + 5$

36. $3 - 2t - 7 = t + 1 + 2t$

37. $(p + 5)(p - 3) = 0$

38. $(q - 1)(q - 10) = 0$

39. $x(x + \frac{3}{4}) = 0$

40. $(x - 3)^2 = 0$

Show your work in each of the following word problems.

41. Rose helped print a book that has 12 chapters and 233 pages. If there are five fewer pages in each of the last 11 chapters than in the first, how many pages are in the first chapter?

42. Hazel ordered some white paper at $1.00 per ream and some yellow paper at $.75 per ream with a total cost of $46.25. If she ordered 15 more reams of yellow than of white paper, how many reams of white paper did she order?

43. The Jets gained 3 yards per play on running plays and lost 7 yards per play on passes in the first half. The number of running plays was 3 times the number of pass plays. How many pass plays did they make if they gained 14 total yards in the first half?

44. In a Colorado town, the temperature was recorded for ten straight days. The recorded low temperature was ⁻10° for a few days, and then it rose to 1° above zero. On how many days was it ⁻10° if the sum of the low temperature readings for the ten days was ⁻34°?

Express each of the following as a sum.

45. $(-3) - 5$ **46.** $0 - (-3)$ **47.** $\frac{1}{3} - \frac{1}{2}$ **48.** $(-x) - y$

Simplify each of the following.

49. $3t - (5 - 2t)$ **50.** $\frac{4}{5}p - (\frac{1}{5}p + 7)$

51. $(x - 3) - (-4x + 5)$ **52.** $(x^2 - 3x + 2) - (2x^2 + x - 5)$

Find the distance between two points whose coordinates are the pair of numbers given.

53. -5 and 3 **54.** $-3\frac{1}{2}$ and $-10\frac{1}{4}$ **55.** a and -7 **56.** x and y

Graph the truth set of each sentence.

57. $|a - 1| = 2$ **58.** $|y - 2| < 3$

59. $|t - 5| = -3$ **60.** $|p + 1| > 2$

Express each quotient as a product, using the meaning of division.

61. $\dfrac{-3}{10}$ **62.** $5 \div (-7)$ **63.** $\dfrac{a}{b}$ **64.** $\dfrac{3}{\frac{3}{8}}$

Give a common name for each of the following, using fewer opposite signs or subtraction symbols.

65. $-\dfrac{x}{-y}$ **66.** $\dfrac{-(a - b)}{y}$ **67.** $-\dfrac{a - 3}{a - 4}$ **68.** $-\dfrac{a - b}{b - a}$

Give a common name for each of the following.

69. $\dfrac{3x}{5} \cdot \dfrac{10y}{-6x}$ **70.** $\dfrac{-2a}{b} \cdot \dfrac{bc}{10} \cdot \dfrac{-5}{3a}$ **71.** $\dfrac{x + 3}{12} + \dfrac{x - 2}{6}$

72. $\dfrac{3a - 1}{b} - \dfrac{2a + 5}{b}$ **73.** $\dfrac{\frac{t}{-5}}{\frac{3t}{10}}$ **74.** $\dfrac{a}{3} \div \dfrac{5ab}{9}$

When two dice are thrown, you can expect the top faces to appear in one of just thirty-six possible ways. The dice may fall so that each of their faces shows one, two, three, four, five, or six dots; that is, each die can fall in one of six possible ways. Hence, combined, the two dice can fall in six times six, or thirty-six, possible ways, each different outcome being equally probable. The two-die array shows all the possible outcomes. (Note that, to distinguish between the two dice and their individual outcomes, you may use a white die with black dots and a black die with white dots, as in the photograph.) In this chapter, you will discover the meaning of probability.

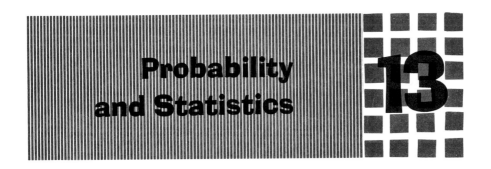

Probability and Statistics

13.1 Measure of Probability

In your everyday talk, you use words that suggest you know something about chance, or probability. You may remark that the "chance" for rain is good today. Your coach may say that the "odds" favor your team to win the game. Your teachers may tell you that you will "probably" get a good grade if you work hard.

■ **P-1** If the odds are 8 to 5 that the Mets will beat the Cubs, whom do you expect to win?

Tossing coins, throwing dice, and drawing marbles from a bag are often used as experiments in probability. They are easy to perform, and the results are easily understood.

If an ordinary coin is tossed, it can land "heads" or "tails." Since it has an equal chance of landing in either one of these two positions, you can expect it to land heads about half the time. It is said that the probability of "heads" is $\frac{1}{2}$, or 0.5. Also, the probability of "tails" is $\frac{1}{2}$.

■ **P-2** If an ordinary die (one of a pair of dice) is tossed, what do you think is the probability of getting a 4?

■ **P-3** If you toss a coin 1000 times, do you think you will get exactly 500 heads and 500 tails?

A man who was in a prisoner of war camp during World War II tried a coin-tossing experiment. He recorded the results of 10 sets of 1000 tosses each. The following list is the number of times heads came up in each set of 1000 tosses.

502, 511, 497, 529, 504, 476, 507, 528, 504, 529

The total number of times heads came up was 5087. The ratio of the number of heads to the number of tosses is $\frac{5087}{10,000}$, or 0.5087. His experiment showed an **experimental probability** of 0.5087 for getting "heads." The **mathematical probability** is $\frac{1}{2}$, or 0.5.

If you were to perform a coin-tossing experiment, you might get an experimental probability different from 0.5087. In fact, each of your classmates would likely get different results for the same number of tosses.

In the coin-tossing experiment, there are two **possible outcomes** for the coin if it is assumed it will not stand on its edge. There is only one **favorable outcome** if you are considering the probability of getting heads.

> You can find a real number that represents probability by the following ratio.
>
> $$\frac{\text{number of favorable outcomes}}{\text{number of possible outcomes}}$$

If you toss an ordinary die, the probability of getting an even number is $\frac{3}{6}$, or $\frac{1}{2}$. The number of possible outcomes is six.

■ **P-4** If, in tossing the die, you want to get an even number, what is the number of favorable outcomes? Why?

$$\text{Thus, } \frac{\text{number of favorable outcomes}}{\text{number of possible outcomes}} = \frac{3}{6}\text{, or }\frac{1}{2}.$$

ORAL EXERCISES 13.1

A bag contains 7 red marbles and 3 green marbles. A marble is drawn from the bag so that all marbles have an equal chance of being drawn.
1. What is the probability that the marble drawn is red?
2. What is the probability that the marble drawn is green?
3. What is the probability that the marble drawn is white?

A spinner like the one shown is used for a game. When it is not clear which numeral the pointer is closer to, another spin is made. A player spins the pointer.
4. What is the probability that he gets 10?
5. What is the probability that he gets 3?
6. What is the probability that he gets less than 5?

7. What is the probability that he gets more than 8?
8. What is the probability that he gets at least 7?
9. What is the probability that he gets 6 or less?
10. What is the probability that he gets 12?
11. Can you tell what the probability is that he will have to spin the pointer again?

A tourist group can travel from Chicago to New York by bus, train, or plane. It can travel from New York to Boston by bus, train, plane, or ship. The following diagram shows these possible routes.

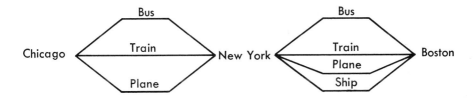

12. In how many different ways can the group travel from Chicago to Boston if they stop in New York first?
13. In how many different ways can the group travel from Chicago to Boston if they are on a bus at least once each trip?
14. In how many ways can the group travel from Chicago to Boston if they are on a ship at least once?

WRITTEN EXERCISES 13.1

A If an ordinary die is tossed, what is the probability of each of the following?
1. That a 6 appears on the die
2. That the lower face will show a 3
3. That a number greater than 4 is shown
4. That a number less than 6 is shown
5. That a number less than or equal to 3 is shown
6. That a number greater than or equal to 5 is shown
7. That a 1 appears on one of the side faces
8. That a 5 appears on one of the side faces
9. That a 7 will appear on the die
10. That the lower face will show a 0

Suppose that 3 black marbles, 5 red marbles, and 6 green marbles are placed in a box. A student who is blindfolded draws one marble from the box. What is the probability of each of the following?

11. That the marble drawn is black

12. That the marble drawn is red

13. That the marble drawn is green

14. That the marble drawn is yellow

Suppose there are 12 channels available on a television set. Television stations use six of these channels to show commercial telecasts and one channel for an educational telecast. The other channels have no telecast. If a channel is selected at random, what is each of the following probabilities?

15. That the selection will be a commercial telecast

16. That the selection will not be that of a telecast

17. That the selection will be the educational channel

18. That the selection will be a channel that is used by a television station

In a class of 20 boys and 14 girls, a student is selected at random by the teacher to give a report.

19. What is the probability that the choice is a girl?

20. What is the probability that the choice is a boy?

21. What is the probability that the student selected is not a boy?

22. What is the probability that the student selected is not a girl?

B Perform the following probability experiment.

23. Toss a nickel and a penny together 100 times. Let

H represent heads for the nickel,
T represent tails for the nickel,
h represent heads for the penny,
t represent tails for the penny.

Record the number of times each of the following pairs appears.

(H, h) appears ? times.
(H, t) appears ? times.
(T, h) appears ? times.
(T, t) appears ? times.

13.2 Sample Spaces

Suppose you toss two coins, such as a penny and a nickel, and note the ways the two coins appear. Such an activity is called a **probability experiment.** You know the different ways the two coins can appear. The possible outcomes for the nickel could be shown by H or T and for the penny by h or t. If the nickel shows a head and the penny shows a head, this outcome can be represented by (H, h). Likewise, (T, h) means the nickel shows a tail and the penny shows a head.

The following table shows the different possible outcomes of the experiment.

	h	t
H	(H, h)	(H, t)
T	(T, h)	(T, t)

You can see there are four possible ways for the two coins to fall.

■ **P-1** What is the probability that both coins show heads?

■ **P-2** What is the probability that one coin shows a head and the other a tail?

■ **P-3** What is the probability that both coins show tails?

The four possible outcomes of this experiment make up its **sample space.** Each toss of the two coins is called a **trial** of the experiment.

> A **sample space** is a set of elements such that any **trial** of an experiment gives exactly one of its elements.

The sample space of the two-coin experiment has **pairs** of letters to represent its elements. The sample space could be shown as

$$\{(H, h), (H, t), (T, h), (T, t)\}.$$

■ **P-4** If the nickel and penny are tossed together, can the outcome possibly be a pair not in the sample space that is shown?

You could try a probability experiment by using three coins and noting the outcomes. Suppose that three nickels are used and that they are called 1, 2, and 3. An outcome shown as (H_1, T_2, H_3) will mean that the first nickel shows a head, the second nickel shows a tail, and the third nickel shows a head.

■ **P-5** What outcome could be shown as (T_1, H_2, H_3)?

You can see that each outcome of this experiment can be represented in this way by **triples** of letters and numerals.

The entire sample space for the three-coin experiment is

$$\{(H_1, H_2, H_3), (H_1, H_2, T_3), (H_1, T_2, H_3), (H_1, T_2, T_3), (T_1, T_2, T_3),$$
$$(T_1, T_2, H_3), (T_1, H_2, T_3), (T_1, H_2, H_3)\}.$$

ORAL EXERCISES 13.2

Use the three-coin experiment to answer the following.
1. How many outcomes are possible when three coins are tossed?
2. Would the sample space be the same if the experiment involved tossing one coin three times?
3. What is the probability that all coins show heads?
4. What is the probability that all coins show tails?
5. What is the probability that two coins show heads and one shows tails?
6. What is the probability that two coins show tails and one shows heads?
7. What is the probability that at least two coins show heads?
8. What is the probability that less than three coins show tails?
9. What is the probability that the faces showing on all three coins are not the same?
10. What is the probability that heads does not appear?

WRITTEN EXERCISES 13.2

A A drawing is made for a basketball tournament of four teams. The teams are numbered 1, 2, 3, and 4. Pairs of numerals are put on pieces of paper in a box. A drawing is then made to determine the first two teams to play. The drawing is a probability experiment, and the sample space can be shown as

$$\{(1, 2), (1, 3), (1, 4), (2, 3), (2, 4), (3, 4)\}.$$

1. What is the probability that team 4 will play in the first game?
2. What is the probability that team 3 will play in the first game?
3. What is the probability that teams 1 and 2 will play in the first game?
4. What is the probability that teams 1 and 4 will play in the first game?

5. Why is the pair (3, 3) not in the sample space?
6. Why is the pair (2, 2) not in the sample space?
7. Why is the pair (2, 1) not included in the sample space?
8. Why is the pair (3, 2) not included in the sample space?

Jack has three cards marked I, II, III, and Bill has three cards marked 1, 2, 3. Each draws a card from the other after shuffling them. If the numerals on the two cards drawn name the same number, Jack gets a point. If the Roman numeral represents a larger number, then Bill gets a point. Complete the table shown below for the sample space of this experiment before attempting the problems that follow.

Jack's Cards

		I	II	III
	1	(1, I)	?	?
Bill's	2	?	?	(2, III)
Cards	3	?	(3, II)	?

9. What is the probability that Jack gets a point?
10. What is the probability that Bill gets a point?
11. What is the probability that Bill draws a card with III on it?
12. What is the probability that Jack draws a card with 2 on it?
13. What is the probability that Jack draws a card with II on it?
14. What is the probability that Bill draws a card with 1 on it?
15. What is the probability that the sum of the numbers represented on the two cards is 4?
16. What is the probability that the sum of the numbers represented on the two cards is less than 3?

13.3 Two-Die Experiment

Suppose you toss two dice, one red and one green die, and record the number of dots that appear on their top faces. Each of the numbers 1, 2, 3, 4, 5, or 6 can denote an outcome for the red die and also for the green die. Let the number shown on the red die be represented by r and the number shown on the green die by g. Then the outcome of the toss of both dice can be shown by the pair (r, g). Thus, if a 3 is shown on the red die and a 5 is shown on the green die, the outcome of the toss is (3, 5).

■ **P-1** How many such pairs (r, g) are possible in the two-die experiment of the previous page?

■ **P-2** Do the pairs (3, 5) and (5, 3) mean the same thing in this two-die experiment?

Since the order in which the numbers appear in such pairs is important, they are often called **ordered pairs.**

The sample space for the two-die experiment is shown by the following table. Notice that there are 6 ways for each die to fall and $6 \cdot 6$, or 36, possible ways for the pair of dice to appear.

Green Die

		1	2	3	4	5	6
	1	(1, 1)	(1, 2)	(1, 3)	(1, 4)	(1, 5)	(1, 6)
	2	(2, 1)	(2, 2)	(2, 3)	(2, 4)	(2, 5)	(2, 6)
Red	3	(3, 1)	(3, 2)	(3, 3)	(3, 4)	(3, 5)	(3, 6)
Die	4	(4, 1)	(4, 2)	(4, 3)	(4, 4)	(4, 5)	(4, 6)
	5	(5, 1)	(5, 2)	(5, 3)	(5, 4)	(5, 5)	(5, 6)
	6	(6, 1)	(6, 2)	(6, 3)	(6, 4)	(6, 5)	(6, 6)

Listing the elements of the sample space in a table as above is sometimes an easy way to discover probabilities. Suppose you want to find the probability that, in tossing two dice, the sum of the numbers shown is 6. By looking at the table, you see that there are 5 ways for this to happen: (5, 1), (4, 2), (3, 3), (2, 4), and (1, 5). From the meaning of probability, $\dfrac{\text{number of favorable outcomes}}{\text{number of possible outcomes}}$, you can see that the probability of this event is $\frac{5}{36}$.

Let the above event, that the sum of the numbers shown is 6, be represented by A. The probability of this event can be represented as follows.

$$P(A) = \tfrac{5}{36}$$

This is read: "The probability of event A is $\frac{5}{36}$."

■ **P-3** What is the probability that the sum of the numbers shown is at least 4?

Let B represent the event that the sum of the numbers shown is greater than 8.

■ **P-4** What is $P(B)$?

ORAL EXERCISES 13.3

Use the table for the two-die experiment to answer the following.

1. What is the probability that both dice show a 6?
2. What is the probability that both dice show a 3?
3. What is the probability that the red die shows 4 and the green die shows 2?
4. What is the probability that the red die shows 2 and the green die shows 4?
5. What is the probability that the green die shows 1?
6. What is the probability that the red die shows 5?
7. What is the probability that the sum of the numbers shown on the two dice is 4?
8. What is the probability that the sum of the numbers shown on the two dice is 13?
9. Why are pairs of numbers as shown in the sample space of the two-die experiment called ordered pairs?
10. How is the symbol $P(R)$ read?
11. How many outcomes are possible in the two-die experiment?
12. Would the sample space of the two-die experiment be different if the dice were the same color?

WRITTEN EXERCISES 13.3

A The following problems are based on the two-die experiment.

1. What is the probability that the numbers on the two dice are equal?
2. What is the probability that the sum of the numbers shown on the two dice is 7?
3. What is the probability that the sum of the numbers shown on the two dice is greater than 9?
4. What is the probability that the sum of the numbers shown on the two dice is less than 5?
5. What is the probability that the sum of the numbers shown on the two dice is not greater than 6?
6. What is the probability that the sum of the numbers shown on the two dice is at least 8?
7. What is the probability that exactly one of the dice shows a prime number?
8. What is the probability that both dice show prime numbers?

9. What is the probability that the number shown on the red die is greater than the number shown on the green die?

10. What is the probability that the number shown on the green die is not greater than the number shown on the red die?

11. What is the probability that at least one of the numbers shown is even?

12. What is the probability that both of the numbers are odd?

Find each of the following probabilities. Let

A represent the set of pairs in which the red die shows an odd number,

B represent the set of pairs in which the green die shows a prime number,

C represent the set of pairs in which the red die shows a number less than 3,

D represent the set of pairs in which the green die shows an even number,

E represent the set of pairs in which the red die shows a number greater than 6,

F represent the set of pairs in which the green die shows a whole number.

13. $P(D)$ 14. $P(C)$ 15. $P(A)$ 16. $P(B)$ 17. $P(E)$

18. $P(F)$ 19. $P(A$ does not occur$)$ 20. $P(E$ does not occur$)$

13.4   Complementary Events

In the two-die experiment, you were asked to find the probability that the sum of the numbers shown is 6. This was called an **event,** and it was named by a capital letter.

An **event** in probability is a subset of the sample space. Thus, an event may have no elements or it may consist of one or more elements of the sample space.

■ **P-1**   What other name can be given to an event if it has no elements?

■ **P-2**   What is the probability of an event with no elements?

It is possible, of course, for an event in probability to be the entire sample space. Using the two-die experiment, let E be the event such that the sum of the numbers shown on the two dice is a whole number greater than 1 and less than 13.

■ **P-3** What is $P(E)$?

Using the meaning of probability,

$$\frac{\text{number of favorable outcomes}}{\text{number of possible outcomes}},$$

you can clearly see that $P(E) = \frac{36}{36} = 1$.

■ **P-4** What is the greatest value any probability can have? the least value?

For the two-die experiment, let B be the event such that the sum of the numbers shown is less than 11. If you count the elements of this set, you can see that there are 33. Suppose you count the elements of the event such that the sum of the numbers shown is *not* less than 11. This set is $\{(6, 5), (5, 6), (6, 6)\}$. It is called the **complement** of set B.

> The **complement** of an event is the set of elements of the sample space that are not elements of that event.

The complement of an event has a special symbol. Thus,

$$B' = \{(6, 5), (5, 6), (6, 6)\}$$

is the complement of set B.

■ **P-5** What is $P(B')$?

Notice that $P(B) = \frac{33}{36}$ and that $P(B') = \frac{3}{36}$. Thus, you can see that the following is true.

$$P(B) + P(B') = \frac{33}{36} + \frac{3}{36}$$
$$= \frac{36}{36}$$
$$= 1$$

It is always true that the sum of the probabilities of an event and its complement is 1. In finding the probability of B, it would be easier to find the probability of B' and then to subtract it from 1.

Let $S = \{(H, h), (H, t), (T, h), (T, t)\}$, the sample space for the two-coin problem.

■ **P-6** If $D = \{(H, h), (T, t)\}$, what is $P(D')$?

■ **P-7** If E represents the event such that a head appears, what is E'? What is $P(E')$?

You can describe the complement of an event by using the word "not" in the description of the event. Let A equal the event that both coins show heads. Then A' equals the event that *not* both coins show heads.

■ **P-8** In the two-die experiment, what is the probability that the sum of the numbers shown is not 2?

ORAL EXERCISES 13.4

For the experiment of tossing three coins, you will remember the following set.

$$\{(H_1, H_2, H_3), (H_1, T_2, H_3), (T_1, T_2, T_3), (T_1, H_2, T_3)$$
$$(H_1, H_2, T_3), (H_1, T_2, T_3), (T_1, T_2, H_3), (T_1, H_2, H_3)\}$$

Consider these events:

A represents the event such that all coins show heads.
B represents the event such that all coins show tails.
C represents the event such that exactly two coins show heads.
D represents the event such that exactly two coins show tails.
E represents the event such that at least two coins show heads.
F represents the event such that at least two coins show tails.

Find each of the following probabilities.
1. $P(A')$ 2. $P(C')$ 3. $P(E')$ 4. $P(B')$ 5. $P(D')$ 6. $P(F')$
7. $P(A) + P(B)$ 8. $P(E) + P(A)$ 9. $P(E) + P(E')$
10. $P(C) + P(D)$
11. What is meant by an event in probability?
12. How is the probability of an event related to the probability of its complement?
13. If $P(A) = \frac{3}{13}$, what is $P(A')$?
14. If $P(B') = \frac{21}{25}$, what is $P(B)$?
15. If $P(X) = 0.3$, what is $P(X')$?
16. If $P(T') = 0.30$, what is $P(T)$?

WRITTEN EXERCISES 13.4

A Use the sample space for the two-die experiment to find the probability of each of the following.

1. The sum of the numbers shown by the dots is not 7.
2. The sum of the numbers shown by the dots is not 8.
3. The red die does not show a 2.
4. The green die does not show a 3.
5. The numbers shown on the two dice are not equal.
6. Not both numbers are primes.
7. The sum of the numbers shown by the dots is less than 4.
8. The sum of the numbers shown by the dots is greater than or equal to 10.
9. The sum of the numbers shown by the dots is greater than or equal to 4.
10. The sum of the numbers shown by the dots is less than 10.

11. How are the probabilities of Exercises 7 and 9 above related.
12. How are the probabilities of Exercises 8 and 10 above related.

Complete the following if

  A represents the event that neither die shows more than two dots, and

  B represents the event that both dice show four or more dots.

13. $P(A) = $? 14. $P(B) = $? 15. $P(B') = $? 16. $P(A') = $?
17. $P(A) + P(B) = $?   18. $P(A') + P(B') = $?
19. $P(A) \cdot P(B) = $?   20. $P(A) \cdot P(B') = $?

In a deck of regular playing cards, there are 13 spades, 13 hearts, 13 diamonds, and 13 clubs. There are four cards of each kind, for example, 4 aces, 4 twos, 4 kings, and so forth. A card is drawn at random from a well-shuffled deck.

21. What is the probability of getting a spade?
22. What is the probability of not getting a heart?
23. What is the probability of not getting a ten?
24. What is the probability of not getting a face card (king, queen, jack)?
25. What is the probability of not getting an odd number? (Ace is the same as one.)
26. What is the probability of not getting an even number?

13.5 Probability of the Union of Two Events

You will recall that the union of two sets is the set of elements belonging to at least one of the sets. It is shown by the symbol $\cup$. If $A = \{a, b, c\}$ and $B = \{b, c, d\}$, then

$$A \cup B = \{a, b, c, d\}.$$

Even though b and c appear in both sets, they are not listed twice in $A \cup B$.

In probability, you will find that it is often useful to work with the union of two events. For example, in the two-die experiment, suppose you want to find the probability that the red die shows a 1 *or* the green die shows a 2. You will have this event if the red die shows a 1 or if the green die shows a 2 or if both of these are true. Let

$\quad R$ represent the event that the red die shows a 1,

$\quad S$ represent the event that the green die shows a 2.

You can see that

$$R = \{(1, 1), (1, 2), (1, 3), (1, 4), (1, 5), (1, 6)\}$$

and

$$S = \{(1, 2), (2, 2), (3, 2), (4, 2), (5, 2), (6, 2)\}.$$

In computing $P(R \ or \ S)$, you would not count the element $(1, 2)$ twice. Hence,

$$P(R \ or \ S) = \tfrac{11}{36}.$$

■ **P-1** How many elements are in $R \cup S$?

■ **P-2** What is $P(R \cup S)$?

It is clear that $P(R \ or \ S)$ is the same as $P(R \cup S)$. Consider the following.

$$W = \{(1, 1), (2, 1), (1, 2)\} \quad \text{and} \quad Y = \{(6, 6)\}$$

■ **P-3** What is $P(W)$?

■ **P-4** What is $P(Y)$?

■ **P-5** What is $P(W \cup Y)$?

■ **P-6** Is the following sentence true?

$$P(W \cup Y) = P(W) + P(Y)$$

Now consider two more events of the two-die experiment. Let

E represent the event that the green die shows less than 3 dots,
F represent the event that the red die shows at least 4 dots.

The table for the two-die experiment is shown again. Event E is represented by the first two columns. Event F is represented by the last three rows.

Green Die

		1	2	3	4	5	6
	1	(1, 1)	(1, 2)	(1, 3)	(1, 4)	(1, 5)	(1, 6)
	2	(2, 1)	(2, 2)	(2, 3)	(2, 4)	(2, 5)	(2, 6)
Red	3	(3, 1)	(3, 2)	(3, 3)	(3, 4)	(3, 5)	(3, 6)
Die	4	(4, 1)	(4, 2)	(4, 3)	(4, 4)	(4, 5)	(4, 6)
	5	(5, 1)	(5, 2)	(5, 3)	(5, 4)	(5, 5)	(5, 6)
	6	(6, 1)	(6, 2)	(6, 3)	(6, 4)	(6, 5)	(6, 6)

■ **P-7** How many elements are in E? What is $P(E)$?

■ **P-8** How many elements are in F? What is $P(F)$?

■ **P-9** How many elements are in $E \cup F$? What is $P(E \cup F)$?

■ **P-10** Is the following sentence true?

$$P(E \cup F) = P(E) + P(F)$$

You can see that, in finding the probability of the union of two events, you must not count their common elements twice.

To describe events of the two-die experiment more conveniently, you will use the following notation from now on: A sentence such as $Q = \{r \leq 2\}$ will mean "Q is the event such that the red die shows 2 or fewer dots."

ORAL EXERCISES 13.5

If events for the two-die experiment are given as

$$K = \{r = 1\}, \quad L = \{g \geq 5\}, \quad M = \{r \text{ is odd}\}, \quad N = \{r = g\},$$

what is each of the following probabilities?

1 $P(K)$ **2.** $P(L)$ **3.** $P(K \cup L)$

4. $P(M)$ **5.** $P(N)$ **6.** $P(M \cup N)$

7. $P(M \cup K)$ **8.** $P(L \cup N)$ **9.** $P(L \cup M)$

10. What is $P(K \cup K')$?

A Using the experiment of tossing three coins, let the events be given as

$$A = \{\text{exactly two coins show heads}\},$$
$$B = \{\text{not more than two coins show tails}\},$$
$$C = \{\text{all coins have the same side up}\},$$
$$D = \{\text{no fewer than 2 tails appear}\}.$$

Find each of the following.

1. $P(A)$ **2.** $P(C)$ **3.** $P(B)$ **4.** $P(D)$

5. $P(A \cup B)$ **6.** $P(C \cup D)$ **7.** $P(A \cup C)$ **8.** $P(B \cup D)$

In the two-die experiment, let the events be given as

$$R = \{r = 5\}, \quad S = \{g \le 2\}, \quad T = \{g = 3\}, \quad W = \{r \ge 4\}.$$

Find each of the following.

9. $P(R)$ **10.** $P(S)$ **11.** $P(T)$ **12.** $P(W)$

13. $P(R \cup S)$ **14.** $P(S \cup T)$ **15.** $P(R \cup T)$ **16.** $P(S \cup W)$

B Perform the following probability experiment.

17. Take an ordinary thumbtack and toss it at least 100 times. Observe whether each time the tack lands with the point up or with the point touching the surface on which the tack lands. Record the number of each outcome. (You can save time by using several tacks at once.)

18. If U represents the event that the tack lands with point up, what do you estimate for $P(U)$?

19. If D represents the event that the tack lands with the point touching the surface, what do you estimate for $P(D)$?

13.6 Probability of the Intersection of Two Events

You should remember what is meant by the **intersection** of two sets. If $A = \{a, b, c\}$ and $B = \{b, c, d\}$, their intersection, $A \cap B$, is the set consisting of the elements b and c. Thus,

$$A \cap B = \{b, c\}.$$

The intersection of two sets is the set of elements that belong to both sets.

In the last section, two sets of outcomes for the two-die problem were given as follows.

$$R = \{(1, 1), (1, 2), (1, 3), (1, 4), (1, 5), (1, 6)\}$$

and

$$S = \{(1, 2), (2, 2), (3, 2), (4, 2), (5, 2), (6, 2)\}$$

■ **P-1** What is $R \cap S$?

■ **P-2** What is the probability of $R \cap S$?

The sample space for the two-die experiment is shown again for your convenience in discussing another example.

Green Die

	1	2	3	4	5	6
1	(1, 1)	(1, 2)	(1, 3)	(1, 4)	(1, 5)	(1, 6)
2	(2, 1)	(2, 2)	(2, 3)	(2, 4)	(2, 5)	(2, 6)
Red 3	(3, 1)	(3, 2)	(3, 3)	(3, 4)	(3, 5)	(3, 6)
Die 4	(4, 1)	(4, 2)	(4, 3)	(4, 4)	(4, 5)	(4, 6)
5	(5, 1)	(5, 2)	(5, 3)	(5, 4)	(5, 5)	(5, 6)
6	(6, 1)	(6, 2)	(6, 3)	(6, 4)	(6, 5)	(6, 6)

Let two sets of outcomes be given as follows.

$$A = \{r < 4\} \quad \text{and} \quad B = \{g \geq 5\}$$

■ **P-3** How many elements are in A? What is $P(A)$?

■ **P-4** How many elements are in B? What is $P(B)$?

■ **P-5** How many elements are in $A \cap B$? What is $P(A \cap B)$?

■ **P-6** Is the sentence $P(A \cap B) = P(A) \cdot P(B)$ true?

This can be shown as follows.

$$P(A \cap B) = P(A) \cdot P(B)$$

$$\begin{array}{c|c} \frac{6}{36} & \frac{18}{36} \cdot \frac{12}{36} \\ \frac{1}{6} & \frac{1}{2} \cdot \frac{1}{3} \\ & \frac{1}{6} \end{array}$$

Suppose now that you have the following two sets of outcomes.

$$R = \{g < 3\} \quad \text{and} \quad S = \{r \neq 4\}$$

■ **P-7** How many elements are in R? What is $P(R)$?

■ **P-8** How many elements are in S? What is $P(S)$?

■ **P-9** How many elements are in $R \cap S$? What is $P(R \cap S)$?

Again you can see that $P(R \cap S) = P(R) \cdot P(S)$ since

$$P(R \cap S) = \tfrac{10}{36} \quad \text{and} \quad P(R) \cdot P(S) = \tfrac{1}{3} \cdot \tfrac{5}{6}, \quad \text{or} \quad \tfrac{5}{18}.$$

You probably now want to ask the question: "Is it always true that $P(A \cap B) = P(A) \cdot P(B)$?" The answer is "No!"

Consider another example from the two-die problem. Let

$$E = \{r + g \geq 9\} \quad \text{and} \quad F = \{r > 4\}.$$

■ **P-10** How many elements are in E? What is $P(E)$?

■ **P-11** How many elements are in F? What is $P(F)$?

■ **P-12** How many elements are in $E \cap F$? What is $P(E \cap F)$?

You can see from this example that the following is true.

$$P(E \cap F) \neq P(E) \cdot P(F)$$

$$
\begin{array}{c|c}
\tfrac{7}{36} & \tfrac{10}{36} \cdot \tfrac{12}{36} \\
 & \tfrac{5}{18} \cdot \tfrac{1}{3} \\
 & \tfrac{5}{54}
\end{array}
$$

Two events A and B are said to be **independent** if it is true that $P(A \cap B) = P(A) \cdot P(B)$. It is not always easy to tell whether two events are independent.

Suppose a penny is tossed twice and you want to consider the probability that both tosses show heads. Let H_1 be the event that "the first toss shows heads" and H_2 be the event that "the second toss shows heads." It is known that these two events are independent.

■ **P-13** What is $P(H_1)$?

■ **P-14** What is $P(H_2)$?

■ **P-15** What is $P(H_1 \text{ and } H_2)$?

Since the events are independent, $P(H_1 \cap H_2) = P(H_1) \cdot P(H_2)$.

■ **P-16** What is the probability of getting heads on the first toss and tails on the second?

ORAL EXERCISES 13.6

1. What are independent events in probability?
2. How can the probability of the intersection of independent events be found?

In the two-die experiment, let $A = \{r \leq 2\}$ and $B = \{r = 6\}$.

3. What is $P(A)$?
4. What is $P(B)$?
5. What is $P(A \cap B)$?
6. Does $P(A \cap B) = P(A) \cdot P(B)$?
7. Are events A and B independent?

If two tosses in succession are made with a single die, find each of the following probabilities.

8. Both tosses yield 6.
9. The first toss is 5 and the second toss is 1.
10. The first toss is less than 4 and the second toss is greater than 3.
11. The first toss is 6 and the second is 7.
12. The first toss is 1 and the second is 2.
13. The first toss is 2 and the second is 1.
14. The sum of the numbers shown by the dots is 3.
15. The first is 5 and the second is not 5.
16. The first is not 1 and the second is not 6.

In a bag, there are 6 red marbles and 5 black marbles.

17. If one marble is drawn, what is the probability that it is red?
18. What is the probability that it is black?
19. Suppose that the marble drawn is red and that a second drawing is made after the first marble is drawn. What is the probability that the second one is red?
20. What is the probability that both marbles are red if you assume that the drawings are independent events?

WRITTEN EXERCISES 13.6

A A penny is tossed twice.

1. What is the probability of getting tails on the first toss and heads on the second?
2. What is the probability of getting tails on both tosses?

Suppose a penny is tossed three times. Three such tosses are independent.

3. What is the probability that all three outcomes are heads?

4. What is the probability that all three outcomes are tails?
5. What is the probability that the outcome of the three tosses is (T_1, T_2, H_3)?
6. What is the probability that the outcome of the three tosses is (H_1, T_2, H_3)?

A bag contains 3 red marbles, 4 black marbles, and 5 green marbles. Two drawings are made, but the first marble is replaced in the bag before a second one is drawn. Two such drawings are independent.

7. What is the probability that both are red?
8. What is the probability that both are black?
9. What is the probability that both are green?
10. What is the probability that the first is red and the second is black?
11. What is the probability that the first is red and the second is green?
12. What is the probability that the first is black and the second is green?

Let U be the event that a thumbtack lands "point up" and D be the event that it lands "on its side." Suppose it is found by experiment that in tossing a thumbtack, $P(U) = 0.6$ and $P(D) = 0.4$. If the thumbtack is tossed twice, find the probability of each of the following. Assume that the tosses are independent.

13. On both tosses, the tack lands with point up.
14. On both tosses, the tack lands on its side.
15. The first toss yields U, and the second, D.
16. The first toss yields D, and the second, U.

Suppose the probability that a basketball player makes a free throw is 0.7. Assume that successive throws are independent.

17. What is the probability that he makes two in succession?
18. What is the probability that he can make three in succession?

On a five-question, true-false quiz, a student guesses at each answer. Assume that the guesses are independent.

19. What is the probability that he gets the first question right?
20. What is the probability that he gets the last question wrong?
21. What is the probability that he gets all 5 questions right?
22. What is the probability that he gets all 5 questions wrong?

13.7 Averages

You have heard the word average used before in mathematics. In fact, you have referred to a number like 10 as the average of 9 and 11. You found this by adding 9 and 11 and dividing the sum by 2. Thus,

$$\frac{9 + 11}{2} = 10.$$

Actually an average that you found in this way has a special name. It is called the **arithmetic mean,** or often just **mean.**

> You find the **arithmetic mean** of several measurements by first adding the measurements and then dividing this sum by the number of measurements in the sample.

■ **P-1** What is the arithmetic mean of the numbers 1, 2, and 3?

■ **P-2** What is the arithmetic mean of the numbers 2, 3, 4, and 5?

Suppose you have had five tests in one term and your scores are

85, 72, 90, 10, and 68.

The arithmetic mean of your scores can be found as follows.

$$\frac{85 + 72 + 90 + 10 + 68}{5} = \frac{325}{5} = 65$$

Notice that this average score is smaller than the top four scores you had. The low score of 10 that you got on one test "pulls your average down."

Sometimes a different average, called the **median,** is used to describe several measurements. For the test scores given above, the median is 72.

> You find the **median** by arranging the scores in order as 90, 85, 72, 68, 10 and locating the middle score.

You might consider 72 a better description of your test work for the term than the mean score of 65.

■ **P-3** What is the median of the numbers 10, $\frac{1}{2}$, 3, 13, 5, 7, $5\frac{1}{2}$?

■ **P-4** Can you find the median of the numbers 1, 2, 3, 4?

> **When there is an even number of measurements to consider, the mean of the two middle numbers is usually taken as the median.**

Thus, $2\frac{1}{2}$ is the median for the numbers 1, 2, 3, and 4. The two middle numbers are 2 and 3, and their arithmetic mean is $2\frac{1}{2}$.

■ **P-5** What is the median for the numbers 10, $8\frac{1}{2}$, 5, 1, 3, 5?

The following table shows a tally record for the scores on an algebra test for a class. For example, 7 students had a score of 70.

Score	Number of Students
100	/
90	//
80	////
70	~~////~~ //
60	~~////~~ /
50	~~////~~
40	////
30	/

Notice that the score obtained by the greatest number of students is 70. This number is called the **mode** of the scores.

> **The mode is the number appearing most often in a collection of measurements.**

The mode is also considered an average. If no measurement appears more than once, the sample does not have a mode.

In the algebra test scores, the mean score is 63, the median is 60, and the mode is 70. Often the mean or median will give a better description of the measurements than the mode. However, in some work, it is nice to know the mode.

The work below suggests an easy way to find the mean of the algebra test scores.

$$\frac{100 + 180 + 320 + 490 + 360 + 250 + 160 + 30}{30} = \frac{1890}{30} = 63$$

■ **P-6** How is the number 320 obtained for the problem on the previous page? the number 250?

■ **P-7** Why is 30 used as the divisor in this problem?

> The **range** of a sample of measurements is the difference between the greatest and the least measurements in the sample.

For the algebra test scores, the range is $100 - 30 = 70$.

ORAL EXERCISES 13.7

The players on a basketball team score 77 points in a game. The number of points scored by each is as follows.

$$25, \quad 18, \quad 12, \quad 12, \quad 5, \quad 3, \quad 2$$

1. What is the mean score?   **2.** What is the median score?

3. What is the mode?   **4.** What is the range?

A football player scores 96 points in 10 games. His scoring for each game is as follows.

$$6, \quad 12, \quad 6, \quad 18, \quad 6, \quad 0, \quad 12, \quad 6, \quad 24, \quad 6$$

5. What is his mean score for the ten games?

6. What is his median score?

7. What is the mode for his scores?

8. What is the range of his scores?

9. What is the mode of the following measurements?

$$5.2, \quad 4.3, \quad 5.5, \quad 4.7, \quad 4.9, \quad 5.0$$

10. What can you say about the mode of the following sample?

$$5, \quad 10, \quad 7, \quad 3, \quad 5, \quad 8, \quad 3$$

The following table shows the distribution of grades in a class of 30 students for a 10-point quiz.

10	//	5	̶H̶H̶ ////
9	̶H̶H̶	4	//
8	///	3	
7	//	2	/
6	////	1	//

11. What is the median score?   **12.** What is the mode?

13. Explain how you would find the mean score.

A To the nearest tenth, find the arithmetic mean of the numbers in each of the following.

1. 5, 12, 4, 13, 17, 10   **2.** 8, 1, $2\frac{1}{2}$, 16, $15\frac{1}{2}$, 5, 10

3. Find the median for the numbers in Exercise 1.

4. Find the median for the numbers in Exercise 2.

5. A spinner is used for a game as shown. One player keeps a tally of his score as follows.

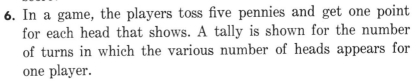

1	⊬⊬⊢
2	IIII
3	⊬⊬⊢ II
4	⊬⊬⊢ I
5	⊬⊬⊢ I
6	⊬⊬⊢ III

Find his total score and his mean score.

6. In a game, the players toss five pennies and get one point for each head that shows. A tally is shown for the number of turns in which the various number of heads appears for one player.

Number of Heads	Number of Turns
5	II
4	⊬⊬⊢ IIII
3	⊬⊬⊢ ⊬⊬⊢ ⊬⊬⊢ III
2	⊬⊬⊢ ⊬⊬⊢ ⊬⊬⊢ ⊬⊬⊢ I
1	⊬⊬⊢ ⊬⊬⊢ III
0	I

Find his total score and his mean score.

7. Some students are asked to estimate the length of a stick to the nearest inch. Here are the estimates: 15, 21, 13, 17, 15, 18, 14, 19, 20, 18, 13. For their estimates, find (a) the mean, (b) the median, (c) the mode, and (d) the range.

8. In ten games, a baseball team scored the following number of runs: 5, 1, 8, 2, 0, 13, 4, 3, 4, 11. For the ten games, find (a) the mean number of runs scored, (b) the median number of runs, (c) the mode, and (d) the range.

9. A single die is tossed to score points in a game. The following tally shows the number of times each face appears. The total score is the total number of dots. There are 100 tosses.

6	~~HHT~~ ~~HHT~~ ~~HHT~~ ~~HHT~~ I	3	~~HHT~~ ~~HHT~~ ~~HHT~~ ~~HHT~~
5	~~HHT~~ ~~HHT~~ IIII	2	~~HHT~~ ~~HHT~~ III
4	~~HHT~~ ~~HHT~~ II	1	~~HHT~~ ~~HHT~~ ~~HHT~~ ~~HHT~~

Find (a) the mean score to the nearest tenth and (b) the mode.

10. A page in a telephone book is chosen at random, and a tally is made for the last digit of each telephone number in one column of the page. The tally is shown below.

9	~~HHT~~ ~~HHT~~	4	~~HHT~~ II
8	~~HHT~~ III	3	~~HHT~~ ~~HHT~~ ~~HHT~~
7	~~HHT~~ ~~HHT~~ I	2	~~HHT~~ I
6	~~HHT~~ I	1	~~HHT~~ I
5	~~HHT~~ ~~HHT~~ III	0	~~HHT~~ I

(a) What is the sum of the numbers represented by the last digits?

(b) What is the arithmetic mean of the numbers represented by the last digits?

(c) What digit is the mode?

C The following are suggested experiments for you to conduct.

11. Toss four pennies together 100 times. By tally marks, record the number of heads, 4, 3, 2, 1, or 0, that appears on each toss. Find the mean number of heads per toss of the four coins.

12. Perform a "random walk" experiment as follows: Toss a coin, and for each head move one unit to the right, and for each tail move one unit to the left on the number line.

When you reach A, record a score of 2. When you reach B, record a score of -1. A game ends when you reach A or B, and then you start at 0 again.

(a) Record by tally marks the number of games ending with a score of -1 and the number ending with a score of 2. Play at least 25 games.

(b) Find the mean score per game.

13.8 Frequency Tables and Graphs

In an experiment, a student tosses 4 pennies sixteen times and observes the number of heads for each toss. The following is a dot-frequency graph showing the results.

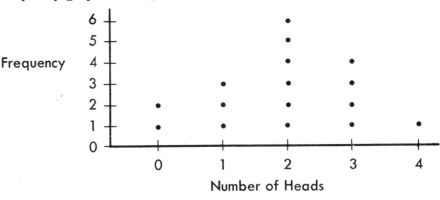

■ **P-1** How many times did 2 heads appear?

■ **P-2** In the experiment, how many times did 3 heads appear? 4 heads?

After grading an algebra test for a class, the teacher records the following scores.

72	76	68
72	68	68
44	60	68
76	68	56
76	80	48
92	92	64
48	60	44
60	68	80
88	56	
60	76	

■ **P-3** What is the mode of the scores?

■ **P-4** What is the range of scores?

In order to show his students a picture of the class results, the teacher grouped the scores in intervals of 10 points. A frequency table is shown for the results.

Interval Boundaries	Interval Midpoints	Frequency
90–100	95	//
80–90	85	///
70–80	75	⊬⊬ /
60–70	65	⊬⊬ ⊬⊬ /
50–60	55	//
40–50	45	////

When a score such as 60 falls between two intervals, it is placed in the upper interval. He then made a dot-frequency graph of the test results. He used the interval midpoint as the score for all the students whose scores fell in that interval.

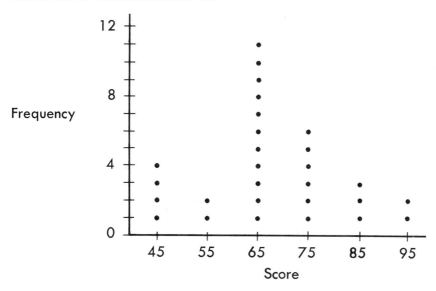

Such a graph gives a clear picture of the work of the class on this test. Notice that, when the column of tally marks in the frequency table is turned sideways and reversed, it looks about the same as the graph.

Some oranges are picked from a tree, and the diameters are measured to the nearest $\frac{1}{4}$ inch. A frequency table for the measurements is shown on the following page.

Interval Boundaries	Interval Midpoints	Frequency
$3\frac{1}{8} - 3\frac{3}{8}$	$3\frac{1}{4}$	III
$2\frac{7}{8} - 3\frac{1}{8}$	3	ℍℍ
$2\frac{5}{8} - 2\frac{7}{8}$	$2\frac{3}{4}$	ℍℍ ℍℍ ℍℍ ℍℍ II
$2\frac{3}{8} - 2\frac{5}{8}$	$2\frac{1}{2}$	ℍℍ ℍℍ ℍℍ I
$2\frac{1}{8} - 2\frac{3}{8}$	$2\frac{1}{4}$	III
$1\frac{7}{8} - 2\frac{1}{8}$	2	II
$1\frac{5}{8} - 1\frac{7}{8}$	$1\frac{3}{4}$	II

■ **P-5** How many oranges have diameters of $3\frac{1}{4}$ inches?

■ **P-6** How many oranges have diameters of $1\frac{3}{4}$ inches?

■ **P-7** What is the mode of these measurements?

■ **P-8** What is the median diameter?

ORAL EXERCISES 13.8

A class takes a test in algebra, and the teacher makes a dot-frequency graph showing the results.

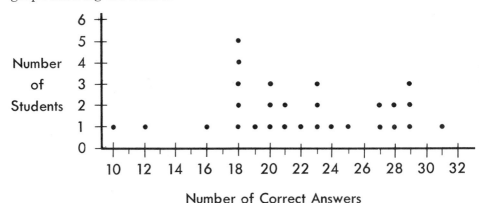

Number of Correct Answers

1. How many students got 10 correct answers?
2. How many students got 31 correct answers?
3. How many students got 17 correct answers?
4. What is the median score?
5. What is the mode?
6. What is the range of scores?

The coach measures the height of players on his team to the nearest inch and records the results in a frequency table.

Interval Boundaries	Interval Midpoints	Frequency	Interval Boundaries	Interval Midpoints	Frequency
76.5–77.5	77	I	69.5–70.5	70	ʜʜ
75.5–76.5	76	II	68.5–69.5	69	IIII
74.5–75.5	75	I	67.5–68.5	68	III
73.5–74.5	74	III	66.5–67.5	67	II
72.5–73.5	73	III	65.5–66.5	66	I
71.5–72.5	72	II	64.5–65.5	65	I
70.5–71.5	71	IIII			

7. How many players are at least 6 feet tall?
8. What is the median height?
9. What is the mode?
10. What is the range of heights?
11. How many players are 6 feet 5 inches tall?
12. How many players are 5 feet 9 inches tall?
13. Is the tallest player exactly 77 inches tall?
14. What is the frequency of players who are under 6 feet in height?

WRITTEN EXERCISES 13.8

A 1. Toss four coins 64 times and record the number of times each possible number of heads appears. Make a dot-frequency graph showing the results.

2. Toss five coins 64 times and record the number of times each possible number of tails appears. Make a dot-frequency graph showing the results.

3. Find the mean for the algebra test scores shown in the frequency table on page 429 of Section 13.8. Use the interval midpoints as scores.

4. Find the mean for the algebra test scores shown by the dot-frequency graph in Oral Exercises 13.8.

5. Find the mean heights of the players shown by the frequency table in Oral Exercises 13.8.

6. Find the mean diameter of the oranges for the measurements shown by the frequency table on page 430 of Section 13.8.

CHAPTER SUMMARY

Important Terms

1. Probability of an event A is
$$P(A) = \frac{\text{number of favorable outcomes}}{\text{number of possible outcomes}}.$$

2. A **sample space** of an experiment is a set of elements such that any trial of the experiment gives exactly one of its elements.

3. In an **ordered pair** of numbers, the order of the numbers is important. Thus, $(1, 5)$ and $(5, 1)$ are different ordered pairs.

4. An **event** in a probability experiment is a subset of its sample space.

5. The **complement** of an event is the set of elements in the sample space that are not elements of that event.

6. The **union** of two sets is the set of elements belonging to at least one of the sets.

7. The **intersection** of two sets is the set of elements that belong to both the sets.

8. Two events A and B are **independent** if
$$P(A \cap B) = P(A) \cdot P(B).$$

9. The **arithmetic mean** of n measurements is
$$\frac{\text{sum of the measurements}}{n}.$$

10. The **median** of a sample of measurements is the middle number when the measurements are arranged in order of size.

11. The **mode** of a sample of measurements is the measurement appearing most often.

12. The **range** of a sample of measurements is the difference between the greatest and least measurements in the sample.

13. The **frequency** of an event is the number of times it happens.

Important Ideas

1. The sum of the probability of an event and the probability of its complement is 1; that is,
$$P(A) + P(A') = 1.$$

2. The greatest value any probability can have is 1.

3. The least value any probability can have is 0.

4. For independent events A and B, it is true that
$$P(A \cap B) = P(A) \cdot P(B).$$

CHAPTER REVIEW

A regular tetrahedron can be used like an ordinary die. Suppose a numeral is written on each of its faces as shown. If a tetrahedron is thrown, show each of the following probabilities.

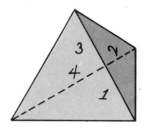

1. That it lands on face 4
2. That it does not land on face 1
3. That it lands on face 6
4. That it does not land on face 10

Suppose a white tetrahedron and a red tetrahedron are thrown.

		Red (r)			
		1	2	3	4
	1	(?, ?)	(?, ?)	(?, ?)	(?, ?)
White	2	(?, ?)	(?, ?)	(?, ?)	(?, ?)
(w)	3	(?, ?)	(?, ?)	(?, ?)	(?, ?)
	4	(?, ?)	(?, ?)	(?, ?)	(?, ?)

Complete the above table for the sample space of this two-tetrahedron experiment, and find each of the following probabilities if

$$A = \{w \leq 3\}, \quad B = \{r = 5\}, \quad C = \{w \neq 3\}, \quad D = \{r = w\}.$$

5. $P(A)$
6. $P(B)$
7. $P(C)$
8. $P(D)$
9. $P(A')$
10. $P(B')$
11. $P(C')$
12. $P(D')$
13. $P(A \text{ or } B)$
14. $P(B \text{ or } C)$
15. $P(A \text{ and } C)$
16. $P(C \text{ and } D)$
17. $P(A \cup C)$
18. $P(C \cup D)$
19. $P(A \cap B)$
20. $P(B \cap D)$

Indicate by *Yes* or *No* whether each of the following pairs of events from the two-tetrahedron experiment is independent.

21. $A; B$
22. $A; C$
23. $A; D$
24. $B; C$
25. $B; D$
26. $C; D$

For each of the following problems, consider the experiment of making three tosses of a single coin in succession.

27. What is the probability of getting (H_1, H_2, T_3)?
28. What is the probability of getting (H_1, T_2, H_3)?
29. How many outcomes are possible that show exactly two heads?
30. How many outcomes involve at least two heads?
31. What is the probability of getting exactly two heads in the three tosses?
32. What is the probability of getting at least two heads in the three tosses?

A "random walk" experiment can be performed by one person as follows. A move of one unit is made on the number line after each spin of the pointer. Starting at 0, a move of one unit to the right is made each time the spinner stops at an odd number. A move of one unit to the left is made each time the spinner stops at an even number. The "walk" ends when either point A or point B is reached. A new "walk" starts again at 0.

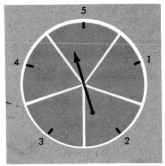

33. What is the probability that the first move of the experiment is to the right?
34. What is the probability that the first move is to the left?
35. What is the probability that the first two moves are to the right?
36. What is the probability that the first two moves are to the left?
37. What is the probability that the first move is to the right and the second is to the left?
38. What is the probability that the "walk" ends after exactly three moves?
39. What is the probability that the "walk" ends after exactly four moves?
40. Will more "walks" likely end at A or at B?

In its first ten games, a basketball team scores the following point totals per game.

$$65, \quad 72, \quad 88, \quad 61, \quad 75, \quad 92, \quad 51, \quad 73, \quad 81, \quad 77$$

Find each of the following.

41. The mean score
42. The median score
43. The range of scores

Suppose a player tosses two dice 36 times and records the sum of the dots on each toss.

44. Make a frequency table showing the expected frequencies for each sum.
45. Make a dot-frequency graph for the expected frequencies.
46. Toss two dice 36 times and make a dot-frequency graph showing the results of the sums of the dots on each toss.

CUMULATIVE REVIEW (CHAPTERS 1–12)

Indicate whether each of the following is *True* or *False* for the sets
$A = \{1, 2, 3, \cdots, 15\}$, $B = \{10, 11, 12, \cdots\}$, $C = \{13, 14, 15\}$, $D = \phi$.

1. C is a subset of A. **2.** A is a subset of B. **3.** D is a subset of B.
4. C is finite. **5.** A is infinite. **6.** B is infinite.
7. D is infinite. **8.** $A \cap B = C$ **9.** $C \cap B = C$
10. $A \cup C = A$ **11.** $B \cup C = C$ **12.** $A \cup \phi = A$
13. $B \cap A = \{10, 11, 12, 13, 14, 15\}$ **14.** $A \cup B = \{$whole numbers$\}$
15. $A \cap \{$whole numbers$\} = A$

Find the value of each of the following phrases when the variable is replaced by 5.

16. $\dfrac{2n + n^2}{5}$ **17.** $\dfrac{2x^2 - 8}{7}$ **18.** $\dfrac{3(x - 3)}{15 - 2x}$

19. $\dfrac{2x^2 - 3x + 2}{3x^2 - 9x - 10}$ **20.** $\dfrac{(x - 3)(2x + 1)}{(x - 2)}$

Find the truth sets of the following compound sentences, using the domain $\{$whole numbers$\}$. Graph the truth set of each.

21. $x \leq 10$ and $x > 5$ **22.** $y < 5\frac{1}{2}$ and $y < 4$
23. $a \geq 2\frac{1}{2}$ or $a > 7$ **24.** $w < 3.6$ or $w = 10$

Indicate by the appropriate letter the number property that is illustrated by each example. The variables a, b, and c represent any real numbers.

A. Addition Property of Zero

B. Multiplication Property of One

C. Closure Property of Addition

D. Closure Property of Multiplication

E. Commutative Property of Addition

F. Commutative Property of Multiplication

G. Associative Property of Addition

H. Associative Property of Multiplication

I. Distributive Property

25. $a + \frac{1}{2} = \frac{1}{2} + a$ **26.** $(2a)b = 2(ab)$
27. $(b + 5)2 = b \cdot 2 + 5 \cdot 2$ **28.** $c + 0 = c$
29. $a(b + c) = a(c + b)$ **30.** $\frac{2}{3}(\frac{5}{5}) = \frac{2}{3}$
31. $(a + b)$ is a real number. **32.** $a(2b) = (2b)a$
33. $(a + b)(a + b) = (a + b)a + (a + b)b$ **34.** $(a)(\pi)$ is a real number.
35. $(2a + b) + 3c = 2a + (b + 3c)$ **36.** $a(bc) = (bc)a$

Write the prime factors of each number using exponents.

37. 360   **38.** 1050   **39.** 396   **40.** 2925

Find the least common multiple of each of the following sets.

41. {4, 6, 15}   **42.** {10, 15, 28}

43. {5, 7, 11}   **44.** {3, 10, 7, 50}

Find the truth set of each of the following open sentences in proportion form.

45. $\dfrac{x}{3} = \dfrac{12}{8}$ **46.** $\dfrac{5}{y} = \dfrac{8}{7}$ **47.** $\dfrac{1}{16} = \dfrac{a}{100}$ **48.** $\dfrac{5}{21} = \dfrac{8}{w}$

49. A basketball team makes about 63% of its shots in a game. How many shots does the team make out of 70 attempts?

50. A sports car that is listed for $4800 sells at a price of $4200. What is the discount expressed as a per cent?

Give the greatest possible error in each of the following measurements.

51. $5\frac{3}{4}$ inches   **52.** 6.32 centimeters

53. 8150 miles   **54.** 13.00 millimeters

For each pair of measurements tell which measurement is more precise and which is more accurate.

55. 5.3 cm; 0.008 cm   **56.** 28,000 mi; 152 mi

57. 25.61 ft; 12.3 ft   **58.** $3\frac{1}{4}$ in; $5\frac{1}{8}$ in

Complete each correspondence.

59. $3\frac{1}{2}$ ft ↔ ? in   **60.** 14 cm ↔ ? mm

61. 51 in ↔ ? yd   **62.** 13.3 cm ↔ ? m

For each of the following, choose a variable to represent the unknown in the problem. Write an open sentence and find its truth set in order to solve the problem.

63. Jane has 3 more records than Mary Ann. Altogether they have 25 records. How many does Mary Ann have?

64. The length of a rectangle is twice the width. If the perimeter is 42 units, what is the width?

65. Bruce raises guinea pigs, and he has 68 in all. If there are three times as many black ones as white ones, how many black guinea pigs does he have?

66. If three times a number is increased by 5, the result is 1. What is the number?

Indicate whether each of the following statements is *True* or *False*.

67. If x is a negative number, then $|x| = x$.

68. If x is a positive number, then $|x| = x$.

69. If x is zero, then $|x| = x$.

70. If x is a negative number, then $-x$ is a positive number.

71. 15 is a rational number.

72. Zero is a real number.

Give the common name for each of the following.

73. $\frac{2}{3} + \left(-\frac{4}{3} + \frac{2}{6}\right)$

74. $-8 + (-5) + (-10)$

75. $x + 5 + \left(-3\frac{1}{8}\right)$

76. $\frac{1}{3} + (-7) + 15$

77. $(-3)(-5)(-2)$

78. $\frac{1}{2}(-5)(8)$

79. $(-1)^3(-2)^4$

80. $5^2(-3)^3$

81. $4a - 7a$

82. $-2x^2 - 3x^2 + 7x^2$

83. $2bc + 3ac - \frac{3}{4}bc$

84. $-5\frac{1}{4}x^2 + \frac{1}{2}x + 2 - \frac{3}{4}x^2$

Write each product as a sum in simplest form.

85. $(p + q)(p + q)$

86. $(m - n)^2$

87. $(2a - 1)(3a + 1)$

88. $(5x - 2)(2x - 5)$

Find the truth set of each sentence.

89. $x + 5 = 2x - 3$

90. $3x - 5 - 5x = 0$

91. $5x - 7 = x - 6 + x$

92. $\frac{2}{3}y + 7 + \frac{5}{3}y = -3$

Find the common name for each of the following. Assume that no divisor is 0.

93. $\dfrac{6x^2}{15ax^3}$

94. $\dfrac{2x^2 + 2x}{3x + 3}$

95. $\dfrac{2a - 1}{1 - 2a}$

96. $\frac{2}{3}x + \frac{5}{2}x$

97. $\dfrac{2}{a - 2} - \dfrac{5}{a - 2}$

98. $\dfrac{1}{x - 1} - \dfrac{1}{1 - x}$

99. $\dfrac{-5y}{12} - \dfrac{3y}{30}$

100. $\dfrac{\dfrac{-5x}{24}}{\dfrac{2x}{30}}$

Summary of
Important Terms and Ideas

Absolute Value

The **absolute value** of a real number, except 0, is the greater of that number and its opposite. The absolute value of 0 is 0.

The absolute value of a real number can never be negative.

The absolute value of a nonzero number is the same as the distance on the number line between that number and zero.

Averages

The **arithmetic mean** of several measurements is found first by the addition of the measurements and then by the division of this sum by the number of measurements in the sample.

The **median** of several measurements is found by the arrangement of the measurements in either increasing or decreasing order; the measurement appearing in the middle of the ordered arrangement is the median. When there is an even number of measurements to consider, the mean of the two middle numbers is usually taken as the median.

The **mode** is the number appearing most often in a collection of measurements.

The **range** of a sample of measurements is the difference between the greatest and the least measurements in the sample.

Binomials

A **binomial** is a phrase that indicates the sum of two numbers.

Each of the two numerals that make up a binomial is called a **term.**

Like terms are made up of exactly the same variable or variables and the same powers of these variables.

The **square of a binomial** is equal to the square of the first term plus twice the product of the two terms plus the square of the second term.

Business Mathematics

The **discount** is the amount that an article of merchandise is reduced in price.

The regular price of an article is called the **list price.**

The price of an article after the discount is deducted is called the **net price.**

Net price = List price − Discount

Interest is a certain per cent of the amount loaned. The amount of money loaned is called the **principal.**

The per cent that is used in an interest problem is called the **rate.**

The interest earned for one year is the product of the rate and the principal.

Divisibility, Factors, and Factorization

If a, b, and c represent integers and $c = a \cdot b$ is true, then c is said to be **divisible** by a and b; c is also a **multiple** of a and b; and a and b are **factors** of c.

An integer is divisible by 2 if the last digit in its common name names an even number; otherwise, it is not divisible by 2.

If the sum of the numbers named by the digits of a given number is divisible by 3, then the given number is divisible by 3; otherwise, it is not divisible by 3.

If the last digit in a numeral is 0 or 5, then the number named by the numeral is divisible by 5; otherwise, it is not divisible by 5.

If the number named by the last two digits of a given number is divisible by 4, then so is the given number; otherwise, it is not divisible by 4.

Numbers that form a product are called **factors**; that is, if a, b, and c represent real numbers and $c = a \cdot b$ is true, then a and b are said to be factors of c.

Any counting number is always divisible by any one of its counting-number factors.

The **proper factors** of a counting number are all of its counting-number factors except 1 and the number itself.

A **prime number** is a counting number greater than 1 that does not have any proper factors.

Counting numbers that are not prime are called **composite numbers.**

In a phrase such as 2^3, 2 is called the **base.** A counting number such as 3 used as an **exponent** shows how many times the base is to be used as a **factor.**

Factorization is the process of factoring.

There is only one selection of factors possible in any **prime factorization.**

Each prime number can be tested as a possible factor of a given number starting with the least prime, 2. Each prime may turn up as a factor more than once. The prime factorization is finished when the last quotient is a prime.

One counting number is divisible by a second counting number if each factor in the prime factorization of the first counting number appears at least as many times as it does in the prime factorization of the second counting number.

The set of counting-number multiples of a number is the set obtained by the multiplication of each counting number by the given number.

The **least common multiple** of two or more counting numbers is the least number in the set of their common counting-number multiples.

To find the least common multiple, express each prime factor the greatest number of times that it appears as a factor of any one of the given numbers.

Measurement

Measurement shows a comparison of the size of an object to a unit of measure.

Every measurement is an approximation.

The **greatest possible error** in a measurement is one half the smallest unit used.

The **precision** of a measurement is given by the least unit used in the measurement. The more precise of two measurements is the one using the smaller unit.

The **relative error** of a measurement is the ratio of the greatest possible error to the measurement itself.

The **accuracy** of a measurement depends upon its relative error. The more accurate of two measurements is the one with the smaller relative error.

The **area** of a plane figure is a number that shows a comparison of the size of the region enclosed by a figure to a unit of measure. The unit that is used is a square region such that each side has one of the standard units for its length.

The **volume** of a solid figure or object is a number that shows a comparison of the size of the space enclosed by the figure with a unit of measure. The unit that is used is a cube with each edge having a standard unit for its length.

Multiplicative Inverse

If the product of two real numbers is 1, they are said to be **multiplicative inverses** of each other.

Every real number except 0 has exactly one multiplicative inverse.

The truth number of the sentence $ax = b$ where a and b represent any real numbers, $a \neq 0$, is the product of b and the multiplicative inverse of a.

Number Line

The number associated with a point on the number line is called the **coordinate** of the point.

The sentence $a > b$ means that, on the number line, the point with coordinate a is to the right of the point with coordinate b.

There is a **one-to-one correspondence** between points of the number line and the real numbers.

The set of points on a number line associated with the elements of a particular set is the **graph** of that set.

The distance between two points is the absolute value of the difference of their coordinates on the number line.

Numerals

Symbols that are used for names of numbers are called **numerals.**

A **numerical phrase** is itself a numeral, and it involves other numerals and one or more signs of operation.

Fractions are numerals that serve as names both for rational numbers and for indicated quotients.

The **common name** of a number is, in general, its simplest name.

The **common name** for a rational number is the fraction whose numerator and denominator do not have a common prime factor.

Operations

Operations on Numbers Named by Fractions
The sum of two real numbers named by fractions that show a common denominator is the sum of the numerators divided by the common denominator; that is, if a, b, and c are real numbers with $b \neq 0$, then

$$\frac{a}{b} + \frac{c}{b} = \frac{a + c}{b}.$$

The difference of two real numbers named by fractions that show a common denominator is the difference of the numerators divided by the common denominator; that is, if a, b, and c are real numbers with $b \neq 0$, then

$$\frac{a}{b} - \frac{c}{b} = \frac{a - c}{b}.$$

The product of two real numbers named by fractions is the number named by a fraction whose numerator is the product of the numerators and whose denominator is the product of the denominators of the two fractions. That is, if a, b, c, and d are real numbers with $b \neq 0$ and $d \neq 0$, then

$$\frac{a}{b} \cdot \frac{c}{d} = \frac{ac}{bd}.$$

The quotient of two real numbers named by fractions is the dividend multiplied by the reciprocal of the divisor. That is, if a, b, c, and d are real numbers with $b \neq 0$, $d \neq 0$, and $c \neq 0$, then

$$\frac{a}{b} \div \frac{c}{d} = \frac{a}{b} \cdot \frac{d}{c}.$$

Addition of Real Numbers

The sum of two positive real numbers is the same as their sum as numbers of arithmetic.

The sum of two negative real numbers is the opposite of the sum of their absolute values.

The sum of a positive real number and a negative real number is
  (a) the difference between their absolute values if the positive real number has the greater absolute value or if the absolute values are equal,
  (b) the opposite of the difference between their absolute values if the negative real number has the greater absolute value.

The sum of any real number and 0 is that real number.

Subtraction of Real Numbers

If a and b are any real numbers, then it is true that
$$a - b = a + (-b);$$
that is, to subtract b from a, add the opposite of b to a.

Multiplication of Real Numbers

The product of two positive real numbers is the same as their product as numbers of arithmetic.

The product of a positive real number and a negative real number is the opposite of the product of their absolute values.

The product of two negative real numbers is the product of their absolute values.

The product of 0 and any real number is 0.

When a real number is multiplied by itself, the product is called the **square** of that number.

Division of Real Numbers

For any real numbers a and b, $b \neq 0$, it is true that
$$\frac{a}{b} = a \cdot \frac{1}{b};$$
that is, to divide a by b, multiply a by the multiplicative inverse of b.

If a is any real number, $\frac{a}{0}$ does not represent a number.

Opposites

If a is any real number, then it is true that

$$-(-a) = a.$$

The opposite of the sum of two real numbers equals the sum of their opposites; that is, if a and b are any real numbers, then it is true that

$$-(a + b) = (-a) + (-b).$$

For any real numbers a and b, if $a < b$ is true, then $-a > -b$ is true. This is called the **Order Property of Opposites.**

Order of Operations

In finding a common name for a numerical phrase, perform the operations from left to right except when the operations of multiplication or division and addition or subtraction occur together; in this case, mathematicians agree to multiply or divide before adding or subtracting.

In finding a common name for a phrase that involves an indicated square of a number, square first and then multiply, divide, add, and subtract, unless parentheses indicate a different order of operations.

Order of Real Numbers

If a is a real number and b is a real number, then exactly one of the following is true:

$$a > b; \qquad a = b; \qquad a < b.$$

Probability

A real number that represents **probability** can be found by the ratio

$$\frac{\text{number of favorable outcomes}}{\text{number of possible outcomes}}.$$

A **sample space** is a set of elements such that any trial of an experiment gives exactly one of its elements.

An **event** in probability is a subset of the sample space. Thus, an event may have no elements or it may consist of one or more elements of the sample space.

The **complement** of an event is the set of elements of the sample space that are not elements of that event.

The number of times a certain event happens is often called the **frequency** of that event.

Properties of Real Numbers

Closure Properties
Closure Property of Addition: For any real numbers a and b, it is true that

$$a + b \text{ is a real number.}$$

(That the set of real numbers is closed under the operation of addition means that the sum of any two real numbers is a real number.)

Closure Property of Multiplication: For any real numbers a and b, it is true that

$$a \cdot b \text{ is a real number.}$$

(That the set of real numbers is closed under the operation of multiplication means that the product of any two real numbers is a real number.)

Identity Properties
Addition Property of Zero: For any real number a, it is true that

$$a + 0 = a.$$

Multiplication Property of One: For any real number a, it is true that

$$a \cdot 1 = a.$$

Inverse Properties
Addition Properties of Opposites: For any real number a, it is true that

$$a + (-a) = 0.$$

Multiplicative Inverse: For any real number a, $a \neq 0$, it is true that

$$a \cdot \frac{1}{a} = 1.$$

Commutative Properties
Commutative Property of Addition: For any real numbers a and b, it is true that

$$a + b = b + a.$$

Commutative Property of Multiplication: For any real numbers a and b, it is true that

$$a \cdot b = b \cdot a.$$

Associative Properties

Associative Property of Addition: For any real numbers a, b, and c, it is true that
$$(a + b) + c = a + (b + c).$$

Associative Property of Multiplication: For any real numbers a, b, and c, it is true that
$$(a \cdot b) \cdot c = a \cdot (b \cdot c).$$

Distributive Property

of Multiplication over Addition: For any real numbers a, b, and c, it is true that
$$a(b + c) = ab + ac \quad \text{and} \quad (b + c)a = ba + ca.$$

of Multiplication over Subtraction: For any real numbers a, b, and c, it is true that
$$a(b - c) = ab - ac \quad \text{and} \quad (b - c)a = ba - ca.$$

Ratio, Proportion, and Per Cent

A quotient of two numbers is called a ratio if it is considered to be a comparison of the two numbers.

The ratio $\dfrac{a}{b}$ can also be shown as $a : b$.

The terms of a ratio are the two numbers that are compared.

A proportion is a true statement of equality of two ratios.

When $\dfrac{a}{b} = \dfrac{c}{d}$ is referred to as a proportion, a, b, c, and d are to be replaced by real numbers that will make the sentence true. Of course, $b \neq 0$ and $d \neq 0$.

If the variables in $\dfrac{a}{b} = \dfrac{c}{d}$ are replaced by numbers that make it a proportion, then it is true that
$$a \cdot d = b \cdot c.$$

If $\dfrac{a}{b} = \dfrac{c}{d}$ is a proportion, then it is true that
$$\frac{a}{c} = \frac{b}{d}, \qquad \frac{b}{a} = \frac{d}{c}, \qquad \frac{c}{a} = \frac{d}{b}.$$

Per cent, which means "per hundred," expresses a ratio in which the second term is 100.

A per cent that names the same number as a decimal can always be found. First, the fraction that names the same number as the decimal is found; then the form of the fraction is changed so that it shows a denominator of 100. The numerator of this fraction is used in the expression of the per cent.

Reciprocals

Two numbers of arithmetic whose product is 1 are said to be reciprocals of each other.

Every real number except zero has a reciprocal.

If a real number has a reciprocal, then it has only one reciprocal.

The truth number of an open sentence of the form $ax = b$, where a and b are real numbers but $a \neq 0$, is b multiplied by the reciprocal of a.

Sentences and Phrases

Two phrases are **equivalent** if they have the same value when the variables are replaced by the same numbers from the domain.

An **open sentence** is a sentence containing a variable that becomes true or false when the variable is replaced by an element from its domain.

Sentences that have = to represent the verb are usually called **equalities,** or **equations.**

Equivalent open sentences are sentences that have the same truth set.

If any real number is added to both sides of an open equation, then the new equation is equivalent to the first.

If both sides of an open equation are multiplied by the same nonzero real number, then the new equation is equivalent to the first.

A **compound sentence** with connective *and* is true only when both clauses are true.

A **compound sentence** with connective *or* is true if the left clause is true, or if the right clause is true, or if both clauses are true.

A **formula** is an open sentence that usually describes a commonly used rule.

Sets

The objects that make up a set are called its **elements.**

A set that has no elements is called the **empty** set, or the **null** set.

Two sets are said to be **equal** if they contain the same elements.

Two sets are said to be **equivalent** if they contain the same number of elements.

If two sets are equivalent, the elements of one set can be put in **one-to-one correspondence** with the elements of the other.

A set is said to be **finite** provided that either it is empty or its elements can be counted and the counting comes to an end. If a set is not finite, it is said to be **infinite.**

When every element of set A is also an element of set B, then A is a **subset** of B.

The empty set is a subset of every set.

Every set is a subset of itself.

The **truth set** of an open sentence is the subset of the domain whose members make the sentence true when they replace the variable in the sentence.

Sets of Numbers

The set of **counting numbers** is the set $\{1, 2, 3, \cdots\}$.

The set of **whole numbers** is the set $\{0, 1, 2, 3, \cdots\}$.

The set of **positive integers** is the set $\{1, 2, 3, \cdots\}$. (Note that the set of positive integers is the same as the set of counting numbers.)

The set of **negative integers** is the set $\{\cdots, {}^-3, {}^-2, {}^-1\}$.

The set of **integers** is the set that is made up of the negative integers, zero, and the positive integers; that is, it is the set

$$\{\cdots, {}^-3, {}^-2, {}^-1, 0, 1, 2, 3, \cdots\}.$$

The set of **positive rational numbers** is the set of numbers each of which can be represented by the quotient $\frac{a}{b}$ where a and b are counting numbers.

The set of **negative rational numbers** is the set of numbers each of which can be represented by the quotient $-\frac{a}{b}$ where a and b are counting numbers.

The set of **rational numbers** is the set that is made up of the negative rational numbers, zero, and the positive rational numbers. (Note that each rational number can be expressed as a repeating decimal.)

The set of **irrational numbers** is the set of numbers each of which can be expressed as nonending and nonrepeating decimals.

The set of **numbers of arithmetic** is the set consisting of 0 and the coordinate points to the right of 0 on the number line.

The set of **real numbers** is the set that is made up of all the rational numbers and all the irrational numbers. The set of real numbers consists of all the coordinate points on the number line.

Symbols for Verbs

When a word sentence is translated into an open sentence, a symbol for the verb must be used. Some of the symbols that represent verbs are $=$, $\neq$, $>$, $<$, $\leq$, and $\geq$.

The symbol for equality, $=$, indicates that the symbols on each side of it name the same thing.

The symbol $\neq$ (read "is not equal to") indicates that the symbols on each side of it name two different things.

The symbol $>$ is read "is greater than," and the symbol $<$ is read "is less than."

The symbol $\geq$ is read "is greater than or equal to," and the symbol $\leq$ is read "is less than or equal to."

Variables

A **variable** is a symbol that may be replaced by any element of a specified set.

A set from which the replacement of a variable may be chosen is called the **domain** of the variable.

Any number that will make an open sentence true when it replaces the variable is called a **truth number.**

Answers to Pivotal Questions

CHAPTER 1

Section 1.1 (page 1)
P-1 Set. P-2 The first three Presidents of the United States.
P-3 Answers will vary.

Section 1.2 (page 4)
P-1 Yes. P-2 No. P-3 Yes; yes.
P-4 No; there are elements in G that are not in H.
P-5 No; there are elements in B that are not in A.
P-6 Yes; {1, 4, 5}, {4, 5} are examples.
P-7 The set of letters in the alphabet.
P-8 A is a subset of B. No; there are no elements in A that are not in B.
P-9 No; there are no elements in R that are not in S.

Section 1.3 (page 8)
P-1 Finite; finite; finite; infinite; infinite.
P-2 {teachers in your school} P-3 Yes. P-4 Yes.
P-5 The set of multiples of 3 that are greater than or equal to 12.
P-6 30, 35, 40 P-7 40, 50, 60, 70, 80 P-8 {1, 3, 5, $\cdots$, 999}
P-9 The set of even numbers from 2 to 100.

Section 1.4 (page 12)
P-1 A = C; B = E P-2 Yes. P-3 Yes; no. P-4 No.
P-5 Answers will vary. P-6 16; 101; 1,000,001
P-7 The set of whole number multiples of 3.
P-8 By adding 1 to every even number.

Section 1.5 (page 16)
P-1 No. P-2 $\frac{1}{2}$ P-3 $2\frac{1}{2}$ P-4 $\{0, \frac{7}{4}, \frac{33}{8}, 5\}$

Section 1.6 (page 20)
P-1 Yes; $5 = \frac{5}{1}$, etc.; $3\frac{1}{8} = \frac{25}{8}$, etc.; $2.56 = \frac{256}{100}$, etc.
P-2 No. P-3 Yes. P-4 Yes; yes. P-5 $\frac{11}{16}$
P-6 $3\frac{6}{16}$; $\frac{5}{8}$; 2.61
P-7 Take their average (i.e., add them and divide by 2).

Section 1.7 (page 23)
P-1 When you divide the symbol 8 in half (lengthwise) you get 3, another symbol.
P-2 8; 10; 0; 0; 15; $\frac{1}{2}$; $\frac{3}{4}$; $\frac{1}{4}$; $\frac{1}{2}$ P-3 Both are common names.

Section 1.8 (page 26)

P-1 10; 14; 3; 1

P-2 9; $20 - 3 \times 5 + 8 \div 2 = 20 - 15 + 4 = 9$; the multiplication and division are done first.

P-3 4; perform addition and subtraction from left to right.

P-4 8; 10

Section 1.9 (page 28)

P-1 24; 10   P-2 25; 6   P-3 3; $22\frac{1}{4}$ P-4 $\dfrac{2 + 3 \times 4}{5 \times 8} = \dfrac{14}{40}$

Section 1.10 (page 31)

P-1 16   P-2 13

Section 1.11 (page 33)

P-1 Yes, it is true.

P-2 It is not a sentence; it is a numerical phrase.   P-3 $\neq$

P-4 True.   P-5 True; false; false; true; true.   P-6 $12 + 7 > 8 - 3$

CHAPTER 2

Section 2.1 (page 41)

P-1 40 in; 60 cm; 10 ft   P-2 4(5)   P-3 $4x$; $x + x + x + x$

P-4 12   P-5 24.8   P-6 $\{2, 2\frac{1}{2}, 5\}$ P-7 $\{6, 7, 15\}$

Section 2.2 (page 44)

P-1 $x + 3$; $2(3) - t$; $5 \cdot y$ P-2 $15n + 2$

P-3 $3x + 10$ P-4 Answers will vary.

Section 2.3 (page 47)

P-1 11   P-2 11

P-3 Subtract 4 from any number of the sequence to find the next number.

P-4 23   P-5 23   P-6 $t - 2$

Section 2.4 (page 50)

P-1 It is an open sentence.   P-2 False.   P-3 True.   P-4 True.

P-5 $x = 2$ P-6 1, 5, 7, for example.   P-7 $x = 6$ P-8 $x = 6$

Section 2.5 (page 53)

P-1 $\{\frac{1}{2}\}$ P-2 $\{0\}$ P-3 No.   P-4 ϕ or $\{ \ \}$ P-5 $\{4\}$; $\{0, 1, 2\}$; $\{4, 5\}$

P-6 Because 0 also makes the sentence true, and the truth set must list all truth numbers.

P-7 Because 3 does not make the sentence true and the truth set contains no elements that make the sentence false.

P-8 {numbers of arithmetic less than 3}

P-9 {numbers of arithmetic}   P-10 No; the truth set is infinite.

Section 2.6 (page 56)

P-1 36; 100; 144; $\frac{1}{4}$; $\frac{9}{16}$ P-2 16; 49; 64; 25; 13

P-3 $\{9, 16, 25\}$ P-4 $x = 6$ P-5 50   P-6 100   P-7 21; 4

Section 2.7 (page 58)

P-1 {numbers of arithmetic greater than or equal to 10} P-2 Yes.

P-3 No. P-4 {whole numbers less than or equal to 5}

P-5 {whole numbers greater than or equal to 5}

P-6 That of P-4 is finite; that of P-5 is infinite.

P-7 y is not less than 6.

Section 2.8 (page 60)

P-1 {1, 4, 6} P-2 Yes; yes; yes.

P-3 $x < 5$ P-4 $x \leq 2$ P-5 {numbers of arithmetic}

Section 2.9 (page 65)

P-1 False. P-2 True.

P-3 {all whole numbers greater than or equal to 3}

P-4 {all whole numbers less than 7}

P-5 {all whole numbers greater than or equal to 3 and less than 7}

P-6 {0, 1, 2, 3} P-7 {1, 2, 3, · · ·}

P-8 {1, 2, 3} P-9 {1, 2, 3}

Section 2.10 (page 68)

P-1 Because 2 is not in the truth set of $x > 2$.

P-2 Because $3\frac{1}{2}$ is in the truth set of both $x > 2$ and $x < 5$.

P-3 None. P-4 {3, 4}

P-5

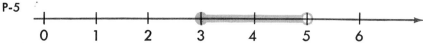

Section 2.11 (page 72)

P-1 True. P-2 False.

P-3 True, because one of the two clauses is true. P-4 False.

P-5 True. P-6 $x = 7$ P-7 {0, 1, 2, 3} P-8 {0, 1, 2, 3, 7}

P-9 {0, 1} P-10 {0, 1, 2, 3, 4, 5}

P-11 {0, 1, 2, 3, 4, 5} P-12 {0, 1, 2, 3, 4, 5}

Section 2.12 (page 75)

P-1 Because 1 is in the truth set of $x < 2$ and, therefore, in the truth set of the *or* sentence.

P-2 6 is in the truth set of $x \geq 5$.

P-3 4 is neither in the truth set of $x < 2$ nor in that of $x \geq 5$.

P-4 Yes, for it belongs to the union of the truth sets of the clauses.

P-5 Yes; no.

CHAPTER 3

Section 3.1 (page 83)

P-1 When added to any number, 0 does not change the number.

P-2 True; false; true. P-3 {0}; {$\frac{5}{6}$}

P-4 When any number is multiplied by 1, the number is not changed.

P-5 True; true; true; true. P-6 {15}; {1}

Section 3.2 (page 85)

P-1 9   P-2 $(3+1)+(5+4)$ is one way.   P-3 24   P-4 Yes.
P-5 No; $4+1=5$, for instance, and 5 is not in A.
P-6 No; $4 \cdot 2 = 8$, for instance, and 8 is not in A.   P-7 No.
P-8 Yes.   P-9 Yes.   P-10 No; $1+1=2$, and 2 is not in R.
P-11 Yes; $0 \cdot 0 = 0$, $1 \cdot 0 = 0 \cdot 1 = 0$, $1 \cdot 1 = 1$; thus, all of the products
   are in R.

Section 3.3 (page 89)

P-1 Move four and one-half units to the right of 0.   P-2 $7\frac{1}{2}$
P-3 Move three units to the right of 0.   P-4 $7\frac{1}{2}$ P-5 Yes.

Section 3.4 (page 92)

P-1 7 and 9; 16   P-2 16 and 4   P-3 20   P-4 9 and 4; 13
P-5 13 and 7   P-6 20   P-7 $\frac{1}{5} + (\frac{3}{4} + \frac{1}{4})$ P-8 $1\frac{1}{5}$

Section 3.5 (page 96)

P-1 $4+4+4$ P-2 $3+3+3+3$ P-3 $2 \cdot 5$ P-4 $5 \cdot 2$ P-5 Yes.

Section 3.6 (page 99)

P-1 10 and 5; 50   P-2 50 and 2   P-3 100   P-4 5 and 2; 10
P-5 10 and 10   P-6 100   P-7 $5(\frac{2}{3} \cdot 3)$ P-8 2   P-9 10   P-10 $21a$

Section 3.7 (page 103)

P-1 Multiply the number of rows by the number of columns; 72.
P-2 $6 \cdot 5 = 30$ P-3 Product.   P-4 Sum.   P-5 No.

Section 3.8 (page 106)

P-1 $(b+c)a$; $b \cdot a$; $c \cdot a$ P-2 $3 \cdot 8 + 5 \cdot 8$ P-3 Yes.
P-4 $4(10+13)$ P-5 $3(8+1)$ P-6 $3(x+5)$
P-7 $(10+13)3$ P-8 $(5+3)x$ P-9 $10y$ P-10 $7t$

Section 3.9 (page 109)

P-1 Commutative Property of Multiplication.
P-2 Associative Property of Multiplication.   P-3 $5a$; $5a$
P-4 $30xy$ P-5 $24abc$ P-6 $20n^2$ P-7 $6x + 2a$

Section 3.10 (page 112)

P-1 $5x$ P-2 a; 7   P-3 $a^2 + 5a$ P-4 $7a + 35$ P-5 $a^2 + 12a + 35$

CHAPTER 4

Section 4.1 (page 119)

P-1 No; the quotient is not a counting number.
P-2 Yes, $28 = 7 \cdot 4$.   P-3 Yes.   P-4 Yes.   P-5 Yes; 15
P-6 Yes; 30   P-7 $\{2, 7\}$ $\{3, 5\}$; $\{2, 3, 6, 9\}$ P-8 ϕ

Section 4.2 (page 122)

P-1 Yes.   P-2 No.   P-3 18   P-4 Yes.
P-5 Yes.   P-6 17; no.   P-7 No.   P-8 Yes.

P-9 No.   P-10 No; no.   P-11 Yes.   P-12 No.
P-13 If it is divisible by 10, then the last digit must be 0.

Section 4.3 (page 126)
P-1 No.   P-2 29   P-3 9 has a proper factor of 3.
P-4 25 and 35   P-5 49   P-6 No.

Section 4.4 (page 130)
P-1 Yes.   P-2 Yes; 36   P-3 2   P-4 3   P-5 Yes.   P-6 2

Section 4.5 (page 133)
P-1 $3 \cdot 3 \cdot 3 \cdot 3$ P-2 5   P-3 3   P-4 125
P-5 The third power of 5.   P-6 x; 6
P-7 $x \cdot x \cdot x \cdot x \cdot x \cdot x$ P-8 $2^2 \cdot 3^3 \cdot 5^2$
P-9 Ten cubed; thirty-five squared; five to the fourth power; two to the fifth power; x to the sixth power; y to the tenth power.
P-10 Two to the fourth power times three squared times five cubed times seven to the fifth power.
P-11 Yes.   P-12 No.

Section 4.6 (page 136)
P-1 $\dfrac{2 \cdot 2 \cdot 3}{2 \cdot 2 \cdot 3}$ P-2 1   P-3 $\frac{1}{5}$ P-4 Yes; no; no; yes.
P-5 $\frac{5}{5}$; $\frac{15}{20}$ P-6 $\frac{3}{3}$; 15   P-7 1; $\frac{5}{5}$; 35   P-8 $\frac{4}{4}$

Section 4.7 (page 141)
P-1 $\frac{15}{28}$ P-2 $\frac{6}{45} = \frac{2}{15}$ P-3 $\frac{20}{3}$ P-4 $\frac{7}{5}$; $\frac{1}{35}$ P-5 $\frac{1}{8}$; $\frac{1}{5}$

Section 4.8 (page 144)
P-1 $\{4, 8, 12, 16, \cdots\}$ P-2 12   P-3 36; 72; 108
P-4 36   P-5 $2 \cdot 2 \cdot 3 \cdot 5 = 60$ P-6 $2^2 \cdot 3 \cdot 5^2 \cdot 7 = 2100$

Section 4.9 (page 148)
P-1 $\frac{7}{24}$ P-2 3
P-3 Because both multiplications yield a fraction with denominator 24.
P-4 $2 \cdot 2 \cdot 3$ P-5 $2 \cdot 3 \cdot 7$
P-6 $2^2 \cdot 3 \cdot 7 = 84$ P-7 $\frac{7}{7}$ P-8 $\frac{2}{2}$

CHAPTER 5

Section 5.1 (page 155)
P-1 1   P-2 1   P-3 $\frac{7}{4}$; $\frac{4}{7}$ P-4 $\frac{1}{3}$; 3
P-5 Express the number as a fraction, and then interchange the numerator and the denominator.
P-6 0   P-7 ϕ P-8 Zero has no reciprocal.
P-9 $\frac{1}{7}$ P-10 No.   P-11 $\frac{4}{7}$; $\frac{10}{28}$ P-12 1

Section 5.2 (page 158)
P-1 $\frac{1}{3} \cdot 15$
P-2 3 is the reciprocal of $\frac{1}{3}$; 10 is the common name of the product.

P-3 $\{30\}$ P-4 $\dfrac{1}{a}$ (b) P-5 0   P-6 $\frac{3}{2}(10) = 15$ P-7 50   P-8 $\frac{1}{15}$

Section 5.3   (page 160)
P-1 The ratio of 3 to 10.   P-2 The ratio of a to b.
P-3 The ratio of 5 to 2.   P-4 $2 : 3$ P-5 $3 : 5$
P-6 $24 : 25$ P-7 $30 : 50$, or $3 : 5$ P-8 $14 : 3$

Section 5.4   (page 163)
P-1 Yes.   P-2 No.   P-3 45   P-4 45
P-5 $12 \cdot 6 \neq 13 \cdot 5$; thus, it is not a proportion.   P-6 No.
P-7 $\frac{3}{9} = \frac{4}{12}$ P-8 $\frac{8}{5} = \frac{16}{10}$ P-9 $\frac{1}{3} = \frac{4}{12}$ P-10 $\frac{3}{1} = \frac{12}{4}$

Section 5.5   (page 166)
P-1 $3x = 24$ P-2 $\frac{1}{3} \cdot 24$ P-3 $\{8\}$ P-4 $\dfrac{x}{96} = \dfrac{5}{12}$

Section 5.6   (page 170)
P-1 5%; 75%; 125%; 4% P-2 25%; 60%; 8%; 30% P-3 $x\%$
P-4 $\dfrac{1}{6} = \dfrac{x}{100}$, or $\dfrac{1}{6} = \dfrac{16\frac{2}{3}}{100}$ P-5 50%; 240%; 25%; 0.2%
P-6 Move the decimal point over two places to the right and then put the per cent sign at the end of the numeral.

Section 5.7   (page 173)
P-1 No.   P-2 Because per cent is wanted, and $x\%$ is $\dfrac{x}{100}$.
P-3 The number of passes completed is less than the number of passes thrown; hence, the ratio of passes completed to passes thrown, $\frac{21}{35}$,

is less than 1 and equal to the per cent of passes completed, $\dfrac{x}{100}$.

P-4 $\frac{1}{35} \cdot 2100$
P-5 The number of passes completed is less than the number of passes

thrown; hence, the ratio of passes completed to passes thrown, $\dfrac{12}{x}$, is

less than 1 and equal to the per cent of the passes completed, $\frac{75}{100}$.
P-6 $\frac{1}{75} \cdot 1200$

Section 5.8   (page 176)
P-1 $\left(\frac{12}{100}\right)75$ P-2 $0.12(3) = 0.36$

P-3 $0.15n$; $\left(\frac{15}{100}\right)n$ P-4 $\left(\dfrac{x}{100}\right)36$, or $0.01x(36)$

Section 5.9   (page 179)
P-1 Principal.   P-2 Interest.   P-3 $12   P-4 $(0.08)(200)$
P-5 $\left(\dfrac{5\frac{1}{2}}{100}\right)d$, or $0.055d$ P-6 $\left(\dfrac{r}{100}\right)75$, or $0.01r(75)$
P-7 $4   P-8 $8; $12   P-9 $2; $1
P-10 $\frac{6}{100}(x) \cdot 2$, or $0.06x(2)$ P-11 $\dfrac{x}{100}(250) \cdot \dfrac{1}{2}$, or $0.01x(250)\frac{1}{2}$

Section 5.10 (page 182)

P-1 Discount.   **P-2** $5; $3: $2   **P-3** $8.50

P-4 $42.50; $300; $400   **P-5** $\frac{p}{100}(25); \ 25 - \frac{p}{100}(25)$

Section 5.11 (page 185)

P-1 45   **P-2** 4; 96   **P-3** 30% solution.   **P-4** 10 pounds.

P-5 0.04y **P-6** $\frac{x}{100}$ **P-7** $\frac{x}{100} = \frac{3}{60}$ **P-8** 5   **P-9** A 5% solution.

CHAPTER 6

Section 6.1 (page 191)

P-1 Inch; pound; meter; foot; car length; arm length.
P-2 Car length; arm length. They differ from car to car and person to person.
P-3 3 inches.   **P-4** $\frac{1}{4}$ inch.   **P-5** $3\frac{1}{2}$ inches.
P-6 Yes; about $\frac{1}{8}$ inch.   **P-7** Less.   **P-8** $3\frac{1}{4}$ **P-9** Greater.

Section 6.2 (page 196)

P-1 2 inches.   **P-2** About $\frac{1}{3}$ inch.   **P-3** Yes.   **P-4** 3 inches.
P-5 Yes.   **P-6** 3 inches.   **P-7** $\frac{1}{16}$ inch.   **P-8** 0.005 inch.
P-9 $\frac{1}{8}$ inch; $\frac{1}{2}$ inch; 0.01 inch; 0.1 inch.

Section 6.3 (page 201)

P-1 15.85 inches.   **P-2** It is $\frac{1}{8}$ foot.   **P-3** $17\frac{3}{4}$ feet.
P-4 13 feet.   **P-5** 2.048; 2.05; 2.0

Section 6.4 (page 204)

P-1 $\frac{1}{2}$ foot.   **P-2** $\frac{\frac{1}{2}}{16} = \frac{1}{32}$ foot.   **P-3** $\frac{1}{2}$ foot.

P-4 $\frac{\frac{1}{2}}{17} = \frac{1}{34}$ foot.   **P-5** 17 feet.   **P-6** 1 mile; 100 miles.

P-7 0.154 foot; 15,400 feet.   **P-8** They all have the same accuracy.

Section 6.5 (page 207)

P-1 4   **P-2** Pound.   **P-3** 8   **P-4** $\frac{8}{21} = \frac{1}{x}$

P-5 $8x = 21$ **P-6** $\frac{1}{8}$ **P-7** $x = \frac{21}{8}$

Section 6.6 (page 210)

P-1 Milligram means one thousandth of a gram.
P-2 Centiliter means one hundredth of a liter.   **P-3** 10
P-4 100   **P-5** 10   **P-6** 100,000
P-7 Divide by 100 (that is, move the decimal point two places to the left).
P-8 Multiply by 10 (that is, move the decimal point one place to the right).

Section 6.7 (page 213)

P-1 It is the square region that is 1 foot on each side.
P-2 Inch.   P-3 Square inch.   P-4 144   P-5 9
P-6 Square centimeter.   P-7 10 mm   P-8 100 mm²

Section 6.8 (page 217)

P-1 18 cubic inches.
P-2 A cube with each edge having a measure of 1 foot; a cube with each edge having a measure of 1 yard; a cube with each edge having a measure of 1 centimeter.
P-3 Cubic yard.   P-4 Cubic meter.
P-5 Cubic foot; cubic yard; cubic millimeter; cubic meter.
P-6 Because cm is the abbreviation for centimeter.
P-7 144   P-8 12   P-9 $(36)^3$ P-10 $(1000)^3$

Section 6.9 (page 221)

P-1 $4n$; 4; 10; 20; 41; 396   P-2 30   P-3 No.
P-4 No; zero is not in the domain.
P-5 $p = 2l + 2w$ P-6 30 inches.

Section 6.10 (page 225)

P-1 8 in³   P-2 20 yd per min, or 1 ft per sec.
P-3 40 km per hour.   P-4 1800 miles.   P-5 10 seconds.

CHAPTER 7

Section 7.1 (page 233)

P-1 Yes. P-2 a has domain {9, 14, 19, 42, 45}. P-3 $a + 8$ P-4 No.
P-5 Since 9 square feet correspond to 1 square yard, $9x$ square feet correspond to x square yards.
P-6 $(0.05x)(2)$

Section 7.2 (page 236)

P-1 No.   P-2 28   P-3 No.
P-4 $p + (p + 6) = 52$ P-5 29   P-6 8
P-7 No.   P-8 9   P-9 No.   P-10 $x + 3$

Section 7.3 (page 240)

P-1 $17 = n - 5$ P-2 $35 < n$ P-3 $n + 42$
P-4 $n + (n + 42) = 56$ P-5 $56 - n = n + 42$
P-6 Yes; let the smaller number be represented by $\dfrac{x - 3}{2}$.

Section 7.4 (page 243)

P-1 Perimeter $= 2l + 2w$.
P-2 $2(x + 3)$ means $2x + 6$, which is more than $2x + 3$.
P-2 $x - 2$ P-4 $A = \frac{1}{2}$(base)(height).

Section 7.5 (page 246)

P-1 $\dfrac{x}{85} = \dfrac{20}{1}$ P-2 Cents.   P-3 $15x$ P-4 $2200n$

P-5 $3(25) = 75$ P-6 $4(50) = 200$ P-7 $5x$; $25y$; $10n$

P-8 180 cents.   P-9 $x + 2$ P-10 $5x$

P-11 The left-hand side of the equation is expressed in cents; so the right-hand side ($1.25) must also be expressed in cents (125 cents).

P-12 The left-hand side of this equation gives the number of coins the boy has but not the value of these coins.

Section 7.6 (page 249)

P-1 350 miles.   P-2 $500 - x$

P-3 No, if x is the length of one of the two pieces.   P-4 No.

P-5 $500x$; $600x$ P-6 $25 - x$ P-7 $60x$; $50(25 - x)$

Section 7.7 (page 253)

P-1 No.   P-2 4400 feet.   P-3 No.

P-4 5500 feet.   P-5 Yes.   P-6 Yes.

P-7 Since the speed of sound is given in feet per second, feet must be used for distance.

P-8 Yes.   P-9 No.   P-10 No.

CHAPTER 8

Section 8.1 (page 259)

P-1 π, for example.   P-2 It is ten units to the left of 0.

P-3 Yes.   P-4 Infinite.   P-5 No.   P-6 Yes; yes.

P-7 {integers}   P-8 {integers less than or equal to $^{-}1$}

P-9 {integers greater than or equal to 1}

Section 8.2 (page 262)

P-1 $\{0, 1\frac{1}{2}, 3, 4\frac{1}{3}\}$ P-2 $\frac{0}{1}$; $\frac{3}{2}$; $\frac{3}{1}$; $\frac{13}{3}$

P-3 Halfway between $^{-}1$ and $^{-}2$.   P-4 Negative thirteen fourths.

P-5 No; no.   P-6 Infinite; infinite.

Section 8.3 (page 265)

P-1 No.   P-2 .3333 $\cdots$ P-3 27   P-4 234; 9; 0   P-5 Irrational.

P-6 Between $^{-}3.14$ and $^{-}3.15$, or between $^{-}3$ and $^{-}4$, but nearer $^{-}3$.

Section 8.4 (page 268)

P-1 Right.   P-2 Left.   P-3 Left.   P-4 2.17181; 2.17181

P-5 $^{-}1.81$; $^{-}1.81$ P-6 x P-7 $x > ^{-}3$

P-8 The set of all points to the left of and including $^{-}2$.

Section 8.5 (page 272)

P-1 $2\frac{1}{2}$ P-2 $^{-}(3\frac{1}{3})$ P-3 0

P-4 Negative ten; the opposite of ten; the opposite of negative ten; the opposite of $\frac{1}{2}$; negative $\frac{1}{2}$; the opposite of negative $\frac{1}{2}$.

P-5 10   P-6 $^{-}10$ P-7 10   P-8 $^{-}3$

Section 8.6 (page 275)
P-1 $3 > {}^-7$ P-2 8   P-3 2   P-4 $8 > 2.$
P-5 $^-5$ P-6 $^-3$ P-7 $^-5 < {}^-3$ P-8 $-x < -y$

Section 8.7 (page 277)
P-1 The opposite of x is greater than 5.   P-2 No.   P-3 Yes.
P-4 $x > 3$ P-5 $\{\frac{1}{2}\}$ P-6 $\{\frac{1}{2}\}$ P-7 $5 \leq x$

Section 8.8 (page 280)
P-1 10   P-2 Its opposite.   P-3 Its opposite.
P-4 Its opposite.   P-5 $\frac{3}{4}$ P-6 $1\frac{1}{2}$ P-7 100; 3; $75\frac{1}{2}$; 0
P-8 π P-9 5 units; 5   P-10 5 units; 5
P-11 $2\frac{1}{2}$ units; $2\frac{1}{2}$ P-12 100 units; 100 units; 100; 100

CHAPTER 9

Section 9.1 (page 287)
P-1 Gain of two yards.   P-2 Loss of three yards.
P-3 Net loss of three yards.   P-4 Gain of ten yards.
P-5 $4 + 6 = 10$ P-6 Loss of thirteen yards.
P-7 $(^-6) + (^-7) = {}^-13$; loss of thirteen yards.   P-8 $^-7$ P-9 0

Section 9.2 (page 290)
P-1 Yes.   P-2 The team is at $^-6$ after two plays.
P-3 $^-2 + (^-4) = {}^-6$ P-4 Yes.   P-5 Yes.
P-6 At 8.   P-7 $5 + 3 = 8$ P-8 $^-3$ P-9 $^-3$

Section 9.3 (page 293)
P-1 $^-8$ P-2 $^-8$ P-3 2   P-4 2   P-5 $^-2$
P-6 $^-2$ P-7 0   P-8 $^-5$ P-9 5

Section 9.4 (page 296)
P-1 Yes.   P-2 $0 + (-0) = 0$ P-3 True.
P-4 Commutative Property of Addition.
P-5 Show that the phrases on either side of the equal sign name the same number.
P-6 No.

Section 9.5 (page 300)
P-1 $^-1$ P-2 14   P-3 Commutative Property of Addition.
P-4 Associative Property of Addition.   P-5 $x + 2$
P-6 Commutative Property of Addition.
P-7 Associative Property of Addition.   P-8 $^-11 + x$ P-9 $^-10 + x$

Section 9.6 (page 303)
P-1 $\{3\}$ P-2 $\{3\}$ P-3 Yes.   P-4 No.
P-5 Yes.   P-6 $\{4\}$ P-7 $\{4\}$ P-8 $\{6\}$ P-9 $\{6\}$

Section 9.7 (page 306)
P-1 $\{3\frac{1}{5}\}$ P-2 To isolate the x.   P-3 $^-5$
P-4 Substitute $^-6$ for x.   P-5 3   P-6 $-a$ P-7 10   P-8 $\{4\}$

Section 9.8 (page 309)

P-1 $x + 2; ^-3$ P-2 Add $^-2$ to both sides.   P-3 $\frac{7}{2}$ P-4 $x + ^-(\frac{7}{2})$
P-5 Add $\frac{7}{2}$ to both sides.   P-6 $^-7$ P-7 $7 + (^-x)$ P-8 $\{2\}$

Section 9.9 (page 311)

P-1 By the Closure Property of Addition of Real Numbers.
P-2 Addition Property of Opposites.
P-3 0   P-4 0   P-5 0   P-6 $5 + ^-8$

CHAPTER 10

Section 10.1 (page 319)

P-1 Addition Property of Opposites.
P-2 For any number of arithmetic a, $a \cdot 0 = 0$.   P-3 $0; 0; 0$
P-4 $^-5$ P-5 $^-10$ P-6 $^-15$ P-7 $^-4; ^-8; ^-12; ^-16; ^-20$
P-8 $^-4; ^-8; ^-12; ^-16; ^-20$ P-9 $^-3; ^-6; ^-9$ P-10 12
P-11 8   P-12 96   P-13 $^-96$

Section 10.2 (page 323)

P-1 5, 10, 15   P-2 $5; 10; 15$ P-3 $4; 8; 12$
P-4 A positive number.   P-5 $7; 5$ P-6 $35; 35$

Section 10.3 (page 326)

P-1 $^-5; 0; ^-(\frac{1}{2})$ P-2 Yes.
P-3 $^-30 = ^-30; 0 = 0; 60 = 60; 5.2 = 5.2; ^-30 = ^-30$

Section 10.4 (page 329)

P-1 Product.   P-2 Sum.   P-3 Commutative Property of Multiplication.
P-4 ^-6x P-5 $6x^2$ P-6 $6x^2y$ P-7 $25x + ^-35$ P-8 $^-5(a + b)$

Section 10.5 (page 331)

P-1 You get the opposite of that number.
P-2 This will prove that $(^-1)a$ is the opposite of a.
P-3 5   P-4 35   P-5 35   P-6 $^-3; ^-12$
P-7 36   P-8 36   P-9 $10; 5$ P-10 $50; 50$

Section 10.6 (page 335)

P-1 $10; -a; ^-5b^2$
P-2 No; r is a factor of one term but not the other.
P-3 No; x^3 is a factor of one term but not the other because the variables are raised to different powers.
P-4 $^-7y^2; 4ab$ P-5 No.   P-6 $4a^2 + ^-5b$ P-7 $3(^-a + b)$
P-8 $x(x + ^-1)$, or $(x + ^-1)x$

Section 10.7 (page 338)

P-1 Step 1: Distributive Property.   Step 3: Using common names.
    Step 2: Distributive Property.   Step 4: Adding like terms.
P-2 $x^2 + 2x + ^-15$ P-3 Distributive Property.
P-4 $3x; (2x + 3)(^-2)$ P-5 $6x^2 + 9x + ^-4x + ^-6$

P-6 $6x^2 + 5x + {}^-6$ P-7 Yes. P-8 $4x^2 + 12x + 9$
P-9 $(x + y)^2 \neq x^2 + y^2$ since $(2+3)^2 = 5^2 = 25$ and $2^2 + 3^2 = 4 + 9 = 13$.

CHAPTER 11

Section 11.1 (page 343)
P-1 1; 1; 1; 1 P-2 No; their product would be negative.
P-3 1 and $^-1$ P-4 ϕ P-5 No. P-6 $\frac{1}{10}$; $^-4$; $\frac{5}{2}$; $^-(\frac{8}{5})$; $^-1$

Section 11.2 (page 345)
P-1 3 P-2 3 P-3 Yes. P-4 4 P-5 $x = 4$; 4
P-6 Yes. P-7 $\{9\}$ P-8 $x = 9$; 9 P-9 Yes.
P-10 To isolate x, each side of the equation was multiplied by the multiplicative inverse of $\frac{3}{5}$, that is, by $\frac{5}{3}$.
P-11 They are multiplicative inverses. P-12 $^-(\frac{1}{4})$ P-13 $x = {}^-7\frac{1}{2}$
P-14 If $a = 0$, a has no multiplicative inverse because 0 has no multiplicative inverse.

Section 11.3 (page 348)
P-1 Addition Property. P-2 Addition Property of Equality.
P-3 Using common names. P-4 Multiplication Property of Equality.
P-5 $x = {}^-6$ P-6 $\{^-6\}$ P-7 $^-5$ P-8 $^-31 = {}^-6x$ P-9 $^-(\frac{1}{6})$

Section 11.4 (page 350)
P-1 $4x + 3$ P-2 $^-3$ P-3 Add $^-3$ to both sides. P-4 No.
P-5 Apply the Distributive Property to express $x(3x + {}^-5)$ as a sum.
P-6 0 P-7 ^-3x

Section 11.5 (page 353)
P-1 $x + 5$; 8 P-2 To get all terms containing x together on one side.
P-3 $2x$ P-4 $^-3$; $3x + 3$ P-5 $5x + {}^-1 = 4$

Section 11.6 (page 356)
P-1 5 P-2 0 P-3 Yes. P-4 $^-2$; $^-5$ P-5 Yes. P-6 $\{0\}$
P-7 $\{0\}$ P-8 $\{1\}$ P-9 $\{5, ^-1\}$ P-10 5 P-11 $^-1$ P-12 $\{5, ^-1\}$
P-13 No; for instance, you could have $a = 10$, $b = \frac{1}{2}$. The method in the example applies only when the product is 0.

Section 11.7 (page 359)
P-1 Yes. P-2 Yes. P-3 Yes. P-4 Yes.

CHAPTER 12

Section 12.1 (page 365)
P-1 3 P-2 3 P-3 $^-3$; 13; 13; $^-3$; 3; $^-5$; 8; 0
P-4 $1 + (^-10)$; $^-7 + (^-3)$; $^-2 + 8$; $x + (^-y)$; $x + y$

Section 12.2 (page 368)
P-1 $5x + (^-2x)$ P-2 $3x$ P-3 $5 + (^-x) + (^-2)$
P-4 $3 - x$ P-5 2 P-6 4 P-7 $(^-a) + (^-b)$, or $-a - b$

Section 12.3 (page 371)

P-1 0   P-2 2   P-3 $a - b + c$ P-4 Definition of subtraction.
P-5 The opposite of a sum is the sum of the opposites.
P-6 Associative Property of Addition.   P-7 Definition of subtraction.
P-8 $3x - 2y - 5$; $2a + 3 + 5b$ P-9 $a - b - c - d + e$
P-10 Yes; yes.   P-11 $6a^2 - 15a$ P-12 $3x^2 - 3xy + 18x$

Section 12.4 (page 374)

P-1 5 P-2 Yes. P-3 No; distance is represented by a positive number.
P-4 Yes. P-5 8 P-6 Yes. P-7 Yes. P-8 6 P-9 Yes. P-10 Yes.
P-11 $|{-2} - (-10)|$, or $|{-10} - (-2)|$ P-12 8   P-13 4 units.
P-14 7 and $^-1$ P-15 No.   P-16 $\{7, {}^-1\}$ P-17 $x - (^-1)$

Section 12.5 (page 378)

P-1 Zero has no multiplicative inverse.
P-2 ${}^-\left(\dfrac{1}{x}\right)$ P-3 $3 \cdot \dfrac{1}{5}$; $^-2 \cdot \dfrac{1}{7}$; $x \cdot {}^-\left(\dfrac{1}{y}\right)$; $a \cdot \dfrac{1}{a}$ P-4 ϕ P-5 0

Section 12.6 (page 381)

P-1 $-\frac{5}{12}$ P-2 By the meaning of division.
P-3 $-\dfrac{1}{b} = \dfrac{1}{-b}$ for any nonzero real number b.
P-4 $-cd = c(-d)$ for any real numbers c, d.
P-5 $-1 \cdot x = -x$ for any real number x.
P-6 Associative Property of Multiplication.
P-7 By the meaning of division.   P-8 $-1 \cdot x = -x$ for any number x.
P-9 $-\frac{7}{12}$ P-10 $-\frac{7}{12}$ P-11 $\dfrac{7}{12}$; $\dfrac{x}{y}$ P-12 $^-1$ P-13 2

Section 12.7 (page 384)

P-1 $\frac{10}{21}$ P-2 $\frac{1}{10}$ P-3 $a \cdot \dfrac{1}{b}$ P-4 $c \cdot \dfrac{1}{d}$
P-5 By the Commutative and Associative Properties of Multiplication.
P-6 $\frac{3}{35}$ P-7 $\dfrac{-10x}{3y}$

Section 12.8 (page 387)

P-1 $-\dfrac{3}{x}$
P-2 Using factored form and then using the rule for the product of numbers named by fractions.
P-3 $\dfrac{a}{a} = 1$ for $a \neq 0$
P-4 Multiplication Property of One, and using the common name.
P-5 $x \neq 2$
P-6 If $x = -\frac{1}{3}$, divisor $6x + 2$ equals 0, but denominator cannot be 0.
P-7 $\dfrac{(-3x)(2y)}{y(-x)}$ P-8 Rule for the product of numbers named by fractions.

Section 12.9   (page 390)

P-1 $\dfrac{5x}{y}$ P-2 $-\dfrac{2}{x-2}$ P-3 6

P-4 $2 \cdot 2 \cdot 3$ P-5 $2 \cdot 3 \cdot 5$ P-6 $2 \cdot 2 \cdot 3 \cdot 5 = 60$

Section 12.10   (page 393)

P-1 $\frac{14}{15}$ P-2 15

P-3 If $c = 0$, the final result will have a zero in the denominator.

P-4 Yes.   P-5 Multiplication Property of One.

P-6 Rule for the product of numbers named by fractions.

P-7 If $a = 0$, the fraction will have a zero in the denominator.   P-8 30

CHAPTER 13

Section 13.1   (page 403)

P-1 Mets.   P-2 $\frac{1}{6}$ P-3 No.

P-4 3; because there are three even numbers on the die.

Section 13.2   (page 407)

P-1 $\frac{1}{4}$ P-2 $\frac{2}{4}$, or $\frac{1}{2}$ P-3 $\frac{1}{4}$ P-4 No.

P-5 The first penny shows a tail, the second a head, the third a head.

Section 13.3   (page 409)

P-1 36   P-2 No.   P-3 $\frac{33}{36} = \frac{11}{12}$ P-4 $\frac{10}{36} = \frac{5}{18}$

Section 13.4   (page 412)

P-1 The empty set.   P-2 0   P-3 1   P-4 1; 0

P-5 $\frac{3}{36}$, or $\frac{1}{12}$ P-6 $\frac{2}{4} = \frac{1}{2}$ P-7 $\{(T, t)\}$; $\frac{1}{4}$ P-8 $\frac{35}{36}$

Section 13.5   (page 416)

P-1 11   P-2 $\frac{11}{36}$ P-3 $\frac{3}{36}$ P-4 $\frac{1}{36}$ P-5 $\frac{4}{36}$ P-6 Yes.

P-7 12; $\frac{12}{36}$ P-8 18; $\frac{18}{36}$ P-9 24; $\frac{24}{36}$ P-10 No.

Section 13.6   (page 418)

P-1 $\{(1, 2)\}$ P-2 $\frac{1}{36}$ P-3 18; $\frac{18}{36}$, or $\frac{1}{2}$ P-4 12; $\frac{12}{36}$, or $\frac{1}{3}$

P-5 6; $\frac{6}{36}$, or $\frac{1}{6}$ P-6 Yes.   P-7 12; $\frac{12}{36}$, or $\frac{1}{3}$

P-8 30; $\frac{30}{36}$, or $\frac{5}{6}$ P-9 10; $\frac{10}{36}$, or $\frac{5}{18}$ P-10 10; $\frac{10}{36}$, or $\frac{5}{18}$

P-11 12; $\frac{12}{36}$, or $\frac{1}{3}$ P-12 7; $\frac{7}{36}$ P-13 $\frac{1}{2}$ P-14 $\frac{1}{2}$ P-15 $\frac{1}{4}$ P-16 $\frac{1}{4}$

Section 13.7   (page 423)

P-1 2   P-2 $\frac{7}{2}$, or $3\frac{1}{2}$ P-3 $5\frac{1}{2}$

P-4 There is no middle number, but the median is $2\frac{1}{2}$.   P-5 5

P-6 Four students obtained scores of 80, and $4 \cdot 80 = 320$; five students obtained scores of 50, and $5 \cdot 50 = 250$.

P-7 There are thirty test scores.

Section 13.8   (page 428)

P-1 6   P-2 4; 1   P-3 68   P-4 $92 - 44 = 48$

P-5 3   P-6 2   P-7 $2\frac{3}{4}$ P-8 $2\frac{3}{4}$

Index

multiplication, of equality, 345–347, 362

multiplication, of one, 83–84, 114, 326

of numbers, 83–84, 109–110

order, of opposites, 276, 284

of reciprocals, 115–157

special, 332–333

sums to products, 106–108

Proportion, 163–164, 166–168, 173–174, 188

  alternation, 164

  as open sentences, 166–168

  cross-products property, 163

  extremes, 163

  inversion, 164

  means, 163

Quotient, 38, 119

  indicated, 25, 36, 45

Range, 425, 432

Ratio, 160–161, 188

Rational numbers, 20–21, 36, 262–263, 284

  negative, 262–263

  positive, 263

Real numbers, 259–266, 284

  addition of, 287–288, 293–294

  comparison of, 269

  distributive property of, 329–330

  division of, 378–383, 393–395

  multiplication of, 319–324

  order of, 268–270

  subtraction of, 365–373, 397

Reciprocals, 155–157, 188

Remainder, 119

Roster method, 1, 9

Sentences, 33–35, 36

  and sentences, 65–66, 80

  equivalent, 303, 314

  formula, 221

  graphs of, 60–64, 79, 80

  open, 41–80, 237–238, 277–278, 306–310, 350–355

  or sentences, 72–73, 80

  proportions as, 166–168

  statements, 33, 50–51

  truth sets of, involving multiplication, 158–159

  word, 237–238

Sets

  closed under addition, 86

  closed under multiplication, 87

  elements of, 1, 36

  empty, 5, 36

  equal, 12, 36

  equivalent, 12, 36

  explanation of, 1, 2, 36

  finite, 8–9, 36

  infinite, 8–9, 36

  intersection of, 66, 418

  null, 5, 36

  subsets of, 4, 36

  truth sets of open sentences, 53–54, 58–59, 79, 306–311, 348–352, 353

  union of, 73, 79, 416–417, 432

  word description of, 8

Special properties

  of division, 381–383

  of multiplication, 332–333, 340

  of subtraction, 371–373

Square of a number, 56

Standard units of measure, 191, 207–209

Statements, 33, 50–51

Subtraction

  closure property of, 370, 397

  difference expressed as a sum, 366

  distance between two points, 375–376

  distributive property of multiplication over, 372–373, 397

  equivalent open phrases, 368

  in open phrases, 368–369

  meaning of, 365–368, 397

  special properties, of, 371–373

Sum

  indicated, 25, 28, 36, 45

  of numbers named by fractions, 39

Symbols

  empty set, 5, 36

  equality, 33

  inequality, 33, 34

  multiplication, 31

  opposite, 272

  raised dot, 31

Tables

  frequency, 429–431

Terms

  of binomials, 112, 114

2
3
G 4
H 5
I 6
J 7